THE MODERN PRACTICAL PLUMBER
VOLUME III

PLATE I

SOIL, BRANCH VENTILATION AND ANTI-SIPHONAGE PIPES FOR RANGES OF W.C.s ADJOINING A BOUNDARY WALL: ALL PIPEWORK BEING NECESSARILY WITHIN THE BUILDING.

The terminals of vents would, of course, penetrate the roof to discharge in the open air. The vert stack of soil pipe on left is cut out in the plate.

[Frontispiece

P.—m.

THE MODERN PRACTICAL PLUMBER

BY

A. C. MARTIN, A.R.S.I.

LECTURER IN PLUMBERS' WORK AND SANITATION
NORTHERN POLYTECHNIC, LONDON, N.

AND

JOHN H. HENWOOD

SANITARY, HEATING AND VENTILATING ENGINEER
AUTHOR OF
"A MANUAL OF GASFITTING AND APPLIANCES"

VOLUME III

CAXTON PUBLISHING COMPANY, LIMITED
CLUN HOUSE, SURREY STREET, LONDON, W.C.2

The Publishers guarantee that the Binding, Printing, Paper and Blocks used in this book are the products of British workers.

Printed in Great Britain by J. Weiner, Ltd.
Bound by Hazell, Watson & Viney, Ltd., London and Aylesbury
P. 2

CONTENTS
VOL. III

CHAPTER I

LIST OF ILLUSTRATIONS

VOLUME III

THE
MODERN PRACTICAL PLUMBER

VOL. III

CHAPTER I

W.C.s

INSANITARY TYPES: Pan—Hoppers and Washout. **MODERN TYPES:** Washdown—Pedestal and Corbel—Valve Closets—Siphonic Closets—Anti-siphonic Action. **WASTE-WATER CLOSETS. EARTH CLOSETS.**

SANITARY knowledge has advanced to such an extent that it is not worth while in this work discussing to a great length the unhygienic features of the sanitary types of many of the older forms of w.c.s. It will be sufficient to just name them and point out the main features which render them insanitary, so that they can be recognised when making a survey of old properties.

INSANITARY TYPES

Pan.—One of the early forms was known as the " pan " closet, and consisted of an earthenware bowl inset to a large cast-iron container. The outlet of the bowl was fitted into the shallow copper dish which trapped a certain amount of water and was supposed to prevent gases from escaping into the room. It was hinged and operated by a handle inset in the timber encasement, the same handle operating the flush when the dish swung out of the way. The inside of the cast-iron container became in time coated with filth, the whole thing being very objectionable and the bad air from this container escaping into the room each time the fitting was flushed.

Usually associated with this fitting was the old form of D-trap, and in some cases with very old work it was found that the bath waste and lavatory waste were connected to the same trap.

Long Hopper.—Fig. 437 shows a " Long Hopper " closet, which is an improvement on the aforementioned; it was generally used for outdoor apartments, servants' closets, etc. It was fitted with a swirling flush, with the idea that such a form of flush in a spiral form would be more cleansing. The opposite effect happened, and the whirlpool action produced in the trap prevented the fitting from being self-cleansing and emptying, it often taking two or three flushings to clear it. It presents a large area subject to fouling; is fragile, being manufactured in thin

I

earthenware ; and entails a wooden encasement. Wooden encasements
are not sanitary features and should be avoided as far as possible.

Short Hopper.—The " Short Hopper " closet (Fig. 438) is a slight
advance on the " Long Hopper." It is
made in two pieces of earthenware with a
trap fixed above the floor line. Its chief
faults are :—its shape is not conducive to
self-cleansing conditions and it is made of
thin earthenware, which entails an encasement to take the weight of the user.

It is often found, when inspecting these
fittings with a view to replacement by a
modern form of sanitary fitting, that a
difficulty occurs in the following manner :
The drain layer (and a few years back drain
layers were not very particular or exact in
their work) has often fixed the outlet pipe
out of centre of the apartment, with the

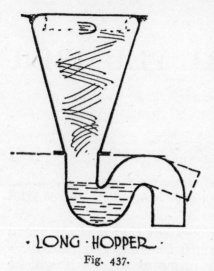

· LONG · HOPPER ·

Fig. 437.

result that, in fixing the fitting in the centre
of the apartment, the trap attached is
necessarily fixed at an oblique angle. This
entails, in fixing a modern fitting in one piece, that the drain has to be
altered and put central to the apartment. Drains should not be interfered with without notifying the local authorities, so that the work may
be inspected and tested. It should be sufficient only to test the one
branch from the nearest manhole.

" *Wash-out*."—Fig. 439 is a type of closet which had a great run when
first placed on the market, known as the " Wash-out." It was fixed on

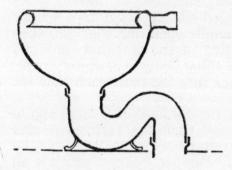

· SHORT · HOPPER ·

Fig. 438.

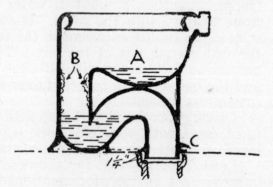

· THE · WASHOUT ·

Fig. 439.

public and private properties to a great extent, and many still exist.
It was thought at the time that it was an ideal fitting, but has not proved
satisfactory for the following reasons : The shallow bowl of water is

insufficient to serve the purpose for which it was intended, i.e. drown excretal matter and odour. Moreover, this stagnant pool, A, destroys, to a great extent, the cleansing power of the flush water, and the inlet leg to the siphon trap becomes foul, as at B, and cannot be cleansed except by hand. The base is often shielded by a continuous flange in the pottery, as at C, so that it is difficult to make a satisfactory joint of the outgo.

MODERN TYPES

Pedestal Wash-down.—For general purposes the wash-down type of water-closet is the most favourable and fairly satisfactory, although not

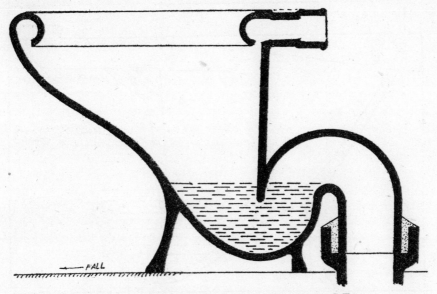

Fig. 440.—The Pedestal Wash-down Closet with S-Trap.

ideal. It is constructed, preferably, of one piece of white glazed stoneware ; it is shaped with a vertical back and a projecting front which is conducive to self-cleansing conditions. Broadly, it is made in two forms, (1) with a " P " trap and (2) with an " S " trap. The " P " trap is usually the most convenient for fixing on first and higher floors or where the floor line to which the fitting is fixed is considerably above the height of the adjoining open areas.

Figs. 440 and 441 show these two types. The outlet should always be clear of the floor or wall line, so that the joint is readily accessible for making, testing and inspecting. The inlet to the flushing rim of the modern type is so arranged that a bend, other than a small offset, is not required in the flushing pipe. The small hole at A is provided to give a small after-flush dribble and ensure that a seal is made in the trap of the fitting should it have been lost by siphonage or other means. The fitting should be so constructed in heavy ware that it is self-supporting. A hinged hardwood polished seat can be attached to the fitting itself, to which it should be secured on special lugs provided, by means of brass bolts.

Special types of water closet may be obtained in which the outgo leaves the fitting at right angles to suit positions of a soil pipe on a side wall. In ordering, right or left hand direction outgo should be stated. An alternative to that is to obtain a type with a separate metal trap. This can be turned in any required direction. Another form for factories and institutes is sometimes adopted which consists of having hardwood

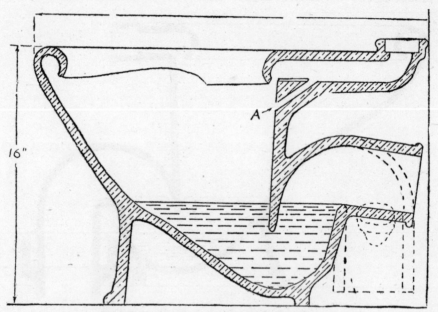

Fig. 441.—Pedestal Wash-down with P-Trap.

insertions secured to the pottery rim ; but, in the writer's opinion, the hardwood hinged seat is to be preferred, and where good conditions are provided they will be used in a proper manner. The faults of washdown fittings may be enumerated as follows : Rather a large area exposed to fouling ; the quantity of water held in the trap is hardly sufficient and it is as much as the limit of two gallons allowed by most Water Board Authorities will clear and replace. As a matter of fact, such fittings would be better with a three-gallon flush, and this would make it that the manufacturers could arrange the construction so that the water line in the fitting could be slightly raised to give a deeper pool of water and reduce the area subject to fouling. Another defect is that the construction of the fitting and the associated flush make it somewhat noisy for indoor w.c.s. This can be reduced somewhat in the case of joist and boarded floors by lagging the space between the joints with slag wool. A quiet type of flushing cistern is also a consideration. These two types are known as " Pedestal " w.c.s.

Corbel Wash-down.—A type which is similar in principle to these is manufactured with the distinct advantage in that the whole fitting is clear of the floor. The type of pedestal which requires floor brackets should

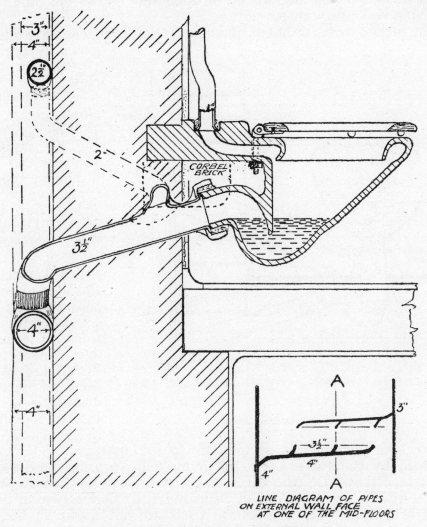

Fig. 442.—The Corbel Wash-down Closet.

always be avoided, as it makes an awkward trap for dirt, which is seldom cleansed, owing to the difficulty of getting at it and is neglected from the fact that it is hidden.

This corbel type is built in the wall and is supported by the lug of stoneware, as shown in the sectional drawing, Fig. 442. It is assumed in the drawing that the fitting is one of three in a range and connected to lead soil pipes, the section being taken through *A—A*. Some forms are constructed to be carried on an iron corbel. The corbel form naturally entails the need of a very solid wall. It is a good plan to give extra support in the one shown in Fig. 442 by building in two white-glazed bull-nose bricks to act as brackets projecting 4½ inches clear of the wall underneath the fitting and spaced on each side of the soil pipe branch, thus giving very adequate support.

In high-class work for hotels and general domestic, one of two forms is generally preferred :
(1) The valve closet.
(2) The siphonic closet.

Valve Closets.— Fig. 443 indicates a somewhat old-fashioned type of a typical valve closet. A lead trap, usually of anti-D form, is fixed between the joists of an ordinary boarded floor and the floor underneath the encasement is covered with a lead safe. The advantages claimed for this fitting are, a large bowl of water reducing the area subject to fouling to a minimum; two

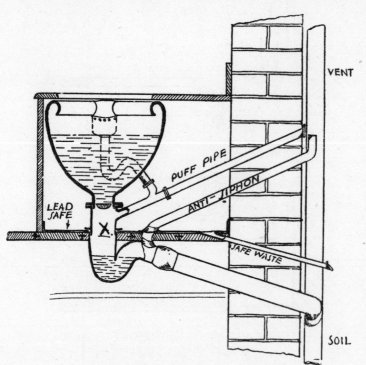

Fig. 443.—The Valve Closet.

water seals against ingress of foul air to the apartment; the pool of water held by the valve assists in giving self-cleansing conditions; it is quiet in action. On the other hand, it is very mechanical in construction and liable to get out of adjustment, so that attention is fairly frequently needed. The mechanical parts are not shown in the figure (the sanitary details only being drawn), and they need a screen to hide them. The large bowl of water reduces odour in the apartment.

The overflow is trapped into the puff pipe as shown to prevent gases escaping from the area *X*, known as the valve box, into the room via the overflow. The puff pipe is necessary to allow this trapped air in the valve box to escape into the open air when the flush is occurring; otherwise it will escape through the flush water into the apartment. If the valve leaks, the bowl becomes empty, and in such a state is far from self-cleansing. The lead safe is provided with a short pipe known as a " safe waste " discharging into the open air and covered with a hinged flap to prevent cold air blowing up. The anti-siphon pipe may be taken through the lead safe as shown, to which it is wiped by means of a flanged joint.

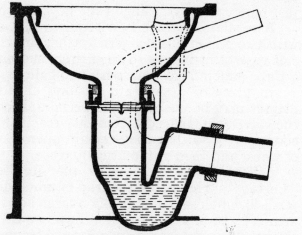

Fig. 444.—Dent and Hellyers "Optimus" Valve Closet.

A more modern form of valve closet is known as the " Optimus " (Fig. 444), and has the trap fixed above the floor. This type has an additional good feature in that the screen hiding the mechanical parts is made D shape in plan, of white glazed stoneware, being a component part of the bowl structure. The trapped overflow is so arranged that at every flush a certain amount of fresh water is discharged into the trap and so prevents the water held in this trap from becoming foul. It has a special screw connection on the outgo of the cast-iron anti-D trap, the lead soil pipe being wiped directly on to this brass connection. In principle of working it is the same as in the older form (Fig. 443). In this the handle is usually inset in the seat, and in raising it it operates in two ways—(1) to tilt the valve and let the contents of the bowl fall through, and (2) it opens the flush to swill down the sides and recharge the bowl with clean water. It can be realised that the bottom valve to the bowl must close before the water flush finishes. This is arranged by a somewhat complicated mechanical arrangement of levers and an " air " vessel. When the flush handle is released, the valve immediately tilts back into position. The

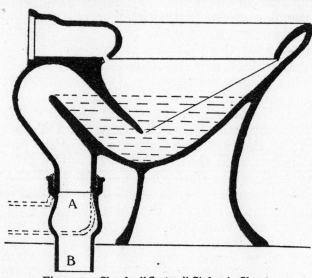

Fig. 445.—Shanks "Certus" Siphonic Closet.

flushing water valve is prevented from shutting immediately by the trapped air in the air vessel holding the plunger back. As this trapped air escapes through a special small valve provided in the air vessel, the water supply is gradually cut off. The rate of escape of air from the air vessel must be adjusted by the man fixing it, so that the water valve shuts off just before the water line in the bowl reaches the overflow level.

A regulation which now requires that all such closets should be fitted with two-gallon flush cisterns rather limits the use and the advantages of this type of fitting, as to be entirely successful it is more satisfactory with a three-gallon flush than with two gallons.

In place of a separate flushing cistern within the apartment, such fittings may be flushed with special anti-concussive valves on a pipe line, the valve being placed within easy reach of the closet. They are internally constructed, so that they remain open to discharge a measured quantity of water and then automatically close.

Siphonic Closets.—One of the simplest forms is known as Shanks "Certus." The seal of the trap is much deeper than that of the ordinary wash-down closet, thus giving a large bowl of water and a limited exposed area. Naturally a two-gallon flush would not be sufficient to thoroughly cleanse down the fitting and pipe and leave such a large pool recharged with clean water. To get over this difficulty it is arranged that the contents of the bowl shall be removed by siphonic action. The siphonic action in this one shown is started by impulse of the flushing water. The special enlarged bulge piece attached to the outgo has a subtle influence in assuring that siphonic action starts. The one indicated is of anti-monial lead and attached to the pottery of the ware by a special patent soldering process. The end is attached to the lead soil pipe by means of a wiped joint, an awkward position, usually between the joists (see Fig. 445).

Another pattern has an enlargement in the pottery itself and is cemented direct into the brass thimble attached to the soil pipe. An essential feature of this particular fitting is that the branch soil pipe shall not be larger than 3 inches. As a matter of fact, it is advocated that it should be $2\frac{1}{2}$ inches. This contention has led to some controversy in various districts, the by-law rating being that the minimum size for all soil pipes attached to w.c.s is $3\frac{1}{2}$ inches. However, the fixing of the fitting has generally been allowed and has given satisfactory results. It has been fixed in other countries to quite a large extent, so the restrictions on the size of the pipe branch attached are not so adamant, and that it has given entire satisfaction under these circumstances suggests that when fixed in good-class properties where it will not receive improper use, the small diameter pipe of $2\frac{1}{2}$ inches can be satisfactory. In most districts the minimum diameter of the main vertical stack of soil and vent pipe is $3\frac{1}{2}$ inches,[1] the wall branch being reduced to meet the requirements of the fitting.

A type is also made with a right angle connection provided where it is required that the soil branch will immediately leave through the wall, but as this part of the fitting forms the long arm of the siphonic pipe, it is better to carry the pipe down as far as possible before striking

[1] The L.C.C. By-Laws, 1930, permit a 3-inch soil pipe.

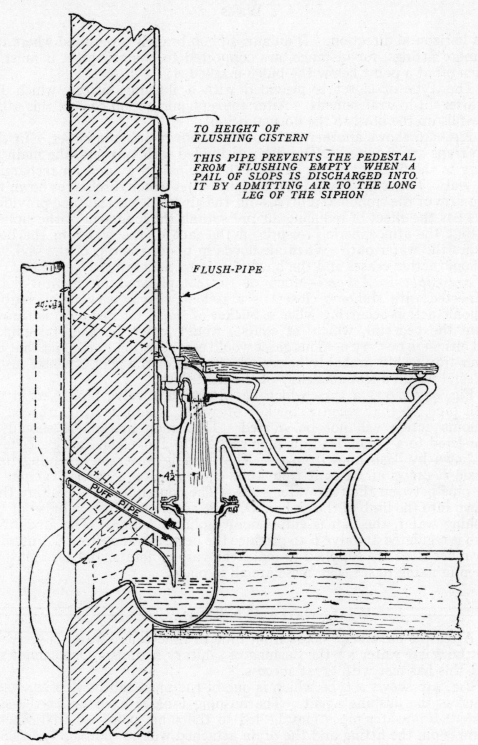

TO HEIGHT OF
FLUSHING CISTERN

THIS PIPE PREVENTS THE PEDESTAL
FROM FLUSHING EMPTY WHEN A
PAIL OF SLOPS IS DISCHARGED INTO
IT BY ADMITTING AIR TO THE LONG
LEG OF THE SIPHON

FLUSH-PIPE

PUFF PIPE

$4\frac{1}{2}"$

Fig. 446.—" Century " Siphonic Closet.

in a horizontal direction.   If an anti-siphon branch is required where two or more fittings, for instance, are connected to one soil pipe, it must be taken off at a point below the bulge marked A.

This type of closet is provided with a flushing cistern which has an after-flush arrangement.   After the siphonic action ceases, this after-flow fills up the bowl to the normal height.

Fig. 446 shows another form of well-known siphonic closet.   In this two traps are required.   The flush is divided into two jets, the main jet going to the flushing of the basin in the ordinary way and for recharging the seal.   The second part is formed into a jet which discharges down the long arm of the siphon and drives out the air in the special pipe provided. This has the effect of reducing air pressure in the long arm of the siphon, so that the atmospheric pressure on the face of the water in the bowl pushes the water out.   When air floods in under the dip of the seal, the siphonic action ceases and the bowl fills up to the normal level again.

Anti-siphonic Action.—Much of the complicated mechanical detail connected with siphonic closets is attached with a view to preventing siphonic action occurring when a bucket of slops, for instance, is thrown down the pedestal, which, of course, would leave the pedestal empty, and although no very noxious gases would escape owing to the fact that the lower trap would probably be sealed, the loss of the pool of water in the pedestal would affect efficiency of the next flush.

Fig. 447 shows a type which has designed a valve box fixed in the flush pipe, so that when a bucket of water is emptied into the basin, siphonic action will not be started.   The union marked A should be connected to a $\frac{3}{4}$-inch lead air pipe carried up above the flushing cistern, as shown by dash lines from A.   The flushing water on emerging from nozzle B draws air after it from tube C, producing a partial vacuum in the pipe between the two water seals.   The contents of the pan are thus drawn into the limb of the siphon D, and, assisted by the impulse of the flushing water, the pan is emptied by siphonic action.   The amount of flush is regulated at valve E to produce the best siphonic effect.   A number of rubber rings are supplied to make the various joints, and care must be taken in fixing to see that these are all in place.

WASTE-WATER AND EARTH CLOSETS

Attempts have been made from time to time where water is scarce to use the waste water for the flushing of sanitary fittings.   One cannot say that this has met with great success.

Fig. 448 shows a type which is one of the most sanitary, using waste water as the flushing agent.   The flushing tank is fixed under the sink waste.   Rainwater pipes may be led to the same point, so that when a storm is on, the fitting and the drain attached will be thoroughly flushed.

In country districts where the water-carriage system is not installed, earth closets may be provided as the next best thing.   They can in such

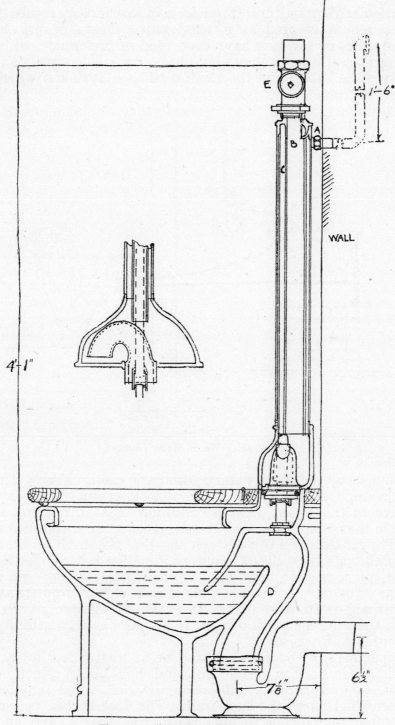

Fig. 447.—" Laydas " Siphonic Closet.

cases, particularly agricultural districts, give satisfactory results providing clean, dry mould is used as a deodorant. Mistakes are frequently made, and ashes or sawdust have been used in preference, with the idea that, being more absorbent they would be better. The reverse is the actual result. It is the bacteria in the earth used as a sprinkler which has the purifying effect.

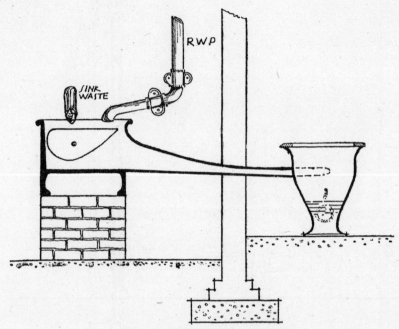

Fig. 448.—Waste Water Closet.

Fig. 449 shows Adamsez patent automatic earth closet. The general remarks as applied later to outdoor water-closet apartments apply with equal force to this type, with the addition that an opening should be provided in the back wall so that the receiver can be withdrawn from that point. The construction can be such also that the earth container can be projecting through the wall to the outer air, so that it can be fed from there. It should, of course, in that case be weathered to prevent rainwater getting in. The one shown is self-contained with an iron encasement or shield, D-shape pattern in plan. It works as follows : When the user rises from the seat, the earth box, *A*, is tilted forward, scattering earth at *B* over contents of receiver.

The apartment to be detached and be at least 6 feet away from the main building (in London area 20 feet) and should be of 9-inch brickwork, and permanent and adequate ventilation provided. This may be a louvre arrangement high up in the back wall. The door should be cut clear at the top and at the bottom to give ventilating spaces, and an air-brick placed under the encasement of the fitting. The floor of the encasement should be perfectly smooth and slope towards the opening at the back of the access, the floor at this point to be 3 or 4 inches higher than the adjacent open area. The floor of the apartment should slope from the riser to the doorway. Permanent natural lighting should be provided with glass area equal to 2 sq. feet as required for the water-closet apartments.

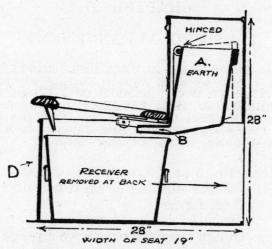

Fig. 449.—" Adamsez " Earth Closet.

CHEMICAL CLOSETS

In their simplest form chemical closets consist of an acid-proofed bucket receptacle within an iron encasement such as shown in Fig. 449, but without the back attachment. A vent pipe from the enclosure is carried to the outer air. Although it is recommended that it can be fixed within a building as with water closets, the writer would not do so, as there is a certain amount of smell of disinfectant which is objectionable. There are other objectionable features, the weekly (or more frequent) necessary emptying and burying and mixing and charging with new chemical; a nuisance in an isolated bungalow, where it is difficult to obtain labour. An improved arrangement consists of a glazed stoneware pedestal, similar to the w.c. without a trap. An iron vessel is buried in the ground below to which the pedestal is attached. From this vessel a drain is carried to a sump hole filled with clinker, etc. When the vessel is full, a valve is opened and the contents allowed to trickle away. The scheme is not suitable for heavy clays, or in districts where the water supply is from wells. The disinfectant is of a corrosive nature, caustic soda, phenol and pine tar disinfectants. In the latest designs the tanks are fitted with anti-splash baffle plate and a mechanical stirrer to break up the solids and give uniform disinfection.

CHAPTER II

FLUSHING ARRANGEMENTS

TYPES : Early Forms—Modern Forms. AUTOMATIC FLUSHING CISTERNS. Water Level
—Flushing for Closets in Ranges—Amount of Water for Flushing—Alternative Fittings for Range
Closets. POINTS GENERAL TO W.C.s. NUMBER OF FITTINGS REQUIRED. TABLE
OF APPROXIMATE NUMBER OF W.C.s NECESSARY : Elementary Schools—Secondary
Schools—Boarding-Schools—Dwellings Occupied by More than One Family. FACTORIES
AND WORKSHOPS : Factory and Workshop Acts—Latrines—Slop Hoppers. URINALS :
Bracket Urinals—Stalls—Flushing—Wastes—Urinettes—Bidets.

THE success or otherwise of any water-closet depends to a great extent
upon the capabilities of the flushing apparatus. Such an apparatus is
divided roughly into three forms :

(1) The single cistern.

(2) A continuous trough cistern fixed above a range of w.c.s.

(3) Patent valves which discharge two or more gallons according to
adjustment and fixed in a special service pipe running to this fitting.

TYPES

Early Forms.—The early form of flushing arrangement consisted of
fixing a weighted valve in a house service tank, a flush pipe being led
from this general store to the sanitary apartment. The valve was
operated by means of long lengths of copper wire and bell cranks. Owing
to the stretching of the wire or sticking of the cranks, it was a frequent
thing for the valve to get stuck up, so that the whole tank of water,
holding from one hundred to four hundred gallons or more according
to the size of the premises, would be emptied down the one fitting. To
avoid this, small compartments were arranged in the tank to prevent the
whole tank being inadvertently emptied.

The next advance was to have a small flushing tank holding from two
to three gallons fixed directly above the fitting within the same apartment,
but operated by means of a weighted valve lifted by lever and handpull.
It is doubtful whether these were a distinct improvement in waste prevention on the old arrangement, as the valves often became leaky, so
that the water leaking down the flush pipe into the w.c. night and day led
to a tremendous amount of waste of water in towns fitted with this type
of flushing tank.

Fig. 450 shows a type of this valve-operated cistern with an attachment which is, probably, the first form of siphonic flushing w.c.

Another defect of the valve-flushing cistern lay in the fact that people would not hold the lever until the tank was empty, particularly in business houses, stations, hotels, etc. To overcome this trouble, a siphon was attached, as shown in the given figure, constructed of lead pipe, so that when the valve was lifted even only for a moment, sufficient water fell down the flush pipe to start the siphonic action, so that the cistern water would empty down to the point A, when, of course, air is admitted. It still, however, has the defect of a possible leaky valve.

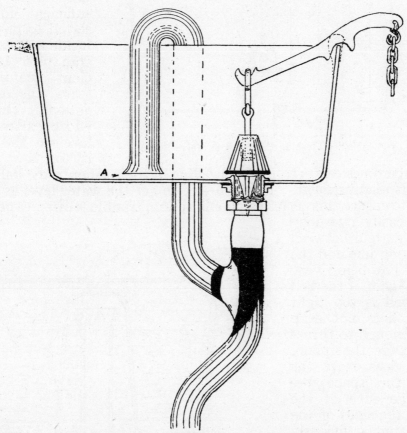

Fig. 450.—Valve Cistern with Improvised Siphon.

The manufacturers' fitting for this type of cistern was evolved as shown in Fig. 451, the whole unit, (a), (b), being self-contained in hard metal. There are many in existence, but they are not approved by most Water Boards, and cannot come under the heading of " waste-water preventers."

Modern Forms.—A type which comes more truly under this heading is shown in Fig. 452. It works as follows : When the bell is raised by pulling the flushing handle down, nothing happens except the water takes the place of the iron. When the handle is released again, the bell falls, and the water which is held inside the well is thrust up inside to fall over the standpipe at (*a*). This falling cascade of water starts the siphonic action and continues flushing until air is drawn under the bottom edge of the bell or dome. From a mechanical point of view it is not one of the best and can

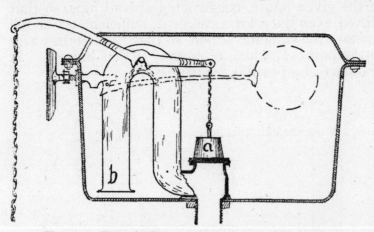

Fig. 451.—Siphonic Flushing Cistern with Valve Start.

become erratic. For instance, if the bell is too loose in fit within the well, it misses the water, so that there is not sufficient force asserted to push it up inside and down the standpipe in sufficient quantities to start the siphonic actions. The same effect exists if the level in the cistern is too low, a state which sometimes exists from the swelling of the washer in the ball valve, and needs readjustment. In the desire to get the water level as high as possible to ensure this certain siphonic action, trouble is often experienced from it easily overflowing, the margin between the working line and the overflow line being very small. Again, if the bell in the well is too tight a fit, it does not drop quickly enough to thrust the water over the siphon, or if it does start the siphon, the space between the edge of the bell and the sides of the well are not sufficiently wide to admit the water quickly enough. This also results in the siphonic action never properly ceasing, owing to the influx of water

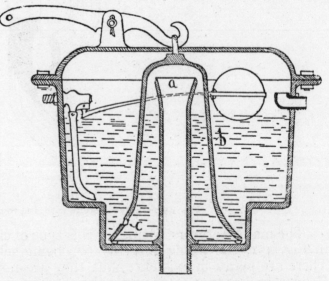

Fig. 452.—Waste Water Preventer Flushing Cistern.

from the ball valve during flushing. While it is a good plan to have a fair fit, the last defect can be overcome by having a small hole drilled in the bell at the point marked (*c*). This has the effect of admitting air into the siphon just before the cistern is empty and so prevents that continuous dribble by siphonic action. The hole should be fitted with a brass bush to prevent rust encrustations closing it.

The early forms have a very fine hole drilled in the crown of the siphon to admit air gradually, but this is not such a good method as the one indicated at c. This hole, which may be about $\frac{3}{16}$ inch in diameter, also has the additional advantage that it avoids the objectionable metallic vibrations, sucking and gurgling noise to a great extent associated with this particular type of cistern at the termination of the flush, the noise of which can often be heard over the whole house of an indoor w.c.

The small pipe fixed to the ball valve leading to the bottom of the cistern is attached with a view to reducing the noise of filling. The overflow pipe can often be raised by fixing an elbow inside as indicated. The

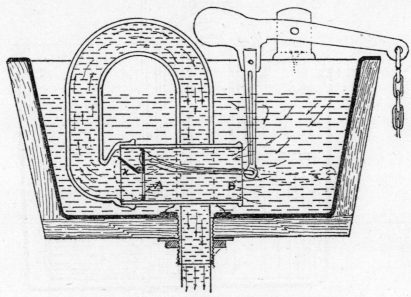

Fig. 453.—Timber Lead-lined Flushing Cistern.

ball valve, however, should not be submerged in the water. As a matter of fact, this is a strong point in Water Board regulations. The silencing pipe should have a small hole drilled in the top to prevent it acting at any time as a siphon. The cistern as shown would have the valve submerged when the water line was near the overflow level, so that it may be considered defective in that respect.

The type of cistern, Fig. 453, is a better mechanical proposition. It may, of course, be in cast iron of any of the usual materials, the one shown being a wooden tank lined with lead. They can also be obtained lined with copper. The horizontal cylinder, about $3\frac{1}{2}$ inches in diameter, is fitted with a piston having a hinged D-shaped valve opening inwards. The given figure is drawn assuming that the handle has just been pulled down. This has thrust the piston along, the valve shown at X being closed by the water pressure during this operation. The water which was in front of this piston has been thrust over the crown of the siphon as indicated by the direction of the arrows within the inverted U pipe and the siphonic action started. The atmospheric pressure on the surface of the water in the cistern pushes it down, opening the valve X, so that the flush is continuous until air is drawn in at the bottom edge of the siphon. The lever then gently rises, the piston receding to point B to be in position ready for the next flush. The ball valve and other details are not shown, but, of course, would be connected in every such cistern. This cistern is quieter in action than the type previously described.

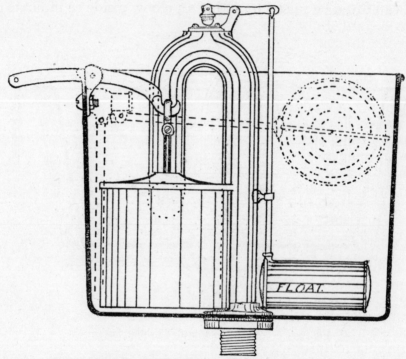

Fig. 454.—Quiet Type of Flushing Cistern.

Fig. 454 shows a type very similar in principle, many of which have been used and give satisfactory results. The cylinder is larger in diameter, giving a bigger volume of water, which, when thrust over the crown of the siphon, ensures a more certain start. It is fitted with a piston with valve opening upwards, this acting as solid piston in the upward movement. When the siphonic action has thus been commenced, it is sustained by the valve opening and the water coming in under the bottom edge of the cylinder. An additional feature on this cistern is contained in an attachment fitted to give quiet flushing effects before the termination of the flush. As can be seen, when the cistern is full, the float has a tendency to rise and close the hole in the crown of the siphon. When the cistern is emptied, the float falls and by its weight lifts up the valve resting over the hole in the siphon. This admits air into the crown of the siphon and stops the siphonic action quietly.

Some cisterns are designed to flush at the opening of the door of the apartment. The one shown in Fig. 455 is such a type of door-action fitting. The chain pull, A, is taken along the ceiling or side wall to door. When users enter the apartment, the ratchet wheel, B, receives a quarter turn, and when leaving the action is completed, the door being opened twice for each flush. The spring, S, returns the lever and keeps the chain taut. The type of cistern required is similar in starting principle to the one shown in Fig. 452. The need for automatic control to such cisterns, however, is gradually disappearing, as the population is educated to the proper requirements in connection with water-closets.

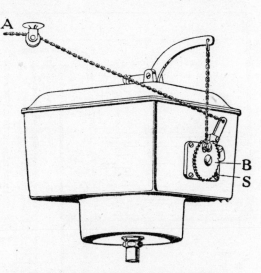

Fig. 455.—Door Action Flushing Cistern.

Automatic Flushing Cisterns

Automatic cisterns are required for flushing drains, grease traps, and ranges of sanitary fittings fixed in places used by irresponsibles, also public urinals and to some extent in sewerage work where intermittent discharge is desired.

The earliest form of automatic flushing cistern consisted of a deep tank so hinged that when full of water it was top-heavy and overset. A small form is shown in a previous figure attached to the waste-water w.c.

The automatic flushing tank proper is shown in Fig. 456. It is an early form by Roger Field, but is quite sound and many are in use at the present time. It works as follows : The bell or dome is fixed giving clearance at the bottom edge at A. The standpipe dips into the well of water, as shown at Z and C. The fitting fills by means of a keyed valve, which is adjusted to fill the cistern and to give discharge at the proper time. They are often fitted in schools, etc., to fill and discharge about three times per day. For public lavatories, however, the discharge must be much more frequent, and the tap is often running full bore in such places. When once the right adjustment has been made, it should not be altered. For this reason, so that the water can be cut off at night without interfering with the regulation, a special stop valve should be fixed within easy reach of the attendant and thus avoid unnecessary waste of water.

Water Level.—Water will only find its level when the conditions of pressure and temperature are equal. In the case of the automatic flushing tank the mechanical parts are so arranged that the air pressure will not be equal. The one in point : as the water rises up the tank when the level outside the dome is at Y, the level of the water inside the dome would be at a point lower, as indicated at X. This difference in levels will increase until there comes a time when the confined air will overcome the resistance and escape as indicated at $Z—C$, when the water inside the dome and outside will flood up to one normal level. This happens several times during the filling of the tank, until there comes a time when the respective water levels will be at X^1 and Y^1 inside and outside the dome. When air now escapes, the water trying to float up to one level, which would be near to Y^1, tipples down the standpipe B at D, which pipe forms the long leg of the siphon, the inside of the dome representing the short leg. This siphonic action will continue until the tank is empty and air is drawn under at A.

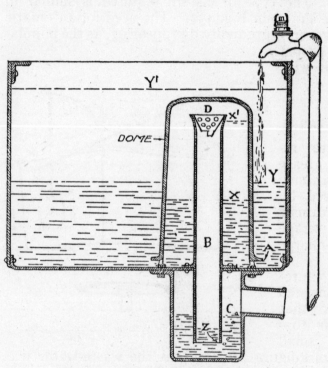

Fig. 456.—Automatic Flushing Cistern.

Although the action of difference in level and discharge has been described as very definite, for the sake of clearness it has been somewhat exaggerated. In practice it may be much more erratic. The relative levels X^1 and Y^1 are not so pronounced as indicated. For instance, it may even so happen that when the air break occurs, the water will flood up to a level which may be only just above the line represented at D. This means that only a dribble of water will escape down the standpipe. The perforated inverted cut cone is fixed as shown with a view to catching this small quantity of water in such a way that it falls down the centre of the standpipe. By doing so it is possible for the siphonic action to be started from the fact that the air is propelled out of this pipe in front of the central cascade to escape via Z and C, and so reducing the air pressure inside the leg of the siphon. If, on the other hand, the water falls down one side of the pipe, it would have no effect on the air and so siphonic action would not be started.

Many of the siphonic cisterns on the market are designed on this principle, but attachments are made with a view to ensuring a start under all conditions. They can, however, become too mechanical and may become erratic owing to the complicated construction. The more simple they are in design generally the more sure they are in action. It is easy to get an automatic flushing cistern which will discharge when water is flowing in at full pelt. It is more difficult to design them to work to a dribble of water. A cistern which may work well when new, sometimes becomes erratic afterwards. As previously stated, most automatic siphonic tanks will flush to a deluge of water when they will not do so at a dribble. For this reason a reverse acting ball valve has been designed. In this type a small pet cock is fixed on the side of the valve which admits the water at the required rate of dribble. When the tank is nearly filled, the float of the ball valve gradually lifts to the rise of the water, and in this case the ball valve is opened, doing the reverse action of the ordinary ball valve. The quick entry of water by this means generally ensures that there will be a start. Such fittings, however, are not approved by most Water Boards, as if anything became faulty the water would be leaking from the valve full bore as compared against a dribble of the ordinary type.

Fig. 457 is a type similar in principle but more compact, so that it does not occupy a large space in the reservoir. It is often used in connection with sewage work, and also can be fixed at the head of a drain in which it has not been possible to give sufficient fall. The relative water levels are arranged to give a wider range over that of the Roger Field type, as indicated at C and F (Fig. 457). The small inverted U pipe as at B is simply a refinement on overcoming the resistance and starting the siphonic action. When the air escapes through the seal at D, the water tipples down the leg of the siphon until the tank is empty. The enlargement shown on the end of the siphon at E has a subtle influence in helping the siphonic action to start. The one shown is assumed to be a concrete tank buried in the ground, as often required in this class of work.

Flushing for Closets in Ranges.—Fig. 458 is an assemble of a type of flushing arrangement adopted for closets in ranges. The two on the left are similar in working principle to that described in Fig. 452, but they are connected together by a 5-inch pipe. The object of this arrangement is to ensure that the water quickly fills up to the flushing height and does not have to rely on a ball valve with its dribbling feed, which often means as much as fifteen to twenty minutes before the water rises to a height which will ensure the siphon starting It also avoids a multiplication of fittings. For instance, one overflow is required for the whole range and one ball valve. A section of this type of cistern is shown inset below on the right, and as can be seen, is exactly the same in principle as Fig. 452. To limit the flush to two gallons, a small well (b) is fixed inside the cistern. The small pipe (a) is attached to the crown of the bell and is led into this well. When the flushing of the cistern starts by means of the hand pull.

water is sucked up through this small pipe (*a*) to empty the well, and by thus admitting air into the crown of the siphon, arrests the siphonic action and, of course, terminates the flush. The big volume of water is not appreciably lowered by this means and quickly fills the small well, so that the fitting is ready almost immediately for a second flush, a design which

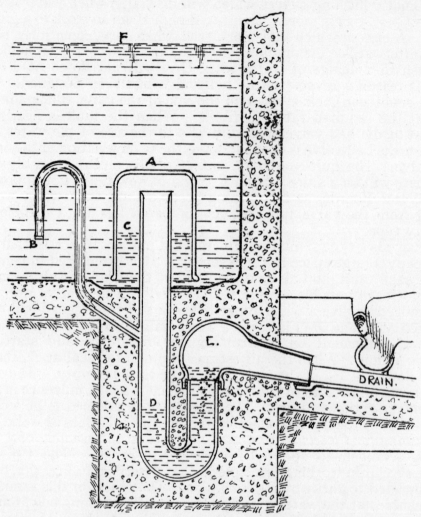

Fig. 457.—Adams' Automatic Flushing Arrangement.

is particularly useful for busy places. The chains are encased by a tubular shield to prevent misusage.

On the top right of this diagram another type is shown, which consists of a continuous cistern the whole length of the range in trough form, as shown in the section on the extreme right. This type may be obtained in galvanised iron or of white glazed stoneware. Again only one overflow is needed and one ball valve. Where the inflow of water to this trough cistern is slow owing to low pressures, an arrangement may be adopted as shown in the sectional drawing *A* of the same figure. In this a large feed tank is fixed over the trough and may be in an adjoining store-room if desired, the trough, of course, being prolonged to that point. The

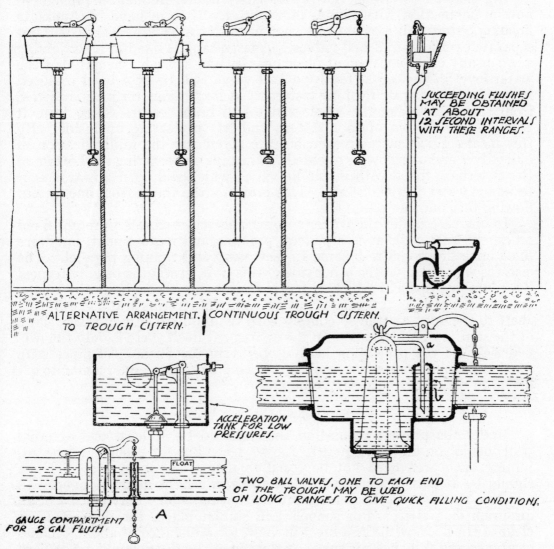

ALTERNATIVE ARRANGEMENT. CONTINUOUS TROUGH CISTERN.
TO TROUGH CISTERN.

SUCCEEDING FLUSHES MAY BE OBTAINED AT ABOUT 12 SECOND INTERVALS WITH THESE RANGES.

ACCELERATION TANK FOR LOW PRESSURES.

FLOAT

TWO BALL VALVES, ONE TO EACH END OF THE TROUGH MAY BE USED ON LONG RANGES TO GIVE QUICK FILLING CONDITIONS.

GAUGE COMPARTMENT FOR 2 GAL FLUSH

A

Fig. 458.—" Adamsez " " Epic " Closet Sets.

float is heavy enough, acting on the lever when the water level in the trough recedes, to lift the valve within the large tank above and so admits a quick discharge of water from that tank into the trough cistern below. The float rising with the water level, shuts off the valve from the large tank, so that the normal flush level in the trough is quickly regained.

Amount of Water for Flushing.—The regulation flushing amounting to two to three gallons is regulated by a device similar to the one in the more conventional form of cistern just previously described, this, by the small bent pipe attached to the crown of the siphon, admitting air when the small cylinder is siphoned empty.

Alternative Fittings for Range Closets.—Another frequent arrangement now in connection with ranges of water closets is to have the separate flushing cisterns all fixed at one level in each compartment, but without separate overflows and ball valves. A large tank is fixed in an adjoining store or any other convenient place near by and at such a height that the water level in this tank, fed by a ball valve, will be at a level required in the line of separate flushing cisterns. A large diameter pipe is carried from this tank along the whole range and branches are taken from it through the bottom of each cistern and left projecting up inside. By this means quick successive flushes are given and the multiplication of ball valves and overflows is avoided. The pipe end entering the bottom of the cisterns is fitted with a spindle valve, which will open upwards only to admit water to the cistern. This prevents the water from one cistern flowing into another one.

In one case under the writer's notice the water-closets were not fixed on an external wall, as is a general practice and requirement, but were fixed on a divisional wall some 12 feet away and running parallel. The cisterns were fixed on the other side of this wall, in what is usually termed " a plumbing space," which space is continuous throughout the range, one end of which, in this case at any rate, should terminate as a ventilating shaft to the open air and so comply with the requirements of the by-laws of the sanitary regulations. In the apartment itself there is only the w.c. pedestal and the projecting handle operating the flush. All pipes were fixed in the plumbing space, such space being large enough for a man to get inside to make any necessary repairs.

Points General to W.C.s

Under the present regulation there should be at least one external wall opening on an area equal to 100 sq. feet,[1] but for basements the adjoining open area need not be equal to more than 40 sq. feet.[2] There should be at least 2 sq. feet of glass fixed in a light made to open. In addition there should be permanent ventilation, which may consist of an air brick or a shaft. For schools and similar places the doors are cut clear of the floor, with this object in view, for a distance of about 3 inches clearance and 6 inches air space at the top. The floor should be of hard impervious material, but for schools, factories, or similar premises, may be of cement trowelled to a smooth surface, or for high-class properties some of the modern patent impervious floor materials, which give a very finished appearance. For outdoor fittings the floor line should be higher than the adjoining open area. The floors should be laid to fall from the

---

[1] See M. of H. Regulations and L.C.C. By-Laws, 1930, p. 293.
[2] See L.C.C. By-Laws, 1930, for modifications, p. 293.

back wall to the doorway at the front, so that the apartment can be cleaned out with a brush and hose if necessary.   It is also a good plan to have the angles rounded, and so avoid sharp quirks which would harbour dirt.   The general recognised minimum width for apartments is 2 feet 3 inches, but 2 feet 6 inches is better.   The height of the fitting should not be more than 17 inches, and when fixed in infant schools, special low fittings should be adopted.   The dividing slabs are best of one of the hard impervious materials now on the market made specially for such purposes, offering a smooth, clean surface.   For ranges these partitions are often now arranged about 6 inches clear of the floor and an open space left at the top, the dividing partitions simply forming a screen about 6 feet 6 inches to 7 feet high.

NUMBER OF FITTINGS REQUIRED

Public elementary schools under Board of Education regulations:— Lavatory basins (wash bowls), should be provided at the rate of two for every fifty children, and equivalent allowances should be made if troughs with sprays are used.   In addition to the supply to the basins, a tap for drawing water should be provided for cleaners' use.

Closets within the main building are not desirable, except for the use of the teachers.

The entries should be screened with an opening at each end and separate provision made for the older boys and girls.

Each closet must not be less than 2 feet 3 inches wide and not more than 3 feet.   The door should be 3 inches short at the bottom and at least 6 inches at the top.   More than one seat in any closet is not allowed.

TABLE LV

APPROXIMATE NUMBER OF W.C.s NECESSARY

Elementary Schools

No. of Children.				Girls.	Boys.	No. of Children.				Girls.	Boys.
Under 30	..	..	..	3	1	Under 150	..	..	..	8	3
„ 50	..	..	..	4	2	„ 200	..	..	..	10	4
„ 70	..	..	..	5	2	„ 300	..	..	..	14	5
„ 100	..	..	..	6	3	„ 400	..	..	..	18	6

In addition, urinal accommodation to the extent of 10 feet per 100 boys is recommended.

The urinal requirement in the specification seems to suggest a running wall panel with a floor channel along the bottom.   Under modern requirements this type is practically obsolete, and the stall type with radial back and channel in one piece of white glazed stoneware should be recommended, even for elementary schools.

Secondary Schools

*Wash-bowl Lavatories—Boys—*1 for every 20 pupils up to 100 and 1 for each succeeding 25.   Eighteen inches to be allowed for each basin.

*Girls—*1 for every 10 up to 100, and 1 for each succeeding 20.

Water-Closets.—The girl's fitting should be in the main building, but suitably isolated. The approaches to each sanitary block must be screened, each closet to be fitted with its own flushing apparatus. The number of closets required is : 1 for every 25 boys ; 1 for every 15 up to 100 and 1 for every succeeding 20 girls.

Urinals.—Separate stalls to be provided to the extent of 1 stall for every 15 boys up to 100, and 1 for each succeeding 20.

Boarding Schools

According to present regulations, *Lavatories* not to be fixed in bedrooms.

Baths.—Two for every twenty boarders—separate provisions for staff to be provided. It is sometimes a policy to fix shower baths, two shower baths occupying the floor space of one ordinary slipper bath.

Number of Closets for day use—1 for every 7 boarders. An up-to-date boarding-school would be fitted with lavatory bowls, baths, and w.c.s within easy access from the bedrooms. A slop hopper should also be fixed in convenient reach of each group of bedrooms or cubicles.

Dwellings Occupied by More Than One Family

1 w.c. for every 12 persons.

It may be pointed out here that for residential hotels, sanitary sets, including w.c., wash-bowl, and baths, are fitted to each suite of rooms, so avoiding the objectionable waiting or even " queuing up " for these fittings, which occurs particularly during holiday seasons.

FACTORIES AND WORKSHOPS
TABLE LVI

Male.	Female.
When less than 100 persons are employed—1 for 25. 100 to 500—4 for first 100, 1 for each 40 after. For 500—1 for each 60, subject to approval. Urinal accommodation must be provided in addition.	1 for every 25 persons employed.

Factory and Workshop Acts.—Under the Factory and Workshop Acts and general sanitary laws, it is essential to arrange a ventilating lobby between any workshop, show-room, etc., and the w.c. apartments, so that the w.c.s can be ventilated to the open air without any fear of a nuisance being created. The arrangement also tends to give a degree of privacy. It is often a difficult problem with existing buildings converted to arrange this ventilating lobby and at the same time provide direct ventilation to the outer air. If the building is not surrounded with other buildings in close contact, the difficulty to such an acute extent does not arise ; but where otherwise, means have to be taken not only to comply with the by-laws, but to produce a satisfactory state of affairs. If the floor concerned is near the roof, it is sometimes possible to arrange a ventilating shaft from the ceiling to the outer air in that direction, or sometimes it is possible to make a staircase form a ventilating shaft, providing an approach lobby can be arranged between.

Where it is impossible to get a change of air by natural means to ventilate the lobby and lavatory apartments of the workshop or whatever the building concerned is, it becomes necessary to adopt some mechanical means to obtain the necessary change of air in the right direction. This consists of rotating fans and shafts, the fans being generally driven by electricity. Lighting is an important detail as well as ventilation. Where the fittings, the apartment, and the surround are all well illuminated and properly ventilated, there is less likelihood of negligence occurring in the general cleansing arrangements. Sunlight and fresh air are nature's disinfectants and superior to any application of chemical fluids or disinfectant powders.

In buildings of factory character, etc., it is always better that the sanitary block shall be away from the main building. A covered approach can be arranged if necessary, and it should go without saying that separate, screened approaches to the separate blocks should be provided for the sexes.

Wherever any foodstuffs, such as at bakeries, sweet factories, etc., are in course of preparation, fixed wash-bowls should be provided for ablution purposes, and if they are to be used properly, cold and hot water should be laid on and clean towels provided. The wash-bowl should be fixed immediately adjacent to the w.c. apartment.

In exceptionally well equipped factories and workshops, slipper baths and shower baths are sometimes provided, particularly, for instance, in connection with large bakeries and collieries, so that the men can have a thorough clean-down and change of clothing before going home.

Fig. 459 shows an arrangement in plan in a small compass which would be suitable, say, for 150 men. If it is to be used properly, there must be a copious supply of hot and cold water, clean towels, and an attendant. The floors are worked to shallow channels in some smooth impervious material, the channels being led direct to the outer wall to discharge over gully traps.

Fig. 460 shows a rather crowded arrangement of lavatory accommodation for the two sexes, and as drawn accommodates 150 men and 60 women.

Fig. 461 shows how lavatory accommodation can be arranged off a staircase under circumstances which do not permit a separate sanitary block.

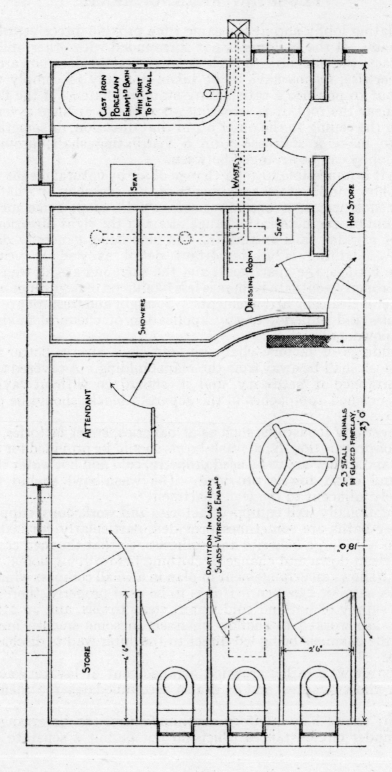

CAST IRON
PORCELAIN
ENAMLD BATH
WITH SKIRT
TO FIT WALL

SEAT

WASTE

HOT STORE

SHOWERS

DRESSING ROOM

SEAT

ATTENDANT

2-3 STALL URINALS
IN GLAZED FIRECLAY.

PARTITION IN CAST IRON
SLABS-VITREOUS ENAML'D

STORE

6' 6"

2' 6"

25' 0"

18' 0"

28

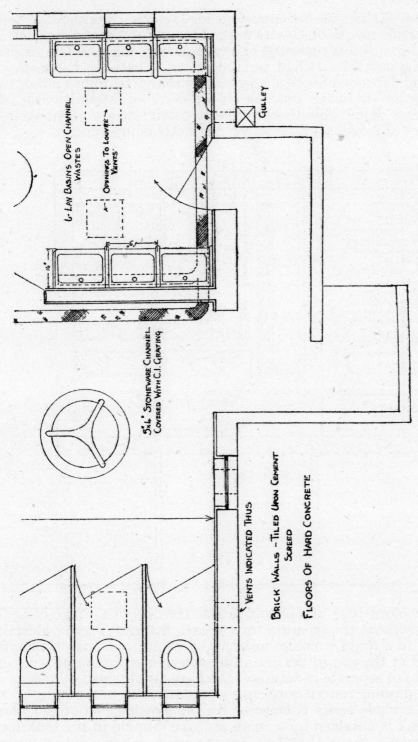

6 Lav Basins Open Channel Wastes

Openings To Louvre Vents

Gulley

5×4" Stoneware Channel Covered With C.I. Grating

Vents Indicated Thus

Brick Walls - Tiled Upon Cement Screed

Floors Of Hard Concrete

Fig. 459.—Sanitary Accommodation for Factories.

Latrines.—It has been the custom for factories, workhouses, schools, etc., to provide ranges of closets flushed by one automatic flushing tank. The early form of this consisted of a trough trapping a certain amount of water in the bottom. It had aerial connection between the seats of the fittings, and depended for cleansing on an intermittent flush either from a tip tank or an automatic flushing cistern working intermittently two or three times a day. This trough type is particularly objectionable, and can in cases of infectious diseases be distinctly dangerous.

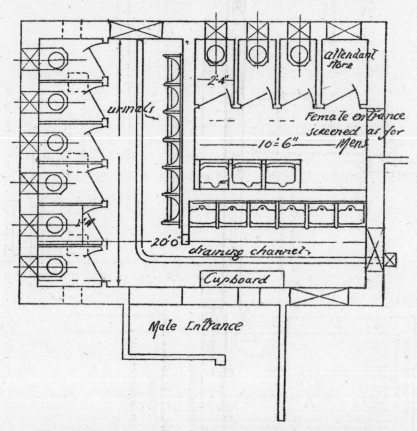

Fig. 460.—Sanitary Accommodation for 150 Men and 60 Women.

An advanced type of siphonic latrine consists of a range of pedestal w.c.s, but without the separate trap to each fitting. These pedestals are connected to a drain running horizontally below, one large siphon as an inverted U at the end of the drain line determines the water level in the whole series of separate pedestals. Discharge is obtained by means of an automatic flushing cistern creating a siphonic action in the range of w.c.s, so that the whole series is emptied by the siphonic action so started. An air break is obtained by a small air pipe dipping in the tank leading from the crown of the U siphon, arresting the siphonic action when the water in the tank gets down to the level of the end of the air pipe. The remainder of the water in the tank continues to discharge until the tank is empty, charging the range of w.c.s with clean water. The time has

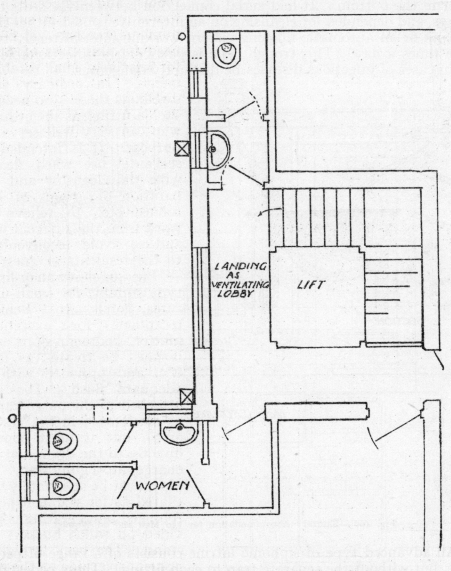

LANDING
AS
VENTILATING
LOBBY

LIFT

WOMEN

Fig. 461.—Office Sanitary Provisions arranged from Staircase.

almost come when these ranges so flushed can be dispensed with, except, in the case of elementary schools and institutes for the mentally defective and for infant schools, the separate fitting independently flushed being much more satisfactory for all general purposes, including factory and institute.

Slop Hoppers.—These fittings are only required where there are large groups of bedrooms, and as we advance in labour-saving devices, such as fixed washing-bowls in bedrooms and adjacent bathrooms and w.c.s in sufficient numbers, the less will be the need for this class of fitting for relatively small establishments. In ordinary small dwellings there is no need for such a fitting, as the ordinary w.c. can very well serve the purpose. It is intended for servants' use when dealing with the cleansing and preparation of groups of bedrooms, etc., to relieve the work from the adjacent w.c.s and so avoid inconvenience to the residents or guests.

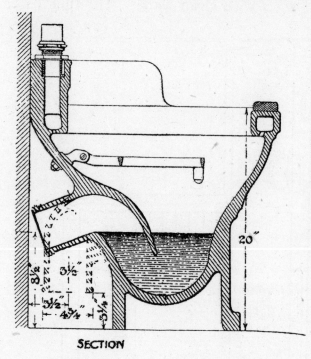

SECTION

Fig. 462 shows an ordinary type suitable for small institutes, hotels, etc. Being a receptacle for excretional matter, bedroom slops, etc., it must be treated as for a w.c. and provided with an adequate flush. The pipe attached to the outgo can be as small as 3 inches (L.C.C. area), but it must connect directly to the drain, not discharge into a gully trap. The pipe must be adequately ventilated as for w.c. soil pipes. A hinged brass grating is provided on which buckets can stand. The back is high to prevent splashing on the wall, and at the front a teak insertion is fixed to prevent fracture of the ware by buckets being knocked heavily against it. A smaller finer grating is often fixed below to intercept floor cloths, etc., which inadvertently get thrown down. It is not advisable to fix a water tap over this fitting, as is often done, for the following reason :

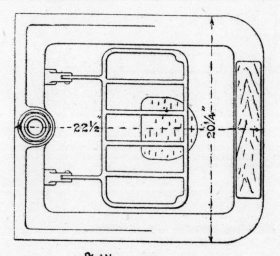

PLAN

Fig. 462.—Slop Hopper.

In emptying a bucket of slops it is quite possible for the nozzle of the tap to become fouled, and the drinking vessels for the bedrooms being filled at this tap, the water is contaminated. If water taps are required, they should be fixed on one side, so that there is no possible risk of fouling.

For large establishments the housemaids' sink and the slop hopper are combined, the slop hopper providing for the emptying and the sink for the cleansing of the utensils used in a bedroom. Hot and cold water are usually provided to the sink section. It is generally arranged that the outlet from the sink discharges to a purpose-made socket provided on the inlet side of the slop-hopper trap to save a special waste pipe, and it is desirable always to economise as far as possible and reduce the number of pipes

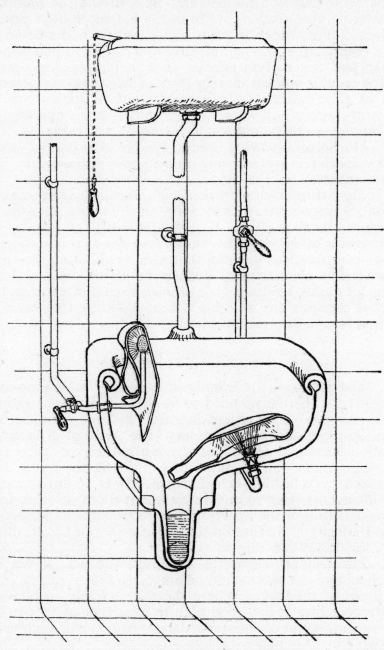

Fig. 463.—Hospital Slop Hopper.

on a building, providing one is not sacrificing efficiency. The outlet from the slop hopper may be connected to a soil pipe to which w.c. outlets are also attached, the fitting being in the same class.   There is one possible unsatisfactory result from this arrangement when dealing with the combined slop hopper and sink, in that at one moment very hot water may be discharging from the hot tap followed quickly by cold.   If the soil pipe, which is probably 4 inches in diameter, is in lead, it can be realised the unequal strains that are set upon this pipe from expansion and contraction effects ; hot water running down one side of this pipe only, it will ultimately lead to fracture, particularly if the soil pipe is of thin material.   It suggests that in such cases for the combined fitting taking hot water, a heavy cast-iron pipe well coated with some bituminous compound would be more serviceable.

For hospital work a special type of slop hopper is provided, which is fitted with jets for cleansing utensils used in the wards.   This arrangement is suggested by Fig. 463.

The fitting itself is flushed by an ordinary flushing cistern and special control valves are provided for flushing the utensils.   The valves are sometimes arranged to be operated with the feet by treadles, with the intention of leaving the hands free for manipulating the utensils.   A two-compartment flushing tank can be obtained for these fittings.   One two-gallon compartment flushes the fitting down and the other supplies the jet flushes to cleanse the utensils used in the wards.   Such an arrangement prevents any possible risk of polluting the water in general service pipes from a general store tank.

URINALS

The provision of urinals is necessary where numbers of men congregate.   There is no need to fit them in domestic properties unless they are premises which entertain guests in large numbers or where there are smoke-room and billiard-room.   The position of urinals should be carefully selected, as the odours from urine are very penetrating and there is nothing more objectionable in a building than the smell of stale urine caused by splashing or otherwise.   It is of importance that the urinal shall not be near to any refreshment-room or store for food, etc.   The construction of the apartment as to smooth, impervious surfaces, proper and adequate ventilation and lighting, are of great importance if satisfactory conditions are to exist.

For ordinary domestic dwellings the w.c. serves the purpose of a urinal, and the seat should be hinged so that it can be conveniently tipped up out of the way.   Where the w.c. is likely to be used as a urinal by irresponsibles, it is a good plan to fix a type of seat to the w.c. which by an arrangement of counter-balance weights will assume a vertical position (swing up automatically).

A special w.c. known as the " Hyback " was manufactured at one time with a view to making a fitting particularly serviceable as a urinal or a w.c.   The back of the pedestal was carried up about 12 inches high above the seat, and the wooden rim seat was so balanced that it tipped up, forming a frame round the pottery back piece. It is not a comfortable or very sanitary fitting, however, as the sitter is likely to foul the clothes by leaning back on the upturned pottery back piece

Bracket Urinals.—Small bracket urinals fixed on a wall are often favoured where the demand for a urinal is somewhat intermittent or the need for a urinal is limited. Fig. 464 shows one such type in section.

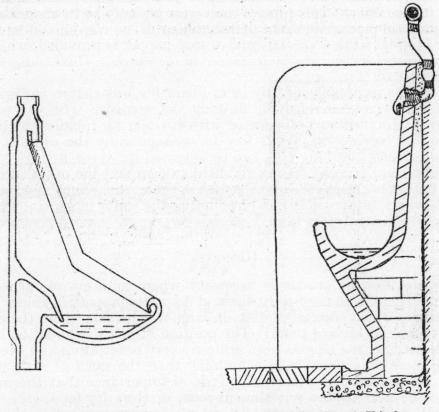

Fig. 464.—Bracket Urinal.   Fig. 465.—Trough Urinal.

Stalls.—While they serve a purpose, they are far from ideal, and, in the writer's opinion, if a urinal is necessary, then nothing but the stall type with radial back and channel or outlet in one piece of white glazed stoneware should be used. The types which, by a weir, trap an amount of dilute urine are not to be recommended, as even dilute urine can become very objectionable, particularly so when water is not constantly running to flush the fitting. A trough type on this principle is shown in Fig. 465. One has only to observe this type in some of our public buildings to realise the faults in comparison with a modern fitment. Rectangular types of stalls, whether in slate or marble, are not satisfactory, as urine fur collects in the angles and on surface which is not flushed. Sparge pipes, consisting of perforated iron or copper pipes running along the length of the stalls, do not give a self-cleansing flush, and a type known as a spreader is to be preferred.

A range of six modern urinals of the stall type is shown in Fig. 466. Each stall covers about 2 feet of wall space, and the screens of side-pottery run sufficiently high and projecting to secure privacy.

The requirements are as follows : A well-lighted position with at least one wall external to the open air. A waste pipe not less than 3 inches in diameter. This pipe, if underground, may be in stoneware or cast-iron drain pipe well coated with bitumen. The trap should be fixed

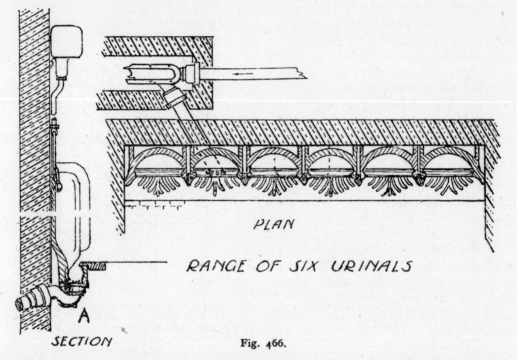

PLAN

RANGE OF SIX URINALS

SECTION

Fig. 466.

directly to the outlet of the channel, which outlet is usually arranged at one end or in the middle of the range.

Flushing.—Single stalls should be provided with flushing cistern giving a one-gallon flush. Where one cistern is fixed to a range, it should have a minimum flush capacity in gallons to give one gallon per stall. The flushing pipe, which is best in copper or in lead, should be graduated in diameter and so arranged that each stall gets a proportional amount of flushing water. Hand-pull cisterns are usually used where the urinal will be used very intermittently ; but in cases where they are used fairly frequently, an automatic type is preferable. The difficulty with the hand-start type lies in the fact that the users will seldom take the trouble of flushing them until there is a distinct odour arising.

Special arrangements with Water Companies have to be made with the automatic type for registering the amount of flushing water used. This is done either by meter or, in some cases, by a special keyed and sealed supply valve. The flush pipe to each stall should be provided with a fan-type spreader. This consists of a cast-brass piece having an oblique slit in it which projects a fan-like stream of water over the whole curved surface of the radial back stall.

Wastes.—The outlet from the channel should be protected with a brass or gunmetal domical bar grating, secured with gunmetal studs or otherwise so fixed that the attendant or any authorised person can remove it for repairs, etc. Adequate supplies of water are necessary in connection with urinals, not only to prevent odours, but particularly to prevent the waste or drain pipe from becoming choked with the fur deposit associated with urine discharge. The waste pipes from urinals fixed on first or higher floors must also be treated as soil pipe, i.e. connected direct to the drain, the only trap being fixed immediately under the channels.

Where two separate fittings or ranges join a stack of pipe, adequate provision must be made against siphonage by fixing anti-siphonage pipes. There should be no objection to branching the waste pipes from urinal ranges to soil pipes if conveniently placed, providing proper anti-siphonage arrangements are made to protect the respective traps.

In the London County Council area not less than a 3-inch waste pipe is allowed.[1] Waste pipes above ground may be of strong lead pipe or of protected cast-iron pipe. There appears to be no objection to using wrought-iron or mild-steel pipes if they are properly coated internally and the special recessed fittings are used as designed for waste-pipe work.

Long lengths of waste pipe should as far as possible be avoided, as the amount of flush is very limited and for single fittings discharging one gallon, it is not sufficient to prevent deposits occurring within the pipe. The writer has a piece of lead pipe 4 inches in diameter, which served as a waste pipe from fittings in a nunnery, which has a passage left about 1 inch in diameter. The writer has several times observed cases where w.c.s have been used solely by women, that the soil pipes and trap to the fitting have quickly become choked with fur, presumably from the fact that the fittings are not flushed after being used as a urinette.

Plain iron fittings in connection with urinals should be avoided, as they are quickly corroded by urine and urine vapours. Walls and floors adjacent to urinals should be of some impervious material.

It may be worth mentioning that fur in urinal fittings and waste pipes may be removed with dilute hydrochloric acid if the pipe is not completely made up. The procedure consists of plugging the bottom end of the pipe temporarily. The pipe should be filled and left overnight. Repeated applications are sometimes necessary to get the pipe clear.

The outgo from channels has not received the attention it should

[1] L.C.C. By-Laws, 1930, permit a 1½-inch waste for a single fitting; 2-inch for two, and 3-inch for ranges of more than two fittings.

do. For instance, in the case of a range fixed on a ground floor, the joint to a stoneware or cast-iron trap has to be made in a blind manner, as it is covered by the base of the channel when putting it in place.[1] One firm

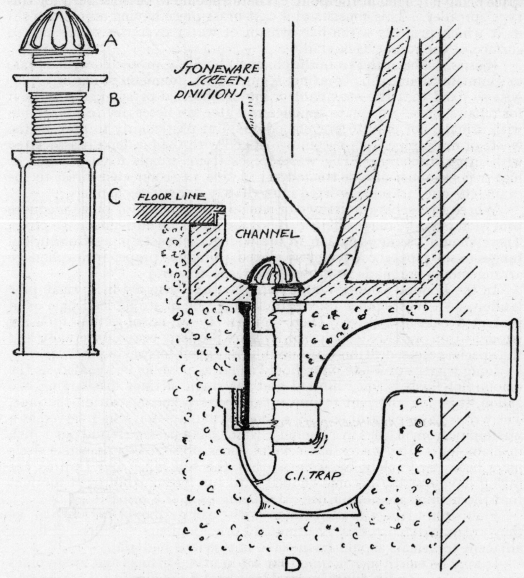

STONEWARE SCREEN DIVISIONS

FLOOR LINE

CHANNEL

C.I. TRAP

Fig. 467.—Burn Bros. Stall Urinal Outlet Fittings.

at least has provided special fittings to meet the need. These are shown in Fig. 467, which gives the separate parts at *A*, *B*, and *C* respectively, *D* showing the fittings *in situ*, the trap being of 4 inches diameter cast-iron. The extension pieces *C* are made in 9-, 12-, and 15-inch lengths.

[1] There is not the same difficulty when connecting to a lead trap.

Urinettes.—These are fittings designed specially for women's use. They are similar to the washdown w.c., but the top is somewhat narrower and elongated and raised at the front. The seat is of horseshoe shape, a space being left open at the front. There appears to be little need for this

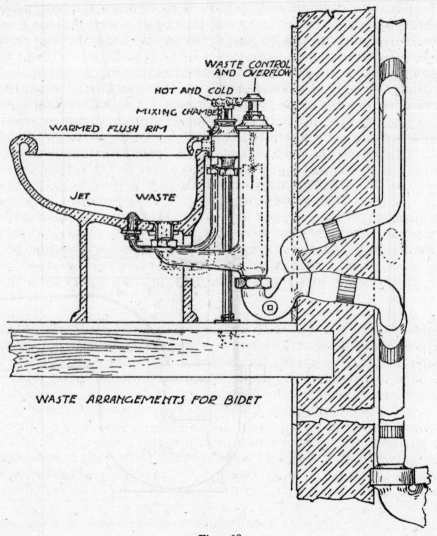

Fig. 468.

fitting, as an ordinary w.c., choosing one with a good projection and a close-fitting seat, should meet the need.

Door action actuating flushes may be arranged for urinals, so that a flush of water is given each time the door is opened. In this case a spring valve is generally used in place of the flushing cistern.

Bidets.—A bidet is a fitting designed on lines similar to a pedestal w.c., but intended particularly as an ablution fitting chiefly for women's use. It may be used also with advantage in certain types of hospital for men or women.

It is not so commonly installed in domestic properties in this country as on the Continent, but is becoming more general.

There is some difference of opinion as to whether the outlet pipe from this fitting should be treated as a soil pipe or as a waste pipe, i.e. whether it should discharge direct to the drain or discharge into a gully trap. The writer believes that the question is being considered by the Committee now sitting with a view to reviewing and readjusting the general sanitary regulations.[1] The fitting is necessarily an ablution provision, and to use it otherwise is probably done from ignorance. The writer heard of a case where a number of refugees to this country, strange to modern sanitation, were temporarily accommodated at a hotel. In the morning it was found that they had used the bath as a w.c. and presumably washed in the w.c. The moral is that it is a question of education, and the public should be educated as to the proper use of the fittings.

Fig. 468 shows a modern sanitary type. It is provided with a douche jet in an upward direction for ablution. Hot and cold valves are fitted with a separate mixing chamber and control valve. Warm water can be used for the flush, so that the rim is rendered comfortable for the person sitting on it. The outlet is small, being $1\frac{1}{4}$ to $1\frac{1}{2}$ inch in diameter. As shown, the waste is fitted as a waste pipe in that, apart from the small trap attached to the fitting, the pipe discharges to the back inlet of a gully trap.

Another form is fitted with a polished or enamelled wooden seat and flap cover. The brass trap shown is one of a special form having an anti-siphon branch as part of the casting. It is not essential, and a branch in the pipe can be made in the ordinary way with a wiped joint if anti-siphonage arrangements are necessary.

The water jet connection should not be branched to any service pipe from which drinking water might be drawn. There was a hinged type of jet on the market which could be turned up and out of the way when the fitting was not in use. It was intended to fit with an ordinary w.c., but was not adopted to any extent. There seem possibilities, however, for such an attachment fitted to the bidet, and so reduce possible risk of water pollution.

---

[1] The L.C.C. Regulations, 1930, have definitely classified the Bidet as an ablution fitting, the waste pipe discharging to a gully trap.

CHAPTER III

WASTE PIPES AND SOIL PIPES

Types of Waste Pipes—External and Interior Fitting—Rainwater Heads—Ventilation Pipe for Wastes—Expansion Joints for Lead Pipes—Soil Pipes—Combined Cast-iron and Lead Pipes—Drainage for Workshops—Ventilation and Anti-siphoning for Ranges—Assemblage of Waste, Soil, and Rainwater Pipes—Hospital Work—L.C.C. Standard Waste and Soil Pipes—Cast-iron Drains.

WASTE pipes from ablution fittings discharge to a gully trap with an aerial break at that point. The pipes taking the discharge from slop hoppers and urinals, although usually called waste pipes, are connected directly to the drain in a similar manner to a soil pipe. The term " soil pipe " is usually applied to the w.c. only.

Types of Waste Pipes.—Waste pipes may be of heavy lead and heavy cast-iron, providing such iron is coated internally and externally, internally to offer a smooth passage and prevent corrosion. In modern practice light-gauge copper pipes are being used for waste pipes, also wrought iron or mild steel. The latter material is easily corroded, so special precautions should be taken to provide a permanent smooth surface. Galvanising is generally considered satisfactory. The fittings of the copper pipe are usually of the compression type, and for wrought-iron waste pipe a special recessed fitting, a sketch of which was given in a previous chapter (Volume I), so that the pipe and the fitting make one even, constant, smooth bore, not with an enlargement and rough edges as is given by the ordinary pipe fitting, for instance, as used in hot-water work.

External and Interior Fitting.—It has been a general practice to keep all waste and soil pipes outside the building as far as possible, and this principle is quite good. It has objectionable features, however, and it is often a sore point with architects that the amount of piping entailed in giving ventilation and anti-siphonage mars the appearance of the building. It is becoming the practice to keep some of the pipes, at any rate, on the internal face of the external wall, and the time may come when plumbing spaces are provided, as in America, where all pipes as far as possible are carried down within this space and access given. At any rate, it is possible to provide this in the larger type of building. In some cases it is a feasible scheme to run the waste pipe on the external face, the branch ventilation and the anti-siphon pipes on the internal face of the wall, or in some cases they can be run within a chasing of the brickwork on the internal face.

Rainwater Heads.—In ordinary domestic work it has been common practice to discharge all waste pipes, where the fittings are conveniently grouped together, into a rainwater head. A rainwater head is not a sanitary fitting, and this particular fitting is far from ideal when applied to such work. For instance, it has a large unequal surface subject to fouling and becomes coated in time with decomposing soap jelly. This rainwater head is necessarily fixed near a window, which means, when the window is opened for ventilation, the gases rising from the pipe under the head must discharge into the room. Under the L.C.C., 1930, By-Laws, this is no longer permitted.

Ventilated Pipe for Wastes.—In best practice the waste pipes will discharge into one common pipe, which is carried up to discharge as a ventilating pipe above the eaves of the building, as required for soil pipes.

Fig. 469 shows a waste-pipe from the bath and lavatory basin connected together and ventilated in this manner. It is assumed that the anti-siphon pipe of the bath waste is on the internal face of the wall.

Occasionally the waste pipe from the lavatory basin, to save pene-

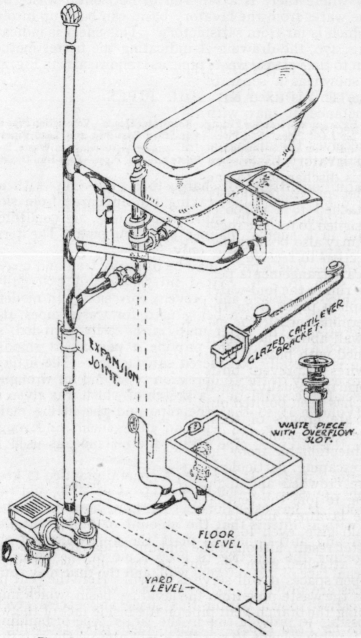

Fig. 469.—Arrangement for Small Domestic Premises.

trating the wall, is connected inside on to the bath waste. This often results, particularly where there is a fair run of horizontal waste bath with bends, that the water from the lavatory basin can back up into the bath, a condition which is far from satisfactory. This effect is indicated in drawing *B* of Fig. 470, the drawing *A* indicating the better method, i.e. direct connection to the vertical waste pipe, as is shown also in Fig. 469.

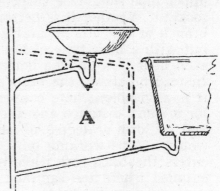

The sink waste is shown as a separate pipe, but where the sink is fixed on a higher floor, for instance, it may with advantage be connected to the same waste pipe which receives the discharge from the bath and lavatory basin. In the present case it is discharging to one of the special inlet pieces previously mentioned and attached to a purpose-made gully trap designed to receive these inlet pieces. They may also be obtained with another connection to receive rainwater where the local arrangements permit the rainwater to run to the foul-water drain. The anti-siphon pipe[1] from the sink is shown as terminating on the external face of the wall above the height of the fitting, finished with beaded edge and cross copper wires to prevent birds entering. In this form it is usually termed a " puff pipe." It has been pointed out that where there are groups of these fittings such a process of terminating the pipe ends can be objectionable from the accumulated gases escaping, particularly where buildings are crowded and high. The dash lines rising to join the ventilating pipe from the lavatory indicate a method which would give, even for the

Best Method of Connecting Waste Pipes.

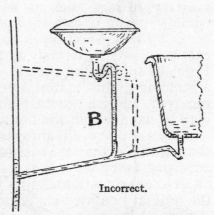

Incorrect.

Fig. 470.

single fitting, a better result, although the amount of gas from the short piece of waste pipe attached from the sink to the gully would not be excessive, and in open spaces it will serve as drawn. Here the vent pipe would have to cross the waste pipe from the lavatory basin, which might be avoided by keeping the branch-vent pipe on the inside face of the wall.

Expansion Joints for Lead Pipes.—Leaden waste pipes receiving the discharge of alternate hot and cold water and particularly from sinks fixed on upper floors can with advantage be fixed with an expansion joint, at least one for every floor immediately below each group of fittings.

[1] A better term, and adopted in L.C.C. By-Laws, 1930, is trap ventilating pipe. Lead expansion joints cannot be used inside a building.

Such a joint [1] is indicated in Fig. 469 immediately below the bath branch. The need applies more particularly to high buildings, and especially so in institutes where very hot water is used. The wall stumps led directly through the wall over the vertical waste pipe have been known to be sawn off from the continual see-saw movement caused by the expansion and contraction through neglect of this provision. The end of the upper pipe should be suspended about 1 inch from the shoulder of the socket. Whether it is better to fix the expansion joint above the wall branch or below is debatable. In the given drawing it is shown below, but with a high type of building with multiplex fittings discharging at each floor it would be better to fix it above, the branch connections. Instead of taking the branch of wall stump directly through the wall, it is advisable, where convenient to so arrange, to strike off sideways for a short distance and then turn through the wall with the branch, and so form a degree of elasticity and freedom of movement which would not be working on a rigid point, as it is when the wall branch enters the brickwork directly. Such a method is usually of necessity entailed where the sanitary fitting is fixed under windows, the waste pipe, of course, not being allowed to traverse across windows, but has to be on one side. It is not the best practice, however, to fix sanitary fittings such as baths and lavatory basins directly under a window, owing to awkward position for opening and cleaning.

Soil Pipes.—Soil pipes are usually of strong drawn lead or of heavy cast-iron coated internally and externally with Dr. Angus Smith's solution. Previous to October 1924 it was not permissible to fix soil pipes within a building of any material other than lead. This barrier has now been removed, and lead or cast-iron, providing the latter is properly coated, may be fixed within the building. L.G. copper tube can also be used.

Generally the advantages of a leaden soil pipe are : It is smaller comparatively than the cast-iron pipe with its thick walls and large sockets occurring every six feet at least, and, therefore, it is less conspicuous on an external elevation and its weather tone is to be preferred rather than the ordinary painted cast-iron. It should not be necessary to add that such a leaden pipe should never be painted. It is more adaptable for the many positions required in practice. It has a smooth bore and is very endurable, and is easily permanently made gas- and watertight. Bends and changes of direction can be worked on the job to suit the circumstances. Its chief weakness lies in the fact that it is easily dented, and for this reason it is not so suitable in situations where it is exposed to damage, as, for instance, in gateways, by-ways, school yards, etc. In such situations the first 6-foot length from the ground level should be in heavy cast-iron, the remainder of the pipe being carried out in lead.

Combined Cast-iron and Lead Pipes.—It is often a proposition to combine the two metals, using cast-iron for the main stack, and in the case of ranges the main branches, and using lead pipes bent to the

---

[1] Expansion joints are sometimes fixed at intervals of 6 feet up the whole stack.

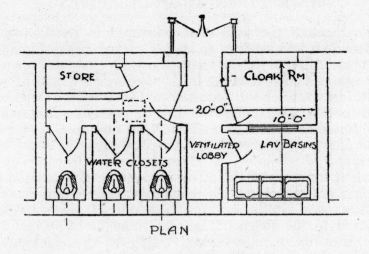

PLAN

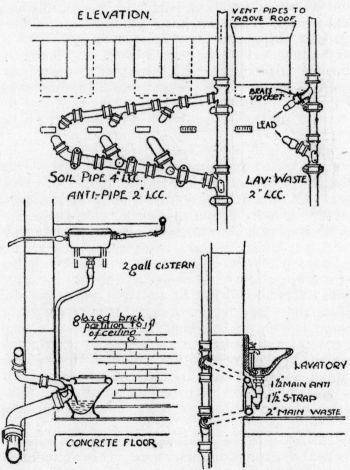

Fig. 471.—Soil and Water Pipes for Workshop on First Floor.

required angle through the wall and connected to the fitting. Where the change is made from cast-iron to lead, a proper type of joint must be made, i.e. a brass thimble wiped on to the lead pipe, the brass thimble being run into the socket with blue lead. Wherever a lead pipe changes to a hard metal in waste or soil pipe work, this detail is required, a brass or other hard-metal socket being required to receive a stoneware outgo and a brass thimble on the spigot end of a lead pipe joining, for instance, a stoneware or cast-iron drain or a cast-iron soil pipe.

Arrangement for Workshops —Fig. 471 shows the drawings of the sanitary arrangement for a workshop, assuming it to be a conversion job of an existing building. The soil and waste arrangements are indicated below, using what is known as " heavy L.C.C. standard pipes and fittings." The socket fitted to the outgo of the w.c. must be of special form and larger than the ordinary pipe socket, owing to the thickness of the stoneware. This point should be observed when ordering. Access should be provided on each junction, particularly so on the main junction into the vertical stack. Lavatory waste pipe and anti-siphon branches are shown as in lead, being more adaptable when any awkward position is met with, and connected to the cast-iron vertical shaft by means of the brass thimble and wiped joint. All these fittings are shown ventilated and anti-siphoned as required, to prevent one fitting siphoning the seal of the trap of the adjoining fitting, and not only that but to provide a current of air flowing up the branch pipes close up to the fitting and out through the ventilating branches, thus aerating and oxidising the internal surfaces of the pipes.

Ventilation and Anti-siphoning for Ranges.—Fig. 472 shows a method of ventilating and anti-siphoning a series of ranges of w.c.s fixed one above the other. The main stack is in cast-iron and branches in lead, a convenient method of carrying out this work. The range on the ground floor is shown with the branches connected directly to an access chamber, which is, perhaps, the safest method, as cases have been known in the course of a stoppage or partial stoppage at the duck-foot bend for the discharge from the upper floors to overflow from the fittings placed on the ground floor. This should not be possible and is generally due to bad workmanship, some lead having escaped during the running of the caulked joints and lodging in this bend at the bottom of the stack, or cement in the case of a stoneware drain. The ventilating pipe on the right has been carried down by dash lines, as at *V*, to the drain. While this is not required under by-laws, it has in a few cases been practised with a view to providing a direct current of air through this pipe from the drain. It is sufficient, however, here to carry the work out as indicated in the firm lines.

Some architects object to the windows being framed round in this way with the two vertical shafts and branch pipes. It is a circumstance which cannot be avoided very well if the pipes are to be outside, but it may be preferred that the main ventilating shaft shall be run close to the 4-inch

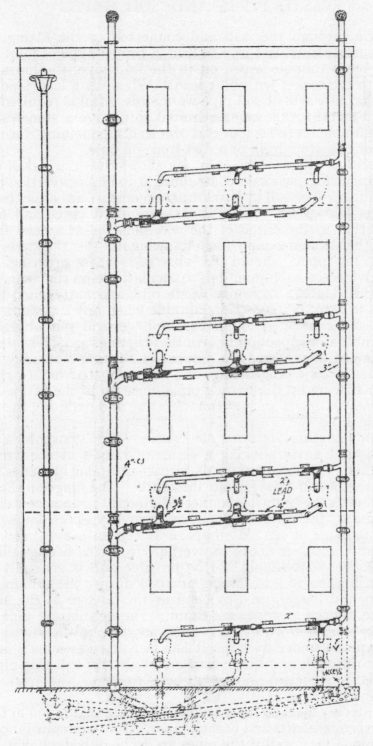

Fig. 472.—Soil and Vent Arrangements for Ranges of W.C.s on several Floors.

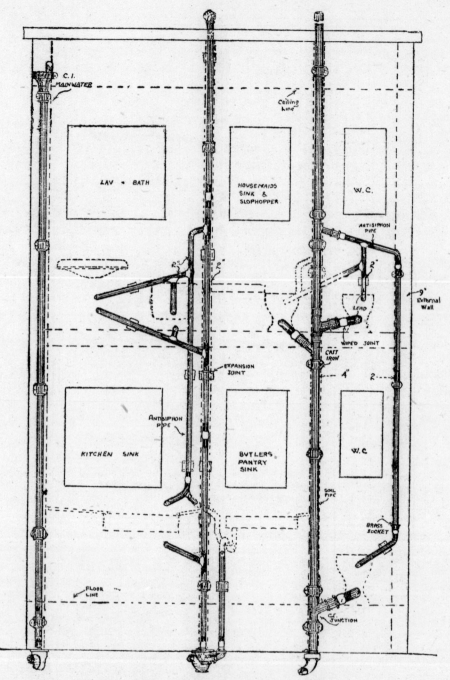

Fig. 473.—Soil and Waste Stacks for a Large House.

stack pipe on the left, in which case the ventilating pipe will have to pass over or behind the side branches, and the horizontal direction run of ventilating pipe will then, of course, have to rise the opposite way, i.e. towards the ventilating shaft placed on the left to provide for the natural rise of the current of air. Plate I shows pipe work for a range of w.c.s fixed on a boundary wall.

Assemblage of Waste, Soil, and Rainwater Pipes.—Fig. 473 shows an assembly of waste, soil, and rainwater pipes as required for fittings in a town house. It will be noticed that the slop hopper outgo is connected to the soil pipe, the main stack of which is of cast-iron ; the short wall branches needed, of course, in connection with this type, are in lead, the object being to so combine the two metals that the work is simplified and carried out in the best possible manner. It could, of course, be carried out in all lead if preferred ; but if very hot water is used in connection with the sink, the trouble described in a previous chapter might be experienced. The bath and lavatories are connected to the one stack, the main ventilating pipe, running along with the waste pipe, entailing the cross over. Pipes are ventilated and anti-siphoned in the manner as required in the best practice.

There is a fault in this diagram in the way the side branches of soil, waste, and anti-siphon pipes have been set out. The work would have a much better appearance if the slope on all the branch pipes were kept at a constant angle of fall and rise as far as possible.

Hospital Work.—Fig. 474 shows the arrangement for a hospital sanitary block. It can be assumed that these sanitary blocks are built clear of the main building and joined by short ventilating lobby or corridor. The position of the slop hopper and combined sink is debatable, and it might be preferred that it should be fixed near the ventilating lobby ; but as arranged, all pipes are on the one elevation and it is possible to take the discharge from the slop hopper into the soil pipe required for the w.c.s. In this case the sink section is provided with a separate waste outlet, not the type discharging into the inlet side of the trap of the slop hopper, but carried out separately as a waste pipe, and, in this case being conveniently near to the main stack of waste pipe serving the bath, it can be connected to it, as it is a pipe of the same classification discharging into a gully trap. (See Plan, Fig. 475, and Elevation, Fig. 474.)

The bath is shown in the centre of the apartment, a usual arrangement for hospitals, making it possible for the patient to be helped from both sides, and at the same time it avoids any awkward corners or angles which would be difficult to cleanse. Lavatory basins are also usually required and could be situated in a position as shown by dotted lines or in any other convenient position in the bathroom.

TABLE LVII

2-inch anti-siphon lead—not less than 45 lb. per 12-foot length. Iron—25 lb. per 6-foot length.

Waste pipes from slop-hoppers and urinals in lead 3 inches in diameter should weigh not less than 60 lb. per 10-foot length. If in cast-iron, not less than 40 lb. per 6-foot length.

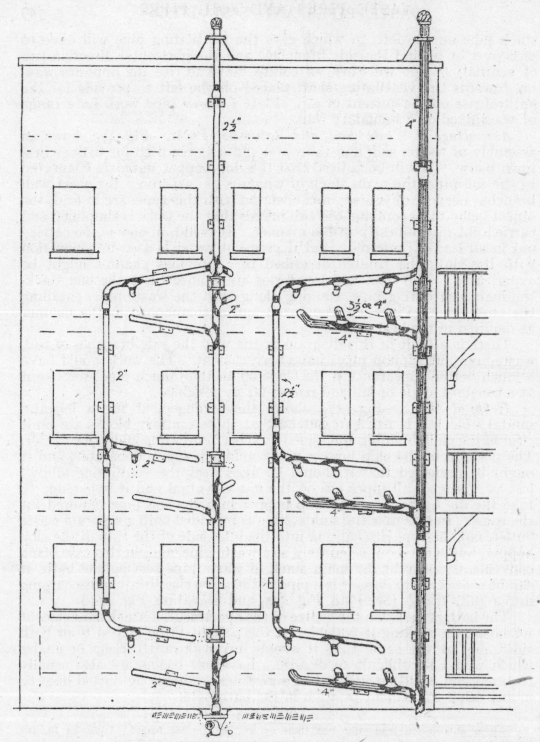

Fig. 474.—Arrangements of Soil and Waste Pipes for a Hospital Sanitary Block.

TABLE LVIII
STANDARD SOIL PIPES
(See page 289 for 1930 L.C.C. By-Laws)

	Lead.		Iron.	
Diameter.	Weight per 10-foot Length not less than	Thickness.	Weight per 6-foot Length including Sockets and Ears	
	65 lb.	$\frac{3}{16}$ inch	48 lb.	
	74 lb.	$\frac{3}{16}$ inch	54 lb.	
	92 lb.	$\frac{1}{2}$ inch	69 lb.	
	110 lb.	$\frac{1}{4}$ inch	84 lb.	

TABLE LIX.
CAST-IRON DRAINS

Internal Diameter.	Minimum Thickness of Metal.	Weight per 9-foot Length including Sockets.
3 inches	$\frac{5}{16}$ inch	110 lb.
4 inches	$\frac{3}{8}$ inch	160 lb.
5 inches	$\frac{3}{8}$ inch	190 lb.
6 inches	$\frac{3}{8}$ inch	230 lb.

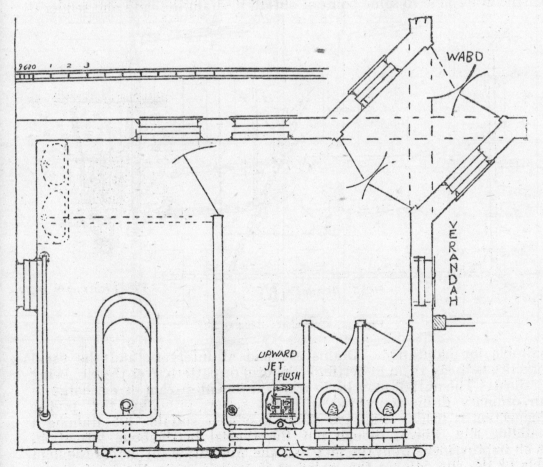

Fig. 475.—Plan of Hospital Sanitary Block.

CHAPTER IV

DRAINAGE

Subsoil Drainage—Rainwater Drainage—Foul-water Drainage. **BUILDING DRAINAGE :**
Separate System—Combined System—Partially-combined System—Country Houses—Planning—
Materials Used—Jointing—Repair Work—" Badger " for Stoneware Drains—Level Laying—
No Drains to be under Buildings—Fittings and Drains—Falls—Ramps—Carrying Capacity of Drains
—Changes in Direction—Trapping—Ventilation of Drains—Connection to Sewer—Testing Drains.

DRAINAGE is roughly divided into three sections :
(1) *Subsoil Drainage.*—Subsoil drainage consists of laying a plain
earthenware pipe to some point of outfall to drain the land and render it

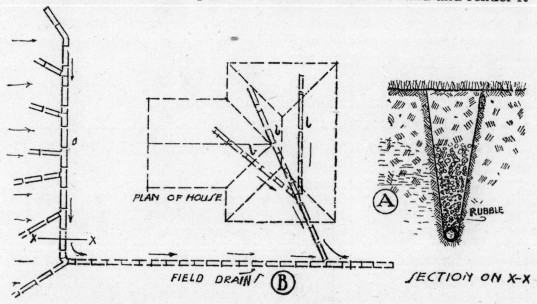

Fig. 476.—Draining a Building Site.

suitable for habitation. Drains are laid at intervals, and the usual
practice is to lay them in herringbone form or pattern over the site being
drained. The outfall may be to any convenient stream or discharge to
an ordinary drain connected with the sewer, providing the proper
connection is made. Fig. 476 shows a scheme suitable for draining a
building site, which, though not the typical herringbone formation,
is an improvement from the fact that the cross drain (*a*) across the high
side of the site catches the water as it travels down the slope in the

strata and diverts the water round the site. A branch set can be laid under the building as shown at (*b*) as an extra precaution in keeping the site dry and healthy. The drawing *A* indicates the type of trench used. The pipes are plain earthenware without sockets laid end to end. A piece of tile is placed over the joints to prevent small stuff filtering in and choking the drain. Broken stone or other rubble is filled in.

(2) *Rainwater Drainage.*—Rainwater drainage, as its name suggests, is a system designed to carry off all the roof water and the water from paved areas.

(3) *Foul-water Drainage.*—In foul-water drainage, drains are arranged to convey all waste waters of sanitary fittings from the vicinity of the building to some convenient outfall.

Building Drainage

Drainage on building work is divided into two classes :

(1) *Separate System.*—In this one set of drains deals with the rainwater only, carrying off all roof water and water from paved areas. Under a district scheme it will discharge to the top water sewer, such sewer dealing only with this water and water from roads, etc., ultimately discharging to the local water-course. Foul-water drains are entailed in the work of carrying off all waste water, and it must discharge to a sewer if one exists within 100 feet of the building ; or if such a sewer does not exist, it may discharge to a cesspool or to a private purification installation.

(2) *Combined System.*—The combined system of drainage consists of laying a drain to carry off the rainwater and the waste water from the sanitary fittings, etc., in one common set of drains, such drains discharging to the foul-water sewer.[1]

Partially-combined System.—In many districts a modification of the scheme exists which allows a certain number of the rainwater pipes to discharge to the foul-water drains, the rest being carried in a separate drain to the storm-water sewer. This is sometimes known as the partially-combined scheme.

The object of separate drainage is to prevent the sewage works being inundated with water during a storm. It can be realised, when one thinks of the miles of paved areas, roofs, etc., over a large town, that this water can be a tremendous deluge which taxes the plant to its utmost and renders the ordinary processes of purification inoperative.

Country Houses.—In country-house drainage, it is often desirable to collect the whole of the rainwater in an underground storage tank for domestic use, laundry, etc., or part of it may be collected in a tank placed in a roof-space of a lower roof to catch the water from a main roof. Such a tank would supply a scullery or laundry by gravitation and save the need of pumping. The general requirements for good drainage are as follows :

---

[1] A " Combined drain " has a different meaning in London.

Planning.—The main thing in planning any system of drainage is simplicity. The lines of drains should be carried in the most direct route from point to point. The number of receiving gullies, etc., should be kept as small as possible; that is, if it can be arranged for one gully to receive several fittings and, in the case of combined drainage, rainwater, then it should be done, making one gully trap do, rather than fix two at distances apart. It cannot be advocated, however, that rainwater pipes, etc., should be run in a horizontal direction on elevations of the building to gain this end; it is more a question of suitably placing the sanitary fittings and, in the case of rainwater, in a position for gutter outlet.

Scale drawings[1] of the scheme of drainage showing the whole system of drainage should be prepared and submitted to the council fourteen days before commencing the work. In cases of alterations to a drain where the work must be carried out at once, notice should be sent to the sanitary authority of the district in writing indicating the need of such proposed alteration, when, by permission, the work may be commenced, subject to the approval of the inspector of the district and subject to the deposit of properly drawn plans within two weeks of the commencement of such alteration. Various Borough Councils provide proper forms on which to draw the plans, and if the space available is insufficient for the drawing, they may be made on tracing linen, and attached to the forms. The forms contain extracts of the by-laws applied to drainage. A block plan showing the position of the building is required for new buildings, and it should be supplied in conjunction with a detailed drainage plan, the minimum scale for the block plan being 1 inch to 22 feet.

Materials Used.—The choice of materials for good drainage is limited —either salt-glazed stoneware or heavy cast-iron drains protected with Dr. Angus Smith's solution. For ordinary villa drainage the deciding factor is generally a question of first cost, and stoneware drains usually score in that respect. Cast-iron drains make a permanently sound job; stoneware drainage is somewhat cheaper. A cast-iron drain when once properly laid will never give any subsequent trouble from blockage, etc., neither will it fracture easily by settlement or subsidence of the building. On the other hand, the stoneware drain is very fragile and would fracture at very little movement. A further advantage of the cast-iron drain is that the lengths are 9 feet against 2 feet for the stoneware pipe, entailing a fewer number of joints, simplicity in laying, and reduced risk of leakage. An exception where a stoneware drain should be selected in preference, irrespective of the question of cost, is in the case where the effluent contains some acid matter which would have a detrimental effect or a corrosive influence on the coating of a cast-iron drain, as, for instance, the discharge from chemical works or process discharging acidiferous fluids.

Jointing.—The methods of jointing employed on drains and fittings are simply by means of sockets and spigots, the stoneware drain joint

[1] Duplicate plans and sections, in ink, to scale not less than one inch to every sixteen feet.

being made with good Portland cement and the cast-iron drain by means of blue lead caulked. The cement used in a stoneware drain should be carefully examined, the best only being used. If it is old stock or what is known as " cold," it will shrink in setting and cause a lot of trouble in getting the joint tight. If, on the other hand, it is what is known as " hot," i.e. new cement, it will probably expand in setting. There is some risk that the whole of the sockets will be split by this expansive force, which it can be realised would be a very serious condition, as the whole of the work would have to be taken up again and relaid with fresh materials. The condition of a bag of cement can be ascertained to some extent by thrusting the hand into the heart of the bag, when some indication is given by the temperature. If the cement is very new, it should be spread out on the mixing board for a few hours, so that it becomes what is known as " air slacked." A little sharp sand should also be added. It is often recommended in specifications that a strand of spun yarn should be inserted in the sockets of these stoneware joints with the object of holding the spigot end concentric to the socket. It will attain this end in a satisfactory manner when used by an experienced man, but there is always some risk where drains are being laid by inexperienced men that some of the yarn will be forced through the joint to the inside of the drain, an obstruction which can cause considerable perpetual trouble by causing the drain to become blocked. Particularly is this so with cut lengths, if such a cut is not made square so that the plain end fits truly on to the shoulder end of the socket it is connected to. In the writer's opinion, it is a mistake to use yarn (which is a kind of soft rope) dry, as in the course of time it must decompose and cause a series of what would be foul points at every 2 feet at least of the drain, for which reason it would be better to steep each length of yarn in liquid cement before using, so that it sets in a homogeneous mass with the cement of the joint.

There are many patent stoneware joints on the market designed to overcome this trouble of getting the spigot end truly concentric to the socket. This is a very important detail, as if it is not true, the irregularity, occurring as it does every 2 feet at least, would offer considerable friction to the passage of matter through the drain. In the case of a drain laid with a slow fall, little pools of liquid matter would be held up at each socket, so that such a drain would never be self-cleansing and the amount of gas evolved and discharging at the vent pipes would be abnormally high over that of a properly jointed and well-laid drainage system. One device consists of providing small projections of stoneware in the bottom of the socket in the form of studs. There are also several patent joints on the market which consist of a bituminous ring of material in the form of a bead round the outside edge of the plain end of the stoneware pipe and another bead of similar material fitted on the inside of the socket. They are turned up and shaped at the factory while hot, and all that is required is to press and twist the two pipes together until the plain end reaches the shoulder of the socket. Some types have the whole depth of the cavity filled with this material ; others have half the depth, the remaining half of the cavity being filled with cement, which is the better type of the two. It is claimed with these types that the drain can be laid in case of alterations without interrupting the normal discharge through the drains, and if necessary such a drain could be laid in a waterlogged trench. If, however, the trenches of drains were waterlogged, the site should be drained by special subsoil drains and so avoid such an unsatisfactory condition of things.

With a cast-iron drain the joint is made in exactly the same way as for cast-iron water mains and cast-iron gas mains laid in the road, in which half the cavity is caulked with yarns and the remainder of the cavity filled with molten lead poured in through a special gasket, as described in a previous chapter. Care must be taken to make a true fit, so that the molten lead cannot run through and settle on the invert of the drain, as if such does occur it is practically impossible to remove it. In place of the gasket of yarn used in caulking, a special lead wool could be used with advantage and so avoid using any material which might subsequently decompose.

Repair Work.—In cases where alterations are being made to a cast-iron drain in use, the whole of the cavity between socket and spigot could be filled with this patent caulking material, and so avoid the use of molten lead and consequent risk to the operator under such conditions.

" Badger " for Stoneware Drains.—It is highly important that the man laying a stoneware drain should use a tool known as a " badger." This consists of a stick of wood about a yard long, which is fitted at the end with a half-circular disc of wood swept to the required radius of the pipe being used. The object of the badger is to remove any surplus cement which may squeeze through into the bore of the drain when making a joint. If one joint alone is neglected, it will cause subsequent trouble ; hence the need of special precaution in this detail. The badger should not be removed from the drain ; otherwise it is easy even for an experienced man to forget. By leaving it lying in the drain he has to thread the next pipe over the handle end of it, and by such process he cannot easily forget and neglect to draw it forward and so sweep off the surplus cement and bring it along into the socket of the drain he has just laid.

In place of the semicircular piece of wood, a piece of old rag tied on to the end of the stick in a bunch a little smaller than the pipe will serve the purpose. This is rubbed about in the location of the joint and has a grouting-in effect to the crevice between spigot and socket on the inside of the drain. Surplus cement must of course be drawn forward out of the pipe.

Level Laying.—All drains, when properly laid, should be as straight as a gun-barrel, and it should be possible—and as a matter of fact drains are often inspected thus—that a lighted candle having been placed at one end, the drain can be seen as a circular tube from end to end.

To avoid subsequent. subsidence, stoneware drains should be laid on a bed of concrete at least 6 inches thick and equal in width to the trench and not less than a projection of 6 inches on each side of the drain. The concrete should be delved out at every point where a socket occurs, so that the drain lies *supported on the barrel* throughout the whole length and not intermittently supported on the sockets. When the drain is laid, the cement should be haunched up to a height equal to half the diameter of the pipe. Another method consists of laying the concrete 3 inches thick. Then laying the drain on bricks laid flat. Fine concrete is then filled in to the necessary depth.

Avoid Drains under Buildings.—A drain should never be laid under a building if it is possible to avoid it. There are cases, of course, where it cannot be avoided, as, for instance, in terrace houses. When such circumstances occur, the drain must be laid in a straight line from end to end throughout the whole distance such drain passes under the building, and access provided at each end. If a stoneware drain is used (some Councils do not allow this), it is required that it shall be not only laid on a bed of concrete 6 inches thick, but that it shall be totally encased to a depth of 6 inches all round the drain. The idea of this, no doubt, is that the drain is a hollow concrete beam with a stoneware lining; but when one considers the quality of the concrete which is often used in drainage and the distance such a beam would be running from rigid point to point, it is very doubtful, if there is no intervening support, whether such drain and beam would support its own weight on the distance between. If it will not do so, it naturally will not fulfil the purpose intended, and any subsequent subsidence of the earth would mean that the stoneware drain with its additional load of concrete would subside and the whole cross-section would fracture. It follows that under a building, at any rate, it is safer to use a cast-iron drain, and it should be supported on a bed of concrete, but not encased.

Fittings and Drains.—Great care should be taken over the selection of suitable fittings for the work in hand, and the drains should be planned to some extent to suit the standard fittings of the catalogue. There should be no make-shift business—that is, if a bend or junction does not take the right line of direction, it should not be made to do so by forming an ill fit in the sockets—the proper fitting should be obtained to suit the job. The stock angles in junctions and bends are as follow: $90°$; $92\frac{1}{2}°$; $95°$; $100°$; $112\frac{1}{2}°$; $120°$; $135°$; $145°$; $157\frac{1}{2}°$. A bend in addition can be obtained at an open angle of $170°$. Traps with outgo at various angles can be obtained, viz. $92\frac{1}{2}°$; $112\frac{1}{2}°$; $135°$; $180°$. The last of course is an S trap, $135°$ is known as a Q trap or half S, and $92\frac{1}{2}°$ is the P trap. Square junctions as sometimes used in water-supply pipes should not be used; i.e. if two pipes meet at right angles, the fitting should have the branch arm swept obliquely in the direction of the flow. Sharp knuckle bends should be avoided and fittings of slow sweep selected in preference. The standard length of the pipe is 9 feet, but to save waste 6-foot, 4-foot, 3-foot, 2-foot, 21-inch, 18-inch, 15-inch, 12-inch, and 9-inch lengths can be obtained for cutting. Double socket lengths for cutting can also be obtained in 3-foot, 4-foot, and 6-foot lengths.

Falls.—One of the most important details in arranging a drainage scheme is to obtain an equal and sufficient fall. It is sometimes contended that a drain can have too much fall. The question is debatable. It is suggested that a small body of water flowing at a high velocity will have a tendency, due to its lack of depth, to leave solids behind. It can be realised that the diameters of the drains will have a bearing on this matter and that a small-diameter drain will give a greater depth of water relatively than a larger-diameter drain carrying the same volume of water. It is, however, a most serious fault to have insufficient fall and every endeavour should be made to get the required amount to give the required velocity, which will have a self-cleansing result on the drain.

A general guide for this work is to multiply the diameter of the drain to be laid by ten : for instance, a 4-inch drain to be laid with no less than a fall of 1 in 40, a 6-inch drain 1 in 60, a 9-inch drain 1 in 90. A certain amount of latitude can, however, be taken each side of these amounts. For instance, the writer has known 4-inch drains laid with a fall of 1 in 48 proving satisfactory, but there must be limits at which a drain ceases to give satisfactory results. The amount of fall required will depend upon the entire distance the drain has to run from its most distant inlet to the point of discharge, and it follows that the greater distance run, the greater the ultimate depth of the drain from a level line. Another factor, of course, will be the depth underground at which the drain commenced.

In exposed positions where there is likely to be traffic over the drain, there should be at least 1 foot of earth over the crown of it, and 2 feet are better. This means, assuming a drain was 6 inches outside, the depth of the trench would be at least 18 inches at the commencement. Where a drain is laid in positions where there would be vehicle traffic over a drain which is not deeper than 1 foot from the crown, the trench should be filled up with concrete to surface level.

The excavations are usually commenced at a point nearest the sewer or other outfall and carried on towards the building. The depth of the trench will, of course, depend to a great extent upon whether there is a fall on the ground site or not. Assuming a level line, with a run of 4-inch drain, say 200 feet long, the depth of a trench at the outfall end would be 200 ÷ 40 = 5 feet, to which should be added the initial 18 inches the depth at which the drain commenced, and 6 inches for concrete, giving a total depth of 7 feet at the low end.

The procedure for setting out the fall of drains on a job is usually by one of two methods, or both can be used. The first consists of setting out the fall by means of sight rails and boning rod. The fall is worked out from point to point, that is, from inlet to access chamber or from access chamber to access chamber as the case may be, obtaining such depths by dividing the standard fall into the run, as in the example just

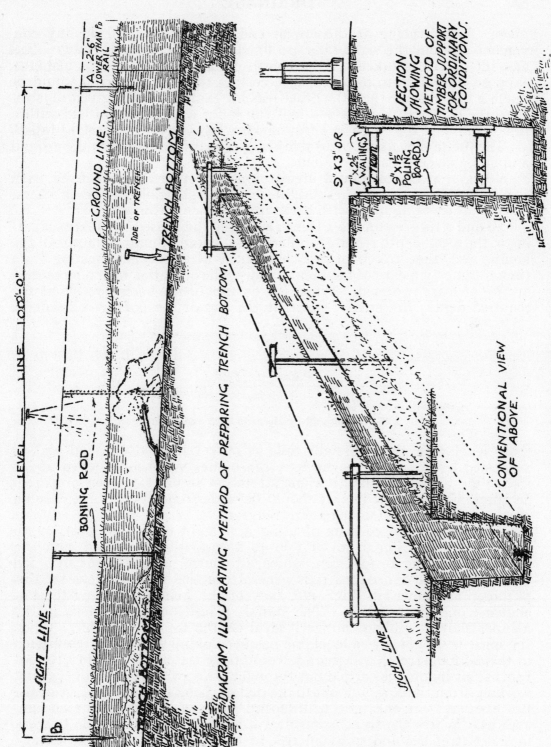

Fig. 477.—Arranging Fall and Excavating for Drains.

LEVEL LINE 100'-0"

A..2'-6"
lower than P.
RAIL

GROUND LINE

SIDE OF TRENCH

TRENCH BOTTOM

SIGHT LINE

BONING ROD

TRENCH BOTTOM

B

DIAGRAM ILLUSTRATING METHOD OF PREPARING TRENCH BOTTOM.

SECTION SHOWING METHOD OF TIMBER SUPPORT FOR ORDINARY CONDITIONS.

9"x3" OR

7"x2½" WALINGS

9"x1½" POLING BOARDS

4"x4"

SIGHT LINE

CONVENTIONAL VIEW OF ABOVE.

given. Commencing at the lowest end of the drain and on any convenient stretch, the sight rails are fixed as indicated in Fig. 477.   The
amount of fall is taken off the length of one sight rail ; for instance,
suppose the fall is to be 2 feet in a certain run, one sight rail would be
made 2 feet shorter than the other—as for example in the given illustration, the sight rail A on a 100-foot run is for a 4-inch drain laid with a
fall of 1 in 40 : 100 ÷ 40 = 2 feet 6 inches less in depth than sight rail B.

   The method of fixing these sight rails is to drive a peg into the ground
and nail a level cross rail to them.

   When working on paved areas, stoneware pipes can be fixed with
socket downwards and the uprights of the sight rails placed in them,
the pipe then being filled with earth to hold them firm.

   To find a true bottom to a trench a boning rod is used.   After excavating to the exact depth required under the sight rails, found by means of the
boning rod, the stretch of trench is excavated between, testing from
time to time by means of the boning rod.   The operation has to be carried
out by at least two men.   When the bottom of the boning rod is at the
required depth, the cross T-piece at the top of the boning rod will be

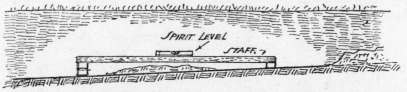

Fig. 478.—Setting Fall by Means of Staff and Spirit Level.

truly level with the two sight rails as observed from one end and as
suggested by the drawn sight line, the boning rod being moved about
from time to time until the whole stretch of trench has been prepared.
In speaking of a sight line, it should be understood that this is only an
imaginary line when looking at the diagram.

   Another method consists of using a straight edge of known length
and spirit-level.   For a fall of 1 in 40 a 10-foot staff is used, giving a
3-inch fall on the 10-foot run, which, of course, is equivalent to a fall
of 1 in 40.   For short runs it is general practice to use bricks for this
purpose, as shown in Fig. 478, two bricks being placed at the low
end and one at the other.   The staff is placed on these bricks in the
manner shown, holding the spirit-level on the top of the staff.   When
the spirit-level indicates a level line has been obtained, the bottom trench
in this 10-foot stretch will give a fall of approximately 3 inches in a 10-foot
run.   This method is carried out throughout the whole length of the run,
working from the low ends out to the distant points.   The distance of the
run excavated at one time will depend to some extent on the circumstances.   Where the trench runs near a building, it is advisable to work
in short stretches and so avoid risk to the building and to the trench.
Timbering for support to the sides of the trenches is necessary for deep

excavations. An ordinary method employed is shown in the inset section drawing on the right of Fig. 477. The walings should be 9 inches × 3 inches in deep trenches.

Where side branches are taken off the main drain line it can be realised that to keep a constant fall throughout the main and the branches, the receiving fittings, such as gully traps, would terminate at different levels. If this practice of fixing fittings at different levels is not carried out, the fittings are fixed to the yard levels and the difference is made up by adjusting the fall to suit, giving either more or a little less as the case may be, although the latter should not be done if it can be avoided. When the true bottom of the trench has been obtained, concrete is put in to the depth of 6 inches unless on a very solid foundation.

Ramps.—There are occasions when there is a considerable difference in levels obtained where a branch drain runs into the main. For instance, assume a case in point where there is an outbuilding, such as a dairy or a stable, some considerable distance back from the dwelling, and it is desired, and is general on the same premises, that there should be only one connection to the sewer. At the point of junction working on equal falls, the depth of the drain of the dwelling at point X (Fig. 479), on indicated run of 4-inch drain, will be 1 foot 3 inches + 1 foot 6 inches = 2 feet 9 inches. Now, taking the run of drain from the outlying building, the depth required at X is $(150 + 50) \div 40 = 5$ feet. To this must be added 1 foot 6 inches, the initial depth, making a total depth of 6 feet 6 inches; then 6 feet 6 inches minus 2 feet 9 inches = 3 feet 9 inches, that is, a difference of 3 feet 9 inches, and the question arises, should the fall be

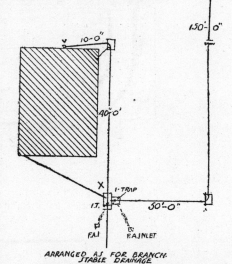

Fig. 479.—Unequal Runs of Drain Meeting at One Point.

increased on the house drain to meet this point 6 feet 6 inches below the ground in the centre of the access chamber X, or should what is known as a " ramp " be formed ? This consists of running the main drains throughout on one equal fall and making adjustment by means of ramps at the point of junction. Stable drainage should not run through a house drain, but should be treated entirely separate and have a separate interceptor, fresh-air inlet, and vent. The stable drain may discharge into the house drain at the intercepting trap, as indicated at Fig. 479.

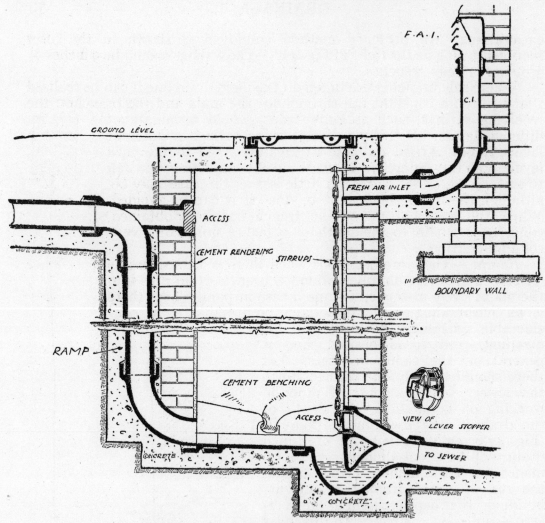

F.A.I.

C.I.

GROUND LEVEL

ACCESS

CEMENT RENDERING

STIRRUPS

FRESH AIR INLET

BOUNDARY WALL

RAMP

CEMENT BENCHING

ACCESS

VIEW OF
LEVER STOPPER

CONCRETE

TO SEWER

CONCRETE

Section on a Ramp and Intercepting Trap.

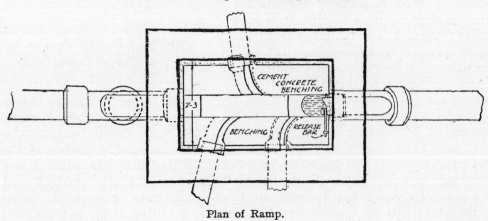

CEMENT
CONCRETE
BENCHING

2-3

BENCHING

RELEASE
BAR

Plan of Ramp.
Fig. 480.

62

Fig. 480 indicates a ramp such as would be required, in which the shallow drain is ramped down outside the access chamber and carried in at the required level. The one shown is in stoneware, but the same method would be suitable for cast-iron drains.

In cases where there is not a great difference in the respective levels, a ramp can be made in the chamber by forming a quick slope in the half-channel pipe passing through the chamber.

On an extensive job, longitudinal sectional drawings should be made of the whole scheme, showing all the depths of the different access chambers and the depth of the drain throughout, working from a datum line, and relative ground levels being shown along the stretch. Vertical scale is usually made twice that of the horizontal scale to show up more clearly the amount of fall and depths of manholes.

On an extensive job the diameters should be carefully dimensioned. There is not much selection, however, the usual standard diameters being 3 inches, 4 inches, 6 inches, and 9 inches. For approximate reference the carrying powers of the drains can be compared by squaring the diameters. Thus $4^2 = 16$; $6^2 = 36$. Therefore a 6-inch drain has more than twice the carrying power of a 4-inch drain, being in effect as 36 is to 16. Owing to this big disparity an intermediate drain has been made 5 inches in diameter, but is not frequently adopted. It generally becomes a question on a small job of where two or more 4-inch branches meet,[1] the next usual standard size is taken of 6 inches and the drain carried on in that diameter. On small dwellings there is no need usually for anything larger than 4 inches in diameter; and for jobs of ordinary dimensions, sizes larger than 6 inches in diameter are seldom required. The relative discharging power of drains is as the square root of the fifth power of their diameters. The intermittent nature of sewage discharge must also be taken into consideration.

Carrying Capacity of Drains.—It is sometimes taken that one-half the daily discharge takes place in six hours, i.e. for each inmate allow 15 gallons per six hours for waste water or $2\frac{1}{2}$ gallons per head per hour.

The following formula is often used for working out velocities and discharge in open channels or drains: $V = 55 \sqrt{\text{of H times 2 F}}$.

V = velocity in feet per minute. 55 is a constant, and it has been contended that this constant under modern conditions of drainage may be increased as high as 100.

H is the hydraulic mean depth. This is found by dividing the sectional area of flowing water in feet by the wetted perimeter in feet, i.e. the wetted surface of the pipe. When the drain is running full or half full, it can be found by simply dividing the diameter of the drain in feet by four.

F is the fall in feet per mile. To find discharge it is necessary to know the velocity either by trial or calculation:

---

[1] Only such cases where the branches will discharge full bore at the same time.

A. Find the velocity of water flowing through a drain 4 inches in diameter laid with a fall of 1 in 40, using the above formula.

$$V = 55 \sqrt{H \times 2 \times F.}$$
$$V = 55 \sqrt{\cdot 0833 \times 2 \times 132}$$
$$V = 55 \sqrt{22}$$
$$V = 55 \times 4\cdot 7$$
$$V = 258 \text{ feet per minute.}$$

Working
$$H = \cdot 33 \div 4 = \cdot 0833$$
$$F = \frac{1760 \text{ yds.} \times 3}{40} = 132.$$

B. Find the discharge in gallons. A convenient form in dealing with a circular pipe is to work to the following formula : Diameter of pipe or cylinder in inches squared multiplied by ·034 gives gallons per foot run. Therefore discharge for 1 foot will be :$4^2 \times \cdot 034 = \cdot 544$, and $\cdot 544 \times 258 =$ 140 gallons approximately, which could be taken as a minimum amount for a well-laid scheme. If the drain was running only half full, the discharge would be one-half, the velocity remaining the same.

It will be realised that this formula is suitable only to apply where water is flowing as in an open channel and under no direct head water. It can be seen that if a 4-inch drain laid on the regulation fall will do this, and considering the intermittent way in which waste waters discharge to a drain, there is little need for very large drains. The largest amount in domestic work that goes down within a short period, as a matter of fact, is from the bath, for which reason, owing to the flushing value of this water falling from the first or higher floor, the bath waste should be kept large and discharge under the grating, not over the grating, of the gully trap, to give good scouring effect. The greatest test on a drain is in a scheme which takes the rainwater from roof and pavement areas in addition to waste waters from the sanitary fittings.[1]

Change in Direction.—For all main changes of direction, bends, junctions, etc., taking foul waste water, access should be provided. For stoneware drains, the method usually employed is to build a 9-inch brick chamber, which must be rendered in cement to be watertight to ground level. The pipe passing through here, whether as a bend or a junction, is in the form of a half-round channel as far as the stoneware pipe is concerned, but the cement concrete should be benched up vertically on each side of this channel to a height of about 3 inches to give a deep-seated channel from which the liquids cannot easily escape. The concrete from that point to the said brickwork is benched up at an angle of about 45°, on each side, so that it can be easily washed down by dashing in a bucket of water should it become foul.

For the side branches, purpose-made inlet pieces can be obtained which are higher on the back, making about ¾ circumference. This ensures that solids in the effluent are not thrown out on to the benching by centrifugal force.

These access chambers are covered with a cast-iron frame and cover having an airtight groove to prevent the escape of gases. The covers

[1] During a storm.

may be of single seal or double seal.   A very special precaution is provided in a manhole cover which, in addition to the ordinary seal made
with tallow, has a condensation seal.   The warm drain-air striking on
the cold plates of the lid condenses the moisture into water, which
trickles down and keeps the channel in which the edges of the plate dip,
full of water.   The strength of the cover must be in proportion to the
traffic which may be anticipated will pass over it, a very heavy type
being required in gateways or archways through which any type of traffic
may pass.   Some are fitted with a recessed lid : this permits the area occupied by the lid being filled with a paving material of the same description

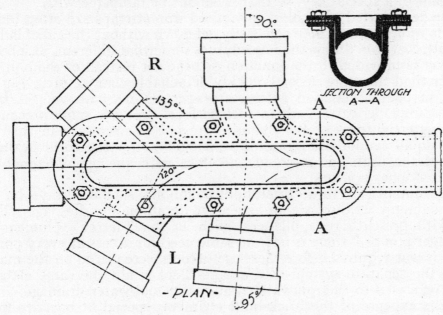

Fig. 481.—Plan of Cast-iron Access Junction.

as that surrounding it, as, for instance, tiles or asphalt, so that only a
double edge of iron about 1 inch wide appears at the surface level.
   Manholes will depend for their size on the depth of the drain and to
the number of junctions coming in at one point.   For instance, three or
four side branches entering on one side will occupy a fair amount of
space and will require a longer manhole than one receiving one side
branch.   Convenient sizes for manholes by Jensen are as follow :
   1 foot 6 inches or less in depth, 2 feet × 1 foot 6 inches in plan.
   1 foot 6 inches to 2 feet 6 inches in depth, 2 feet 6 inches × 2 feet in
plan.
   Above 2 feet 6 inches in depth, 3 feet 6 inches × 2 feet 6 inches in plan.
   Manholes more than 7 feet 6 inches in depth may be contracted in size
to 2 feet × 2 feet at a height of 5 feet above the invert of the drain.   The
top of a manhole may be contracted to the size of the cast-iron cover

by means of over-sailing courses, but with long comparatively narrow types a stone slab is placed over the part which the standard size access lid does not cover. The point is to give comparatively easy access for a man working inside with drain rods to clear from point to point should the need arise. An arch may be turned in place of the slab.

It is sometimes contended that if a drain is no deeper than 2 feet a brick-built manhole is not necessary and a shaft can be carried up as a bend or junction from the drain and finish at ground level. A cast-iron "Kemp's" mechanical stopper is then cemented in the socket, which socket finishes flush with the yard level. The lid of this cover is removed by means of a special key, so that it cannot be tampered with.

For deep-seated manholes, galvanised iron stirrups are often built in the side wall, so that a man can easily get down without the aid of ladders.

With cast-iron drains the procedure is somewhat different, as a bolted-on cover is provided to the junction or bend, or instead of the bolts and nuts method there are special quickly detachable clamps, etc. Fig. 481 shows in plan, a junction with a cross-section inset above. A brick-built chamber is carried up to surface level, but the same precautions as to watertightness of the chamber are not so necessary in this case, as the liquid cannot rise up inside it, should a stoppage occur in the low parts of the drain, as it could and does with the open-channel type when a stoppage occurs.

The number of these brick-built manholes should always be kept to a minimum, as they are an expensive detail on any drainage scheme, and with present-day appliances, such as the "ferret" plungers and "plunger pumps," there is not the same need for access at every possible point as was required before these useful tools were placed on the market.

In the separate system of drainage there is not the same elaborate need for access to the rainwater drain as in foul-water drainage, and to save the expense of the brick-built chamber, special fittings are manufactured which have what is known as "inspection eyes," these consisting of a large socket on the top of the bend or junction, as the case may be, and fitted with a stopper. Pipes may be obtained to fit these sockets to carry up to ground level if required, the stoppers being fixed in the top of the shaft.

Trapping.—An intercepting trap of good form must be placed[1] on the main drain line as near to the sewer as possible, but within the curtailage of the owner's property. Access must be provided to this intercepting trap. This chamber, being at the low end of the drain, is usually the deepest. All inlets to drain other than w.c.s, urinals, and slop hoppers will be fitted with a gully trap at yard level and outside the building. It is sometimes possible to simplify the drain lines by fixing what is known as a "master gully." This master gully can be obtained with a number of purpose-made inlets. Side branches from ablution fittings and also rainwater in a combined scheme will

---

[1] See L.C.C. By-Laws, 1930, giving option on the fixing of intercepting traps, p. 286.

discharge to this gully.   Such a gully will often save the cost of a manhole, in addition to sometimes avoiding the expense of a multiplication of gully traps on a job.   Generally on one building and under ordinary circumstances there is only one connection to the sewer, each separate building having its own connection.   Extensive buildings, however, may have several connections to the sewers.

Ventilation of Drains.—Every drainage system must be so arranged that a current of air may pass through the whole system from end to end.[1]   The usual method is to provide an air inlet at one extremity and an outlet at the other.   Such inlet and outlet are not less than 4 inches diameter in any drain, with the exception that where a $3\frac{1}{2}$-inch soil pipe is fixed to serve a fitting near the extremity of the drain, this shaft carried up above the eaves full size may serve as the main ventilating shaft to the drain, providing no part of the drain is more than 4 inches in diameter.   With certain restrictions the L.C.C. permit a 3-inch soil and ventilating pipe.

Long main branches should be fitted with a specially full-sized air vent.   The usual practice is to fix the air inlet as near the sewer end as convenient, i.e. in the intercepting chamber and led to an adjacent wall on which a mica flap fresh-air inlet is fitted, as shown in Fig. 480. This, while admitting fresh air to the drain, closes to a back draught, the intention being to prevent the escape of foul air.   It should, however, be kept as far away from windows as possible.   The ventilating shaft forming the outlet must terminate 2 feet 6 inches above the eaves and should be 20 feet away from any window or ventilator, measured on a horizontal line.   If this distance cannot be obtained, the shaft should be carried higher.   Bends and particularly sharp bends should, as far as possible, be omitted to avoid friction to the moving air.

Change of air in a drainage scheme depends upon (1) the action of the wind blowing across the ends of the pipes ; (2) the difference in the weight of masses of gas, i.e. the air inside the drain and the external air ; (3) the discharge of effluent through the drains.   An air current when a discharge is not taking place will raise up the drain to the high points and escape at the ventilating shaft provided here, the drain air being usually warmer than the surrounding atmosphere, therefore having a tendency to rise.   The fresh-air inlet pipe should be taken from as near the top of the chamber as possible to avoid stagnant pockets of air in the chamber.

An alternative to a fresh-air inlet near to the sewer end of the drain and to the ventilating shaft at the high end is to fix the fresh-air inlet on this high end and arrange the high ventilating shaft at the other, beginning from the intercepting chamber, with underground drains.   This, perhaps, has an advantage, where a soil pipe from a w.c. fixed on a front elevation can form also the ventilating shaft to the drains, but to fix a special ventilating shaft on a front wall is not encouraged by the architect.

Another way is to fix two ventilating shafts, one at each extremity

[1] See L.C.C. By-Laws, p. 286.

of the drain and both terminating above the height of the eaves, but one higher than the other, with the object of determining which shall be the inlet and which the outlet, it being assumed that the longer shaft may have an aspirating effect on the gas and so form the outlet. It entails this rather ugly pipe on a front elevation and the expense of a double shaft, so that it has not been generally adopted, nor is it allowed in most districts.

Where there are two or more main drain runs into one common drain-pipe, each main branch should be supplied with its own ventilating shaft, thus the cross-sectional area of the fresh-air inlet must be large enough to admit air to serve these separate shafts. For instance, for two 4-inch main branches, a 6-inch fresh-air inlet should be fitted. In the case of cast-iron drains, instead of the fresh-air inlet shaft connecting into an access chamber, the pipe is connected to the drain itself at the lowest access point.

Stable drainage must be kept distinct from house drainage, as the discharge consists mainly of urine and is consequently very foul. It may be connected to a house drain at the intercepting trap, provided it is fitted with its own intercepting trap, the fresh-air inlet and vent shaft being, in fact, a separate scheme from that point. Occasionally stable drainage is taken as a separate connection to the sewer, but in these days of the motor-car, the difficulty of stable drainage does not so frequently occur.

As a general principle drains are kept outside the building, but occasionally circumstances so exist that the drain must pass through and, in some jobs, be exposed in the basement. In such cases they must, of course, be of heavy cast-iron with properly caulked joints and access provided. There are three alternative methods of support : (1) by brick-built piers ; (2) by special cast-iron corbels built into the wall, where the drain runs conveniently alongside a wall ; and (3) by suspending them from the ceiling by a special form of iron sling. Such a scheme is outlined in Fig. 482, which shows both a corbel and the sling method. These slings are fitted with means of adjustment which allow the fall in the drain to be arranged to a nicety.

There are occasions where the whole of the drainage scheme must be kept inside, including inlet gullies. In this case the gully traps must be provided with mechanically sealed tops, as shown in the same diagram.

It is not necessary always to provide gully traps on short underground rainwater branches. The alternative is to provide what are known as rainwater shoes, such a one being indicated on the same drawing. The drain from the shoe must discharge into a gully trap above the water seal on the inlet side.

Where a drain passes through a wall in which subsidence may be anticipated, a relief arch or lintel should be fixed clear of the drain to prevent fracture should it occur.

Connection to Sewer.—Pains must be taken to make a completely satisfactory job at the connection of drain to sewer. Brick-built sewers should be fitted with a purpose-made junction block in one piece of stone-ware, and in such shape that it will fit exactly into the brickwork and take the place of the bricks displaced. The junction block is provided with a socket of standard form to receive the drain end, the joint between the two being made with Portland cement. The junction block and the cross

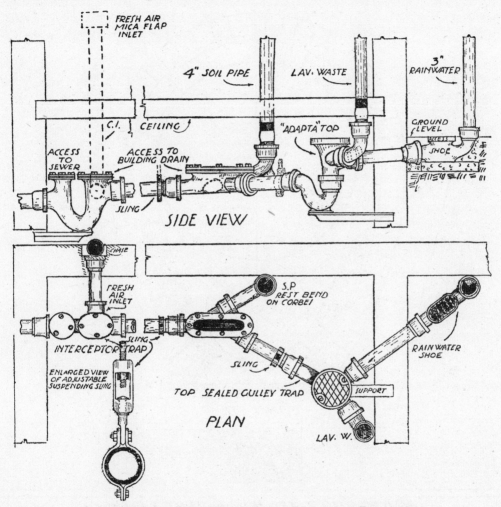

Fig. 482.—Exposed Cast-iron Drain carried across a Basement.

section on a two-ring brick-built sewer is shown in Fig. 483. The connection must be oblique and in the direction of the flow. This is effected by fitting a slow-swept bend to the junction block, the bend being at such an angle that it comes into line with the building to receive the line of drain.

In cases of existing large stoneware sewers, the most convenient method of connecting is to make a hole in the pipe in the side near the top and fit a special saddle-piece branch, as shown in sketch *D* of Fig. 484. The procedure is as follows: The sewer should not be completely exposed, but just the part at which the junction is to be made. A small hole is then carefully drilled through, using a very sharp small chisel

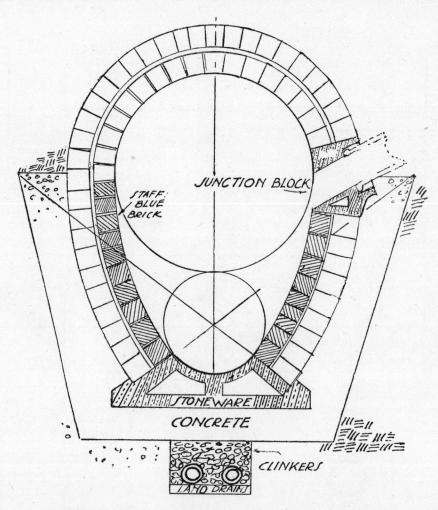

STAFF.
BLUE
BRICK

JUNCTION BLOCK

STONEWARE

CONCRETE

CLINKERS

LAND DRAINS

BRICK BUILT SEWER AND INLET BLOCK

Fig. 483

and a small hammer, applying quick light blows. When the small hole has been made it is enlarged by working on the edge of the hole at an angle as indicated in the diagram *C*. To hold the chisel upright and hit directly downwards would probably result in fracturing the stoneware sewer, a serious business. By working thus obliquely the hole is gradually enlarged to the required dimensions to receive the purpose-made saddle-piece, which is cemented in place, using Portland cement. A slow bend is fitted to the saddle-piece junction to receive the drain, as shown in plan drawing *B*, and at *D* in elevation.

An alternative method is to fit a junction in place of one of the pipes in the sewer, such junction being a special form and provided only

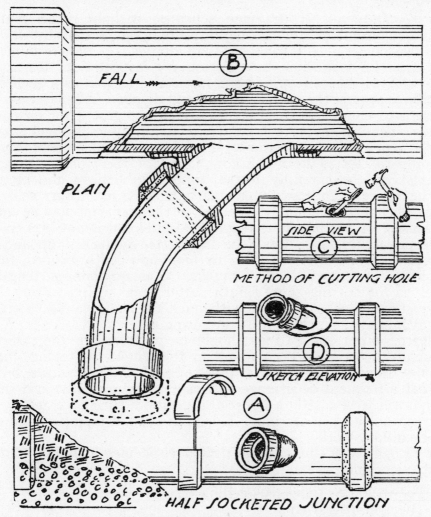

Fig. 484.—Connection of Drain to Stoneware Sewer.

with half-sockets. It can be realised that with the complete standard socket it would be impossible to enter the junction in a proper manner. The top half of the socket is a separate piece cemented on afterwards. This method of connection is indicated in sketch *A*. It is not so convenient as the other method, and is more costly, and when dealing with a sewer carrying large volumes of effluent it is difficult to carry out the work without interruption to the flow.

In cases where large branches are required, for instance, an equal diameter branch to the main drain, the proper junction then will be the best method. Double sockets can be obtained as separate units which will simplify the work somewhat, using such a socket on two plain ends to make a joint. Such a fitment, however, should be avoided in ordinary work.

Testing Drains.—All drainage schemes, including the plumber's work above ground, have to be inspected and tested by the local authorities' officer. It follows that all drains laid underground must be left open for inspection by the sanitary inspector for his approval or otherwise, so that a test is one of inspection as well as a general trial of soundness against the escape of gases and liquids. All materials before they are used should be carefully inspected and tested for flaws, for if defective pipes or fittings are fixed, it is often a troublesome and expensive matter to replace them afterwards, the defects of course being found out when properly tested near the completion of the work. Cement for jointing should be carefully tested, pipes and fittings and stoneware should be inspected for flaws, particularly in the internal surface. Badly warped or bent pipes should be rejected, or the plain end may be smashed and reserved for cutting short lengths. If the end is not broken, there is some possibility that it will be inadvertently picked up and used. If fittings are suspended in the air by hand and gently tapped, the ring or rather lack of ring will indicate cracks. Cracked plain end lengths can be reserved for cutting short lengths, after breaking pieces out for the reason just explained. A length with cracked sockets should be smashed, and so avoid anyone picking it up and using it.

Cast-iron pipes and fittings should be inspected in the same way. Occasionally holes have been found in the lengths of piping, but this should not occur in properly cast pipes up to L.C.C. standards, but they are rather a frequent occurrence with a light type of cast-iron soil and vent pipe which is cast in a horizontal position, shrinkage taking place at the pour holes when casting. This light type of piping should not be used for sanitary work.

The recognised testings for all drainage schemes, including plumbers' work above ground, are :

(1) The rocket or pungent-smelling test.
(2) The compressed-air test.
(3) Water or hydraulic test.

The pungent-smelling test is a crude sort of test applied by a visiting inspector on old properties. It consists of inserting a pungent-smelling chemical into the drainage scheme, when any odour in the building or in the near vicinity will indicate imperfections in the sanitary arrangements. The rockets consist of small cylinders of cardboard and in some cases glass, containing a chemical. The cardboard lid of the cylinder is attached to the cylinder with paper tabs, a light spring inside pressing the lid

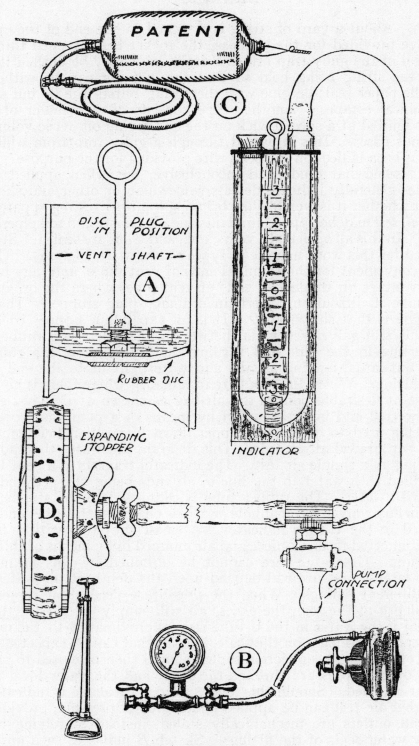

PATENT

C

DISC IN PLUG POSITION

← VENT SHAFT →

A

RUBBER DISC

3
2
1
0
1
2
3
0
0

INDICATOR

EXPANDING STOPPER

D

PUMP CONNECTION

1 2 3 4 5 6 7 8 9 0

B

Fig. 485.—Drain-testing Appliances.

upwards. About a yard of string is attached to one end of the cylinder on an eye provided for the purpose, the rocket being passed through a water seal of the gully trap into the drain, or it may be flushed through a w.c., the string being held so that the cylinder can be withdrawn. When the paper seals become wet, the spring bursts the lid out so that the chemical escapes. Another type consists of a cylinder of metal which is ignited at a special wick on the end giving off dense volumes of sulphurous gases. This is passed through a gully trap from which the water has been ladled, on a special wire provided for the purpose. These tests are somewhat crude and inconclusive, but when applied to old properties generally indicate defects somewhere or other and show the operator whether it is worth while bringing a proper testing apparatus.

The air test may be applied to drains and also waste and soil pipes above ground. In this all open ends, vents, etc., and traps are sealed. Stoppers employed for this work may be of types shown at D, Fig. 485. The one at A is convenient for the terminal ends of vent pipes, and may be used with advantage on the leaden ends of vent pipes where the ornamentations make it difficult to insert an ordinary plug stopper. The most usual type is that shown at D. It is an expanding stopper consisting of two discs of galvanised metal between which there is a rubber ring. By inserting in the pipe and turning the thumbscrew the rubber is pressed outwards, making an air- and watertight fit to the end of the pipe or fitting. Where the pipes are irregular or where there is no means of access at desirable points, the air-bag as shown at C may be used. This is wetted and inflated *in situ* by means of a pump as shown, the cable being used to draw the stopper down in position before inflation and for withdrawal afterwards. This diagram illustrates the apparatus for putting on a simple air test. The indicator consists of a bent U-tube and is filled with water to the line o, all ends being stopped and traps sealed with water. The rubber tube is connected to the stopper D as shown, in any convenient manhole or access chamber, the other end being connected to the U-tube indicator. A small air pump with a flexible tube is connected to the T-piece and air pumped in by means of this small hand pump. Great pressure cannot be obtained by this means. In fact the largest pressure will depend upon the depth of the water seals of the different fittings. When the pressure exceeds that represented by the depth of the seal, the excess air will simply bubble out through it, so that if the water in the U-tube rises approximately to the mark 2, which represents inches on the scale, it is all that can be expected. The air-cock of the pump connection shown should then be closed to prevent leakage by back pressure through the pump and the water level in the indicator watched. Should this level subside, a leakage is indicated.

Another air test can be applied under greater pressure, providing all inlets and outlets are mechanically sealed, instead of relying on the ordinary water seals of the fittings. Sketch B indicates such an outfit, a pressure gauge being used in place of the U-tube. It is sufficient to test any drainage scheme, particularly in stoneware, up to 5 lb. per sq. inch.   This outfit, although very convenient to apply, and portable, simply proves a leakage, and there is no means by this apparatus of finding it.   Generally leakages in new drainage schemes are very elusive and difficult to find by inspection.   In gas services leakages may be found when the pipes are put under air pressure, by painting the joints, etc.,

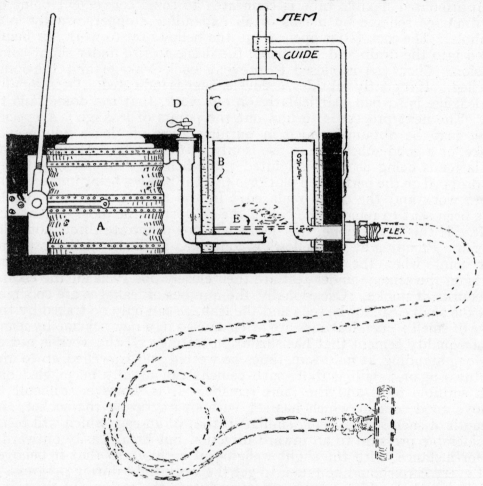

Fig. 486.—Smoke-testing Machine.

over with soapy solutions, when the bubbles produced would indicate the point of leakage ; but in a drainage scheme this is hardly feasible or convenient to apply, owing to the extensive character of the work, number of joints, etc., so that usually a testing outfit is used which contains apparatus for applying air pressure, and attached to it an outfit for applying a smoke test, the smoke test being used to indicate the points of leakage, so that they may be made good.

Fig. 486 indicates a very usual apparatus for applying this double test. It consists of a hardwood skeleton frame about 18 inches long × 9 inches × 9 inches, in which are (A) bellows and a copper cylinder with a water-jacket (B) outside it. A copper dome (C) is put over the cylinder (B) so that the edges are immersed in the water-jacket. To apply the test, all points are sealed, open vent, etc., by means of mechanical stoppers and other fittings by the ordinary water seal. The machine by means of an armoured flexible tube is connected to some convenient point of the drainage scheme by means of an expanding stopper, usually in a manhole. The cock (D) is opened and the bellows set to work, air being forced into the drain and so causing the dome to rise under slight compression. Cock (D) is closed to prevent back leakage and the dome watched. If it gently subsides, a slow leakage is indicated. Occasionally the leakage is so bad, particularly on old work, that the dome fails to rise. The next process is to find out the points of leakage. A special paper may be obtained which in burning gives off dense volumes of smoke, or a good substitute to use is oily cotton waste. Assuming that the latter is being used, it is ignited and when it is smouldering freely it is dropped on the perforated platform (E), the bellows being immediately set to work and the dome replaced. In the meantime a man should have been sent to remove the cap of the stopper in the most distant air-shaft. If this is not done, the smoke will not penetrate throughout the scheme. Pumping at the bellows is continued until the smoke issues at that point, when the cap of the stopper is replaced. All points and joints on the scheme under test are then closely observed for the escape of tendrils of smoke. Occasionally the number of leakages are so slight that the smoke cannot be seen and the leakage can only be traced by the sense of smell ; such leakages are often caused in a new scheme by using a poor-quality cement that has shrunk in setting. If the work is not of too long standing, it may sometimes be wetted and trowelled up to air-tightness again ; failing that, such cement can usually be piggled out with suitable tools and the joint remade. It is, however, difficult to remove good cement which has set, without fracturing the socket, the strength of such socket being similar to that of an egg, which will resist considerable pressure to an inward direction but break easily outwards, as, for instance, with the slight wedging of a chisel, so that it behoves that every care should be taken to get the work tight during progress.

The pipes should not be knelt upon during the making of the joint, nor should they be walked upon while the cement is setting, as such carelessness is sure to produce a bad result.

In testing, whether by this means or by the water test, it is often most convenient to apply the test to sections only, dealing with one section and making it good before proceeding to another. By such a method leakages are more easily traced.

When the job is considered in a satisfactory state, the excavations can be carefully filled in, which remark applies more to a stoneware drain than to a cast-iron drain. A well-laid iron drain will stand any amount of ill-usage and often subsequent subsidence and vibrations, but the same cannot be said of the stoneware drain. The test must be left on until the whole excavation is filled. Small soft earth should be thrown in first and carefully tucked and rammed in at the sides of the stoneware drain, the ramming of the earth being made continuous during the whole process of filling-in up to ground level. If this is not done there will be a subsequent subsidence, which will affect the paving.

The air and smoke test is the most convenient one to apply for old properties. It can be realised that to fill the whole drain scheme with water, as is necessary in the hydraulic test, would be inconvenient and difficult to apply in an occupied property. With a leaky drain underground the smoke will rise through the earth, indicating the points at which defects may be anticipated. Where the smoke does not easily appear, long iron pins may be wriggled through the earth over the line of drains. They should not, of course, be struck with a hammer or the drain would be fractured if the point rested on it. The smoke will issue through the holes when the iron pins are withdrawn. This air and smoke test is considered sufficient for both old and new work in some parts of the country, but under the London County Council only the water or hydraulic test is countenanced.

The hydraulic test consists of filling the whole of the drains with water under an artificial head produced to put the drain under a little more pressure than it would have to withstand in practice. It is sometimes contended that the hydraulic pressure is too severe for a stoneware drainage scheme, but it must be realised that should a drain become choked at a low point, for instance at the intercepting trap, the drain will receive the hydraulic test automatically, at any rate up to ground level, the trouble not usually being found out until this occurs. To apply the test, a stopper should be fixed in the mouth of the pipe at the lowest point, and any convenient water tap opened to discharge into a gully trap. As the water fills up, it is necessary to take means to provide for the escape of trapped air at the crown of the gully traps, as indicated at *a*, Fig. 487. This may be done by inserting a piece of light compo tube under the lip of the water seal while the trap is dry. This permits the air to escape freely and the water to fill up solid to the crown of the siphon. If this is not done, the elastic pad of trapped air will cause fluctuations in the water level, making it difficult to determine whether there is any subsidences of the level and consequent leakage. If the gully traps are fixed at different levels, the low ones must be mechanically sealed at the top as they fill up. A mechanical seal for gully traps consists of two square plates with the rubber pad between in standard size to fit the place of the ordinary grating. In addition a mechanical claw is fitted which is inserted below the lip of the dip in the water seal. Without this precaution there is some probability of a stoneware gully trap being burst by the expansive force exerted in turning the thumbscrew in endeavouring to make the top watertight, and at the same time resist the back pressure. Some idea of this back pressure may be obtained if a simple calculation is made. Suppose, for instance, the drains and piping are to be filled to first-floor level, say, a height of 10 feet above the height of the topmost gully, and assuming the gully 9 inches square, the area of the plate subject to water pressure would be 9 times 9 = 81 sq. inches, and the pressure for 1 foot of head on 1 sq. inch is ·434 lb. Therefore, for 10 feet it will be ·434 × 10 = 4·34 lb. pressure per sq. inch and 4·34 × 81 = 346·5 lb. total pressure tending to push the stopper out.

It is a general practice in good work to fill the drain up to first-floor

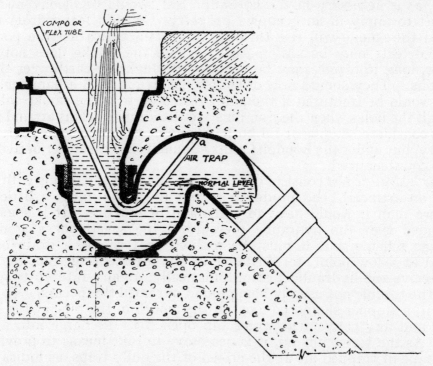

Fig. 487.—Removing Trapped Air from Crown of Gully Trap during Hydraulic Test.

level, which may be done by flushing w.c.s or pouring in buckets of water. If the level of water in these fittings remains constant, the watertightness of the drain is proved, with reverse if a subsidence takes place. Leakage is indicated at the exposed joints and pipes by a dampness appearing and, of course, in very bad cases, trickles of water. On wet days these points are difficult to trace, but the difficulty may be overcome by adding a little permanganate of potash to the water when filling, the bright red fluid thus being easily detected.

[1] The strength of a stoneware pipe is limited, and it is advisable to put no more than about 5 lb. per sq. inch pressure on such a drain, which is equivalent, under normal circumstances, to the first-floor level height.

---

[1] L.C.C. Regulations, 1930, stipulate a test pressure at a 2-foot head only.

Roughly 2 feet 3 inches of height gives 1 lb. pressure per sq. inch. It can be realised that with a very deep-seated drain, the pressure would be greater than this, and therefore it would not be advisable to subject the lower parts of a stoneware drain to the pressure produced in filling up to first-floor height.

In new buildings it often occurs, of course, that the stack pipes have not been fixed when it is wished to put the underground drains under hydraulic test. To meet such cases it is sufficient to give an ordinary head of 2 or 3 feet above ground level. This may be done by temporarily fixing a couple of lengths of pipe in a vertical position on the vent or soil pipe and filling these with water. A more convenient method, however, is to use a special appliance for this, as illustrated in Fig. 488. This consists of a tube about 1 inch in diameter, about 4 feet long, connected to a special expanding stopper. When the whole of the underground work has been filled to surface level, this expanding stopper and pipe attached is fixed in an open end and then filled with water. This can be considered quite a severe test, as a comparatively small leakage of water in this small pipe would show an appreciable subsidence.

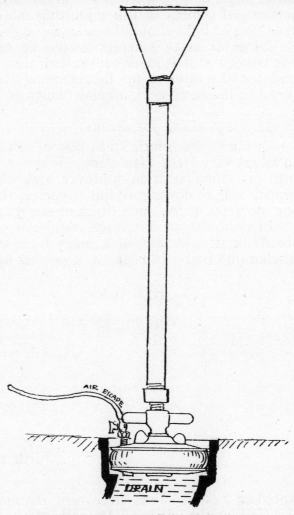

Fig. 488.—Heading-up Tube for Drain Test.

Although all drainage fittings and pipes are supposed to be impervious, a little moisture is generally taken up, and this absorption should be allowed for if subsidence occurs, by filling up again and then watching the level. If it remains fairly constant for ten to fifteen minutes, it can be assumed that the drain is in a satisfactory condition. There is, however, generally little trouble with drains in cast-iron, and the bulk of the points remarked upon apply more particularly to the fragile stoneware drains and fittings.

It is sometimes desirable to inspect the bore of a drain length from end to end. This may conveniently be done by a periscopic principle. A lighted candle is placed at one end and the inspector may look through the length to the light by inserting a mirror on the end of a stick, holding it at an angle of 45°, when if the drain is truly laid and there are no projections of cement or other jointing material on the side of the pipe, a true ring of light should be seen throughout the whole length.

Large drainage schemes should be tested section by section. With the water test it is more convenient then to start on the high stretches and use the same water by removing the plug and allowing it to run down to the next section below which is to be tested.

Proportional sizing for drains.

Owing to the intermittent flow of drainage matter, it is not necessary to adopt very large diameters. Where a number of properties discharge into one common drain, however, and where it is anticipated that each branch will be flowing at full capacity, the following method of finding the diameter of the main drain or sewer can be employed, thus:

Fifty houses in a terrace require a 3-inch rainwater drain. What should be the diameter of a main drain at the outlet end? The relative discharging power is as the 2 : 5 powers of their diameters.

$$D = \sqrt[5]{\sqrt{((D^5) \times N)^2}}$$

Working by aid of Logarithms

Log. 3 =	·4771
5th power	5
$\sqrt[2]{}$ —	2)2·3855
	1·1928
Log. 50 =	1·6990
	2·8918
Squared	2
Fifth root	5)5·7836
	1·1567

Anti-Log. 1567 = 1434 necessary diameter 14·34 inches. If it was certain that the whole 50 drains would be discharging full bore at one time the nearest standard size above would be selected, i.e. a 15-inch drain.

CHAPTER V

SEWAGE DISPOSAL

Broad Irrigation—Sub-irrigation and Chemical Precipitation—Activated Sludge Process—Cesspool Catchment—Intensive Purification by Bacteria—Filtration—Sprinklers—Tray Filter Beds.

THIS work is undertaken by the local council, with the exception of isolated buildings out of convenient reach of sewers. It is not proposed to undertake the treatment of sewerage on such large scales, and it will be sufficient to enumerate the general outlines.

Broad Irrigation.—The early form of sewage disposal under water-carriage system consisted of what is known as " broad irrigation," which entailed a large amount of light, loamy soil suitable for agricultural purposes. The sewage was impounded and distributed over the land to encourage the growth of rough vegetation, the outfall works often being termed " a sewage farm." As districts became more thickly populated such a means was inadequate, owing to the amount of land required, and to the fact that in many cases the land would not be suitable.

Under the broad irrigation scheme it is generally considered that one acre of land is required for every 300 persons, and a natural further outfall to a flowing stream or river. Under the Rivers Pollution Act of 1876 crude sewage must not discharge to any stream or water-course.

Sub-irrigation and Chemical Precipitation.—Purification of sewage may be intensified by what is known as intermittent downward filtration. In this sludge tanks are required for settlement and the land specially prepared with underground drains. In this scheme it is considered that one acre of land is sufficient for 2,000 persons. Mechanical precipitation means are often taken to hurry the settlement and precipitation of solids, the method being to add 5 to 15 grains of lime, according to the type of sewage, strength, etc., for each gallon. Iron sulphate is sometimes used as an additional precipitative, when the amount of lime can be reduced.

Screens, scum boards, detritus tanks, settlement tanks, pumping apparatus, drying lagoons, and means of getting rid of the sludge in a convenient manner are required.

Activated Sludge Process.—Recently much interest has been taken in what is known as the " Activated Sludge " process. This consists of forcing air through the sewage in specially constructed tanks, solids having first been removed by screens, etc. It is necessary for the success of the operation for a certain amount of the sludge from a previous operation to be added to that under course of treatment. The blowers or diffusers, used to give a finely divided admixture of air, consist of shallow cast-iron boxes with covers of porous tiles, through which the air is forced. The action is principally one of oxidisation. It may be considered that it is still in its experimental stages. Although good results have been obtained both in this country and in America, there is still much to be done to give entire satisfaction. Certain trade wastes upset the action to some extent.

A modern scheme of sewerage may embrace all that is best of several processes, the least of which is not the bacteriological purification of sewage, a process which is of more particular interest, perhaps, to the bulk of the readers of this work. Schemes can be evolved in an installation which will deal with a single building or a small community in rural districts.

Cesspool Catchment.—Cesspools are very often built on properties where a water-carriage scheme is required. The system has its limitations and cannot be strongly recommended. It consists of a brick-built chamber underground, or it may be in concrete. It should be perfectly impervious against leakage to ground level. The position should be carefully chosen. The requirements are that it shall be 50 feet from any dwelling and 100 feet from any natural water supply and should not be larger in capacity than the volume represented by three months' catchment, the basis of calculation being the amount of waste water per head on the premises. It should not be less in capacity that 1,000 gallons. Overflows on cesspools are not allowed. If there is any well in the vicinity, the position of the cesspool should be chosen so that the relative positions of the fall in the earth's strata is from the well towards the cesspool and not the reverse from the cesspool towards the well, so that should any leakage occur from, for instance, subsequent subsidence, the foul matter from the cesspool will travel in a direction from the well and so reduce risk of pollution.

Occasionally in rural work, old houses are found in which the occupants do not know the position of the cesspool. It can be assumed under such circumstances that such a cesspool must be leaky, from the fact that it is never emptied.

Sometimes cesspools are intentionally built so that they shall be porous, and such a procedure has even been followed in some of the modern country building estates, the escaping liquids being purified in the earth by natural processes, but there is a great risk under such circumstances, especially if the land is not particularly suitable, of the earth becoming sewage sick, and unhealthy conditions subsequently arising. In districts where it is specified that all cesspools shall be directly watertight to ground level, cases have been known where the occupant has knocked a few bricks out in the bottom, so that the liquefying matter gradually escapes, and so avoids the need of periodical emptying. Such a practice cannot be too strongly condemned, particularly if in the vicinity of well water. In fact, conditions would arise which would make the well water positively dangerous to drink. Generally arrangements can be made for rural sanitary authorities to perform the periodical emptying of these cesspools, when they undertake to do it in a very inoffensive manner.

In agricultural districts a permanent pump may be fixed in the cesspool with the outlet at such a height that the effluent can be directly

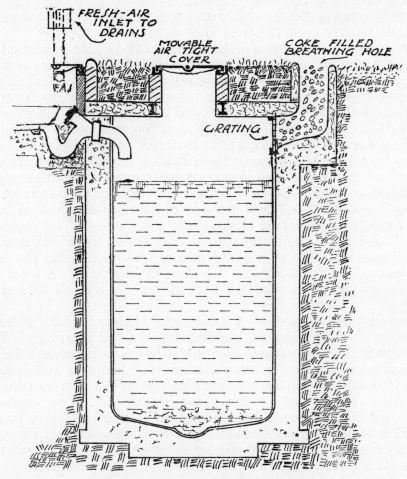

FRESH-AIR INLET TO DRAINS

MOVABLE AIR TIGHT COVER

COKE FILLED BREATHING HOLE

GRATING

Fig. 489.—Cesspool for Collection of Sewage.

pumped into a tank cart, so that it can be taken away and emptied on the land as a manure.

Fig. 489 shows a cesspool *in situ*, with the general requirements. A vent pipe should be fixed in some inconspicuous position at a point where it will not be offensive to allow the generated gases to escape, and so avoid back pressure. The requirements for the drainage scheme will be exactly the same as for that where discharging to a sewer. The intercepting trap is generally in a chamber immediately adjoining the cesspool, but it may be some little distance away if more convenient to so place it. Access must be given to the cesspool, the manhole being covered with an airtight cast-iron cover. In place of the vent pipe, what is known as a " breathing hole " may be constructed, as shown in the diagram. In this an iron grating is fixed in the mouth of the opening and the chamber filled up with coke; the air percolating through this coke is deodorised to some extent.

If a public sewer exists within 100 feet of the owner's property, the local authority may enforce connection of the drain thereto.

The cesspool catchment and hand removal as just described cannot be strongly recommended for every isolated building; there is a scheme much to be preferred if there is no sewer available.

Intensive Purification by Bacteria.—This scheme entails the construction of plant which will produce types of bacteria on an intensive system which will liquefy and purify sewage in a compass much less than that occupied by natural processes, as, for instance, in broad or sub-irrigation. In the top stratum of the earth there exist a number of bacteria whose life work consists of breaking down all organic matter and converting it into inoffensive matter. If such land is overloaded it becomes what is known as " sewage sick," and periods of rest would have to be given for it to recover its purifying effect.

On a broad basis the purification plant under the given heading for a small scheme entails the construction of two sections to intensify the natural method of purification : (1) a septic tank ; (2) a filter bed, or series of beds. A scheme can be designed to serve a small villa or a large estate.

The septic tank consists of a watertight chamber which receives the sewage from the building or buildings under consideration. It must be so constructed that it is dark and unventilated to encourage the growth of a type of microbe known as the " anaerobic " bacteria, and in sufficient numbers to deal with the daily flow of sewage. The process which takes place in this tank is not to any great extent one of purification, the microbes simply breaking down all organic solid matter into liquid and gases. The amount of gas evolved, that is, if the apparatus is carefully sized, should not be great, but means must be taken to permit this gas to escape at a point where it will cause the least nuisance. It should be taken from near the top of the tank, or a breathing-hole can be arranged as described for the cesspool. The conditions in this tank must be such that everything is quiet and disturbance avoided by any violent discharge of effluent into it. For this reason the inlet pipe in the drains is immersed below the surface, the detail described being shown in the sectional drawing of Fig. 490. It should be long and narrow to give slow, still movement from end to end, the length being three to four times that of the width, one specialist, at least, advocating that the length should be equal to seven times the width. It would not be convenient to build a septic tank to such extreme lengths, but the same effect may

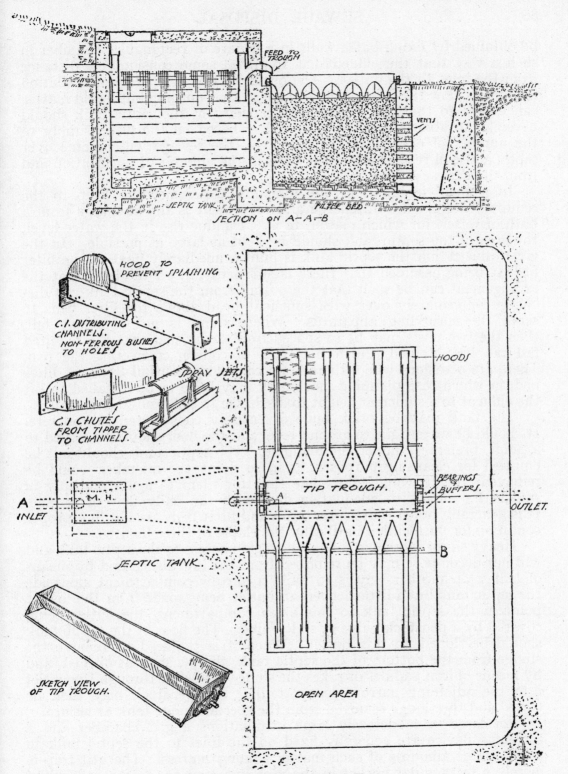

FEED TO TROUGH

VENTS

SEPTIC TANK.

FILTER BED.

SECTION ON A-A-B

HOOD TO PREVENT SPLASHING

C.I. DISTRIBUTING CHANNELS.
NON-FERROUS BUSHES TO HOLES

SPRAY JETS

C.I CHUTES FROM TIPPER TO CHANNELS.

HOODS

TIP TROUGH.

BEARINGS & BUFFERS.

A
INLET

M. H.

A

OUTLET.

B

SEPTIC TANK.

OPEN AREA

SKETCH VIEW OF TIP TROUGH.

Fig. 490—Plan of Purification Plant.

be obtained by fixing baffle walls in a square or rectangular chamber in such a way that the effluent has to travel some considerable distance from the inlet to the outlet. The outlet of this part of the installation is dipped below the level of the sewage so that nothing but liquid matter can escape to the filter beds. The capacity of the septic tank should be equal to about $1\frac{1}{2}$ days' sewage flow based on the water-supply to the number of occupants. If too large, the sewage will become over septic and evil results will ensue both in the amount of purification and from the gases escaping.

In a small installation, one difficulty experienced to keep to the requirements of quiet discharge and movement is the discharge from a bath of water, for which reason, to avoid undue rise in the water level, the area of the septic tank should be kept as large as possible. In the given illustration the septic tank is built immediately next to the filter bed, it being assumed that there is sufficient fall on the land that the arrangement can be such that the outfall from the septic tank can discharge immediately over with sufficient head above the filter beds to serve the sprinkling apparatus. Where there is not sufficient fall, then the two units may be so spaced from each other that the required fall can be obtained, the outlet pipe, of course, connecting the two. There are occasions where there is no convenient outfall from the filter bed, in which case pumping machinery may have to be installed to lift the effluent to a sufficient height to discharge to some suitable outfall.

The tank may be brick built or entirely constructed in concrete. It should be watertight to ground level and the floor should be sloped to a point, preferably under the manhole. The septic tank should not be emptied for cleansing purposes, as in so doing the microbes would be removed, and it would take some time for them to again multiply in sufficient numbers to adequately deal with the daily flow of sewage. It is generally taken that septic tanks and filter beds are not in a proper condition for purification until after the elapse of three months.

Heavy silt or inorganic solids which gain access to the septic tank and will not decompose may be removed from the low dished end by means of ladles, or another way is to build a narrow compartment alongside the septic tank but a little deeper, an outlet being made from the lowest point in the septic tank to this extra compartment, the outlet being covered by a penstock valve or slide valve. The floor of the septic tank should be sloped to this outlet. When it is required to remove the sludge from the bottom of the septic tank, the penstock is opened, and by means of iron paddles or rakes the sludge is pushed through the outlet into the adjoining narrow deeper tank. The penstock may then be closed and the sludge removed from the special sludge tank at leisure.

For large or moderately large installations a grit chamber and a screening device are generally fixed on the inlet to the septic tank to avoid undue amounts of such matter gaining ingress. The grit trap is merely a rectangular pocket in the pipe line, and the screen consists of a barred grating sloped at an angle of about 45°, the bars running from top to bottom, not crossways.

A distinct type of septic tank is favoured by one firm producing sanitary appliances (Adamsez, Ltd.). This consists of a deep cylindrical tube made up of stoneware pipes in sections to the depth of 12 feet by four pieces joined together by a special scarf joint in place of the ordinary socket and spigot. The pipes are 2 to 3 feet in diameter. Special junction arms, inlet and outlet, are arranged about 4 feet below ground level to take the place of the dip pipes, as detailed in the larger septic tanks. The outlet is covered with a mesh grating, to prevent the escape of solid matter. The top is covered with special cast-iron lids, giving easy access. The mesh grating can be removed from this point if required for clearing. It is claimed that as much as 60 per cent. purification takes place in this type of septic tank. The junction arms finish at ground level as an open end for access, but protected by a small cast-iron disc cover. A great appeal is that they are easy to install and occupy little space.

Filtration.—Broadly, filters are of two forms: (*a*) contact filters, and (*b*) intermittent downward filters. The former are not so suitable for small works, and even for big works the intermittent downward filter is taking its place.

Contact filters consist of brick-built chambers filled with a filtering media, such as broken clinker or any similar suitable rubble. These tanks are charged and allowed to drain, when the bacteria set to work and purify the solid matter left. The cycle of operations for such filters is as follows: Filling, one hour; standing, two hours; draining, one hour; aerating, four hours. This allows for three fillings and emptyings per twenty-four hours. The liquid capacity of these beds is about 33 per cent. and they are usually constructed about 4 feet deep. The number and size of tanks can be found from that data for the gross amount of sewage to be purified.

Downward-percolating filters can be rectangular or circular in plan, the determinating factor being the type of sprinkling apparatus adopted for sprinkling the sewage over the filter bed. The filters may be built on an open platform of concrete with a retaining wall constructed of expanding metal, the object being to give a thorough oxidising effect by allowing free passage of air through the filtering media. There is a possible objection to this type, apart from appearance, it being contended that such an arrangement may form breeding-grounds for flies.

This second section of the purification installation relies for its success upon the propagation of multitudes of a type of bacteria which need sunlight and fresh air, known as " aerobic " bacteria. The filtering media must be of a substance, preferably rough and cellular, to give a maximum amount of surface to provide for the colonies. Broken brick, stone, unglazed pottery in a pottery district, flint, coke breeze, clinker, and gravel may be used.

Some authorities prefer graduated layers commencing large at the bottom to small at the top in a few of the materials mentioned.

It is generally accepted that small breeze on a foundation of clinker, the whole lying over a special perforated tile, is the best form of filtering media. Broken pottery and gravel are too smooth to attain the desired object. They have the fault that the effluent may trace its way through the media at such a rate that the bacteria do not have time to have a full purifying effect.

There is some difference of opinion as to whether a continuous downward filtration is better than the intermittent type of downward traverse filter. For small plants the intermittent downward filtration can be accepted as the more suitable, this intermittent discharge, by special arrangement, giving period of rest for penetration of air to oxidise and purify the interstices of the media. The depth of the filter will depend to some extent upon the available point of outfall, the outlet from the filter being at the bottom.

Where a suitable low outfall is not available, a type of filter may be obtained to work in an upward direction with the outlet at the top, but this type is not so effective as the downward filtration type, and the latter should always be chosen in preference when conditions permit.

Although in the usual diagram and text-book the septic tank and the filtration plant are shown immediately adjacent to each other, the necessary amount of fall between the two sections may often be obtained by spacing these two units some distance apart, the slow, gradual fall on the line between the two units giving the required amount to allow for the gravity fall of the effluent and sufficient head to operate whatever intermittent type of sprinkling arrangement is adopted.

For enclosed plots of land where the appearance of a filter bed with open area round would be objected to, the brick-built type of chamber is favoured, and where required, as in a garden, the whole thing can be disguised by means of rockery, crazy pavement, growing shrubs, flowers, etc.

Aeration to the filter media is obtained by means of perforated lengths of 4-inch pipe penetrating into the filtering media and terminating above ground level with a suitable cowl or bonnet.

The type shown in Fig. 490 can give very good results, and consists of a rectangular chamber with three sides built up in honeycomb brickwork. An open area with concrete retaining walls is arranged on three sides, thus giving every facility for aeration. The filter bed is made up, first, with a special perforated tile lying on a sloped concrete foundation, the slope leading to one point of outfall. Ordinary tiles may be used in preference, allowing the locks of one line to rest on the top of the plain end of the other. Another alternative is to lay a course of unglazed butt-end field-drains, the object being to allow free space for the escape of the purified effluent to the outlet. A layer of broken clinker or flint stones may be used to cover these. The rest of the filter bed is made up of breeze, similar in size and grading to that used on the blacksmith's hearth. Over the whole top area of the filter bed special perforated channels are laid, the details of which are shown in the several fragmental drawings imposed on the same figure. The tip trough placed under the outlet across the filter bed receives the discharge from the septic tank. When one half-section of this trough is filled, the load causes it to overset and throw the effluent in an even cascade down the chutes into the perforated channels covering one-half of the filter bed, the effluent escaping through the perforated holes to trickle through the filtering media of that section. In the meantime, the other half of the tip trough is filling, which, in turn, oversets and a like operation is repeated on the other half, so that each half is working alternately with the other and intermittently, thus giving the periods of rest which are advocated with this type of filter. If the filter is properly proportioned and doing its work, the effluent at the outlet will be practically pure water, and it may discharge into the land, if suitably drained, or any adjacent water-course or stream.

It is sometimes desirable with an extensive scheme to arrange two or more filters, so that one filter may be working while the other is resting. It gives conditions convenient for repair or changing the filtering media if desirable. At abnormal times, both filters may be put to work. Where the fall of the land permits, and where it is considered that one filter will not do the work, it is possible to arrange that the effluent from the first filter can discharge in a similar manner to that explained over a second filter bed, and thus ensure a very pure ultimate effluent.

Where the discharge is to the earth, a piece of suitable land is prepared by sub-irrigation with pipes laid level and radiating out in grid-iron form from the one inlet pipe. If there is a suitable stream to receive the discharge, the pipe should not be laid direct to this, but a field drain should be laid in the ground 2 or 3 yards away from the bank, running parallel with it, but at such a depth that it is above or near the water line of the stream. The effluent discharging into this pipe line and trickling through the earth to the water-course receives any further necessary purification, and, escaping through what is virtually an additional filter, there is reduced risk of an unsuitable effluent escaping to pollute the water-course.

It should be noted that rain from roof and paved areas should not discharge to the plant, as it only increases the size, which size is not required at normal times ; and if the plant is constructed in capacity for the normal dry-weather flow, it is flooded out during a storm, thus upsetting the purification and work of the bacteria.

Grease from the scullery sinks should not be allowed to escape into the drain and, of course, eventually to the plant, as it clogs the filter beds, and in time renders them inoperative. Grease gully traps should be fixed on the inlet points to intercept grease and fats. Oils and petrol from the garage also should not discharge into it.

Sprinklers.—There are many forms of sprinkler on the market, the object being to produce a rain-like effect over the filter bed. One such type consists of covering the whole area of the bed with channels having V-shaped notches in the sides. Between these notches pieces of wire are placed from channel to channel, so that the effluent runs along these wires and drops off in the form of beads.

Another type has the channels fitted with numerous small pendants from the bottoms of the channels, the effluent dribbling over the sides and from the pendant points.

It is sometimes contended that a system which allows the water to drop or be sprinkled in a haphazard sort of manner is to be preferred to one which allows the sewage to drop off at fixed points, as the constant drip of water in the same spot forms permanent channels through the filtering media, so that the effluent escapes too quickly and before the bacteria have time to do their work.

The " Fiddan " type of sprinkler is designed to eliminate this disadvantage. The filter bed is circular in plan, with a rail running on top of the retaining wall. The sprinkler is in the form of a paddle-wheel running from the centre to the outskirts of the circle. The effluent from the septic tank drips on one side of this paddle-wheel, which produces a load on the one side. The paddle-wheel is pivoted in the centre and supported by a ball socket, and the other end has a grooved wheel engaging the rail. The load causes the paddle-wheel to move forward as long as sewage is dropping on to it, so that it travels round and round, giving work and periods of rest and allowing the effluent to fall in a haphazard, rain-like manner.

Another type for large sewage works is similar in principle. In this case the sprinkler travels as a paddle-wheel from end to end of a rectangular bed, and by engaging a lever at the end, the special arm is moved to discharge on the other side of the paddle-wheel, so that it is automatically reversed and retraces its step, so to speak, over the filter bed, traversing thus from end to end as long as sewage drops on it. In large works the paddle-wheel is driven by machinery.

A form which is particularly favoured in municipal works or any plant on an extensive area consists of rotating perforated arms pivoted in the centre. The centre column, which supports, is surmounted with a small circular feed tank to supply the rotating arms. The perforations in the arms are set at an angle of about $45°$ from the vertical in a downward direction. The stream of effluent impinging from all these holes pressing on the atmosphere has the effect of pushing the bar backwards, so that the arms are constantly swinging round and round the filter beds as long as sewage is escaping. To obtain free movement, the centre pillar is arranged to rotate in a pad of trapped air, similar in principle to the gasometer cover ; another type uses mercury ; still another, water. Ball or roller bearings working in oil are arranged at points where desirable.

Another type of sprinkler consists of covering the area of the filtering bed with rows of pipes perforated with holes pointing upwards at about an angle of 45°. The pipes are fed from the septic tank by means of what is known as a " Dosing " tank, which dosing tank consists of an automatic siphon, or it may be a simple tip tank, the arrangement of the " Dosing " tank giving a better result and more equal intermittent discharge over the bed than would be obtained if the sewage from the septic tank were allowed to merely escape direct to the pipe lines. When the " Dosing " tank discharges, the whole series of pipes are filled under a slight pressure causing a battery of fountains to spray over the whole area of the filter media. The fountains shortening in the distance throw out, as the pressure falls, thus avoiding forming definite channels through the media and also giving the conditions required, as previously pointed out, for slow filtration with intermittent periods of rest.

Tray Filter Beds.—One of the early forms of filter beds consisted of a series of trays filled with coke, broken clinker, etc. The effluent from the top tray drips over on to a slightly larger tray below, each tray being larger than the one above. While fairly successful as a filter of semi-contact form, it has been found that if, in cleaning this section of the plant down, the filtering media are mixed from the special trays and put back so mixed into the trays, the filter ceases to act properly. It is assumed that each tray breeds its own form of microbe, and when so mixed they are antagonistic to each other, so that the ordinary work of purification is upset. It is generally found that the types of plant as described do not become what is known as " ripe " until an interval of about three months has passed, so that when first installed, perhaps it will be found the purification is not altogether what could be desired, but will improve when the bacteria develop in sufficient numbers. For this reason it is not desirable to interfere with the filtering media, if properly constructed, which remark applies equally to the cleansing of the septic tank, etc. A small tank is sometimes formed on the outlet from the filter bed with a view to catching colloidal matter which has passed through the plant and owing to its gelatine nature is not decomposed by bacteria. The amount of this substance, however, from a small plant is practically negligible.

Where there is no suitable outfall the purified effluent is sometimes caught in an underground tank. A pump is installed to raise it for use in watering gardens, etc.

CHAPTER VI

THE "ONE-PIPE" SYSTEM OF SANITATION

Some Defects of Existing Systems—Principles of "One-pipe" System—Where, and where not, suitable—Ministry of Health By-laws—Advantages of "One-pipe" System—Materials—Access—Sizing. of "Soil-waste" Pipes—Group Planning—Traps—Venting—Example of Installation.

IT can generally be observed that things move and repeat themselves in cycles. For instance, at one time, pipes were always kept inside a building and buried in the walls. There then came a period, now apparently coming to an end, at least for large and high buildings, of keeping all pipes as far as possible on the external face of our buildings. The modern tendency is to revert to putting our sanitary pipes inside the building. Further, at one time all sanitary fitments were discharged *into one* common *pipe*, but owing to a wave of infectious and malignant disease in the country, a commission was set up to enquire and formulate plans for removing the evil. Their "findings" resulted in our present system of sanitation, and the now recognised best materials, and means of construction. Briefly the principles of this are :

1. Smooth-bore pipes ;
2. Small-diameter bores to produce self-cleansing velocities ;
3. Open ends of all soil and waste pipes to diffuse the small amount of gases generated at a safe point, high above the buildings ;
4. The separation of ablution fitments from those used to take discharge of human excretal matter, by pipes to take the discharge entirely separate on or within the building.
5. The fixing of a trap, known as the "intercepting trap" to isolate sewer gas from building-drain gases.
6. To provide inlet and outlet vent pipes at each end of a drainage scheme to ensure an air flush throughout the drainage system ;
7. To disconnect waste pipes of ablution fittings from a.drain at ground level by making them discharge above the water seal of a trapped gully and so reduce risk of drain air escaping into a building through any defect in the plumbing schemes.

That broadly is the scheme, and that it has been a success there can be no doubt when one consults the rates of mortality for the country since its inception and considers the general improvement in sanitary hygienic conditions from fitments and combined with good workmanship on sound principles.

Some Defects of Existing Systems.—The system, though sound generally, results in a maze of pipes on high buildings, which from an architectural point of view are ugly and also are expensive.   As an example, where a bathroom repeats one over each other for eight or ten stories, and assuming each bathroom has a W.C., a bath and a lavatory basin, this entails a waste stack with branches at each floor and a branch ventilating stack

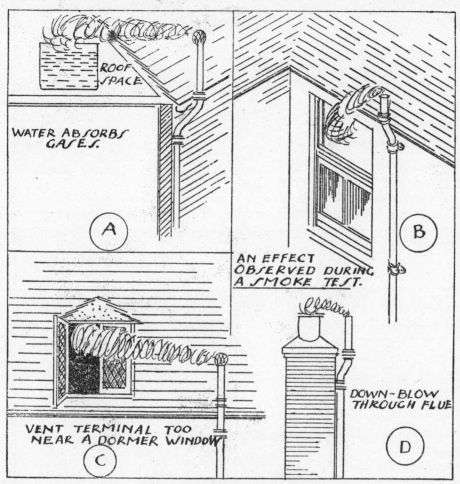

Fig. 491.—Faults which can occur.

with branches to the traps.   Immediately adjacent must be a stack of soil pipe with branches at each floor and its adjacent branch ventilating stack with branches.   This produces four vertical stacks practically the whole height of the building, but the apparent anomaly is, immediately we get to ground level they unite to discharge to one pipe, the "drain."

Further, the scheme of present-day sanitation, though an improvement, has resulted in quite a number of minor defects.   These are illustrated in Fig. 491 and Fig. 492.   Sketch *A* shows how the water in the storage tank can be polluted by gases from the drains and soil pipe.   Sketch *B* shows what happens in some cases.   It was noted during a smoke test of the drains.   When the plug was removed from the end of the vent after the test, the smoke swept down and in at the window below.   The smoke, of course, could be seen, drain air is invisible, and it naturally follows that

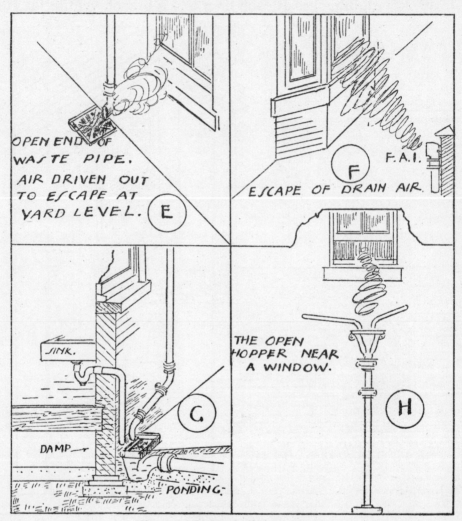

Fig. 492.—Faults of existing schemes.

the drains were being ventilated into the building when the window was open and the wind in a certain direction.   Sketches *C* and *D* illustrate two further faults which may occur, the latter more particularly when a fire is not burning.   Sketch *E* illustrates another defect in connection with gully traps and the waste pipe.   Here, although the pipe air normally climbs upwards as decomposition sets up on the scum on the walls of the pipe, it is pushed down when a fitting discharges, to escape and be breathed at ground level. It also results in yard flooding or at its best in fouling the paving by splashes of soapy compounds which, when dry, fly up as dust. Sketch *F* shows the inherent fault of the dwarf " Fresh Air Inlet " to drains. The opening is certainly protected with a mica-flap closing against back pressure as occurs when liquid discharge is taking place along the drain. Though it prevents the main escape of drain air, it is not airtight, and puffs of air escape at each liquid discharge down the drain. In one district, the sanitary authorities always religiously smoke-tested the attached pipe, but plastered the grated face over with clay for purposes of the test. Sketch *G* illustrates a common nuisance in connection with gully traps with the waste pipes discharging over the grating. The " cement pointing " behind is gradually washed out and the wall and surrounding ground constantly saturated with liquid filth. The circumstances can, however, be much improved or the faults (displayed in *E* and *G*) entirely eliminated by adopt-

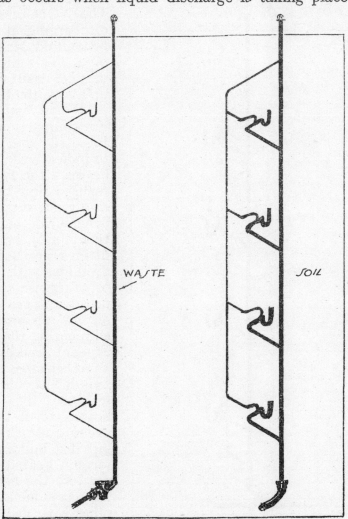

Fig. 493.—Typical System for 4 W.C.'s and 4 Baths.

ing a form of sunk gully with proper waste-pipe sockets discharging below the grating as previously illustrated (see Figs. 419, Vol. II, and 469, etc., Vol. III). Sketch *H*, Fig. 492, illustrates in a graphical manner the fault which exists in connection with the open hopper-head near a window, a fitting which is now taboo under the L.C.C. 1930 By-Laws.

Drainpipe of " One-pipe " System.—The " One-pipe " System is really a revival of the original English system with the faults eliminated, materials improved, plus a system of very thorough ventilation to make it safe. It does not necessarily remove all the faults illustrated, but it goes a long way in that direction. The Americans never had cause to forsake the old English method ; they, by trial and error, gradually improved upon it so that it has become perfectly safe in that country.

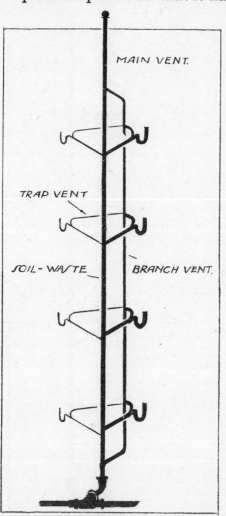

Fig. 494.—The same number of fittings on the " One-pipe " System.

The " One-pipe " System consists of discharging all sanitary fittings, ablution and otherwise into one common pipe. This pipe may be likened to a vertical drain with an open end high up above the buildings it serves.

Where, and Where not, Suitable.—For comparison the skeleton diagrams, Figs. 493 and 494, have been drawn to indicate the principle and difference between the two systems. It can be realised first that there will be little if any advantage in the " One-pipe " Scheme for buildings no higher than two stories, and particularly so if the fittings are scattered. For ordinary dwellings with lavatories in bedrooms or otherwise scattered the system has no advantages and it is better to hold on to our present, safe system, but eliminating the faulty details for this type of building as far as possible. Whether pipes are inside or outside a building should depend entirely upon whether the building is centrally heated or not. Frost is the great enemy and risk with internal plumbing, but if a building is properly and uniformly heated, then the walls will not lose the heat accumulated during the day sufficiently to cause the waste pipes with dribbling taps to freeze in, say the night, in times of frost. If internal means of carrying the sanitary installation is resorted to then the gully traps should be eliminated entirely or alternatively mechanically cover-sealed traps resorted to. In any case where the One-pipe " System ("Soil-waste Pipe," for want of a better term) is adopted, the gully trap must be cut out and the " Soil-waste " connected directly to the drain by means of a slow bend. A system of connection which has proved very satisfactory in America is by means of a pitched junction coupled with an obtuse bend as illustrated in Fig. 495. It is efficient, both in avoiding stoppages occurring and also in preventing "backing up." This latter feature is an important factor as if it occurs to any extent, the discharge from fittings on a high floor might back up in the fittings on the ground floor. Coupled with this, judicious pipe sizing is a very important feature.

Ministry of Health Model By-Laws.—The "One-pipe" System is a topic of much discussion between architects, sanitarians, surveyors and the plumbing trade in general. The practical adoption of the scheme is made possible by the Ministry of Health Published Model By-Laws, the vital sections of which can be found in the Series IV, *New Streets and Buildings* (Urban Series), 1s. 3d. net ; IVa, *New Buildings and Certain Matters in Connection with Buildings* (Rural Series), 9d. ; IVc, *New Streets and Buildings* (Intermediate Series), 1s., and IVb, *With Respect to drainage of existing Buildings*, 6d. net. Published at His Majesty's Stationery Office, Adastral House, Kingsway, London, also Edinburgh, Manchester, Cardiff and Belfast.

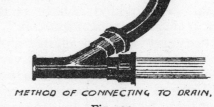

METHOD OF CONNECTING TO DRAIN.

Fig. 495.

The model by-laws do not specifically mention what is now spoken of as the " One-pipe " System of sanitation, but on the other hand they do not prevent it. There is, therefore, no legal obstacle to the "One-pipe" System in any district where by-laws based on the current edition of the model by-laws are in force. The system has been adopted in Scotland and in London, for instance, as at the Cumberland Hotel (Marble Arch, London), containing over a thousand bathrooms. The principle is also favoured by the majority of the professional bodies connected with building. The crux of the matter is that for high and extensive buildings, for which the system is most suited, the " One-pipe " System will be more generally adopted. Section 64 of IV in paragraph 1 convey that inlets to a drain may be made within a building in connection with water-closets, bath, sink or lavatory where the drain is carried through the building. Paragraph 5 says, in effect, that where a *waste pipe* from a bath, sink (not being a slop sink) or lavatory, and every pipe carrying off foul water, where it discharges to a pipe or drain *other than a soil pipe* (the italics are the present writer's) from a water-closet it shall discharge to a properly trapped gully. The inference is that a waste pipe from ablution fittings can discharge to a soil pipe. It also states that if it is more than six feet in length it shall be provided with a proper trap. Again the inference is that where such a waste pipe discharges to a gully trap, and the length of the pipe entailed is less than six feet, it need not be trapped. No Public Health body should have permitted such latitude in that respect. First of all, if a hole exists in a wall and the wind is blowing on that wall, the air pressure is considerable and the hole in the wall forms a relief through which the air travels at high velocity. An untrapped pipe is in effect a hole in the wall. That a waste pipe can be self-clearing and possibly self-cleansing (note the distinction), if proper precautions are taken and provisions made (see Volume II, pp. 235, 236 and Figs. 410, 411), can be admitted, but only those intimately connected with the practical handling of such waste pipes will realise the filthy state in which the internal state of waste pipes frequently exist, trapped or untrapped, if the inlet to such a pipe is throttled by a grating or otherwise. And particularly so if only cold water or indifferently hot water is " on tap."

While all in favour of simplification of sanitary arrangements, no risks should be taken of spreading infectious disease, the source of which is often difficult to trace. The next paragraph says :

" (C) Where a *waste pipe discharges to a soil pipe* from a water closet, it shall be provided, whatever its length, with a proper trap *adequately secured against siphonic action.*" Again the italics are the present writer's. Adequately secured against siphonic action, in the writer's opinion, is not sufficient. There may be very varied opinions on what is *adequate*. Any man with an elementary knowledge of hydraulics, and little conscience as regards sanitary requirements, could so fix any trap that its contents would not be *siphoned*. He has only to throttle the inlet and enlarge the outlet by connecting to a relatively large pipe, but that does not lead to sanitary conditions, in fact it leads to very unsatisfactory conditions, producing slow emptying and foul traps and waste pipes. A 1-inch inlet piece, a 1½-inch trap and a 2-inch waste pipe, for instance, would be difficult to siphon and more so if the 1-inch inlet has a grating reducing its available area to say one half. Further, prevention of siphonage is not the only precaution to be taken, particularly in connection with high buildings where momentary compression effects can cause puffs of foul air to break through the seals of traps situated on the lower floors. Also by providing branch ventilating pipes to the branch wastes the current of air passing along, though admittedly slow, has an oxidising effect which prevents the surfaces of the pipe becoming sour or septic and forms a by-pass which makes the scheme safe in all respects. Where the " One-pipe " System is adopted one of the essential features for safety is the provision of branch and trap ventilating pipes. Only concientious firms and sound craftsmen should be employed in work of this character.

Paragraph 10 of Section 65 states that if the water-closet is constructed to discharge into a soil pipe of an internal diameter not greater then 3 inches[1] which also receives the discharge from any other water-

[1] The index figure gives a statement as follows : If the Local Authority desire to provide against siphonic action where more water-closets than one are connected to a soil pipe even of greater diameter than three inches, the Minister will be prepared to consider the proposal.

closet, or into a soil pipe of whatever diameter which also receives the discharge from a bath, sink or lavatory, the trap of the water-closet shall be ventilated by a pipe which shall (*a*) have an internal diameter not less than $1\frac{1}{2}$ inches, and if it ventilates the traps of two or more water-closets, not less than 2 inches.

It is required that where a branch ventilating pipe rejoins the main vent, it must do so at a point at least 3 feet above the highest connection of any water-closet (and presumably above any other fitting) or otherwise have an open end as high as the top of the soil pipe.

ADVANTAGES OF THE "ONE-PIPE" SYSTEM

1. For large buildings the "One-pipe" System is cheaper than the "two-pipe" system.

2. The quantity of water flushing the single stack is materially increased by the addition of bath water, sinks and lavatory bowls, and this water has a greater cleansing value than the water flushed from a W.C. as it is usually or periodically quite hot.

3. The introduction of the lavatory basin and bath hot water tends to decrease the deterioration of the piping and give it longer life. The great enemy to the metals of piping is carbon dioxide, which is generated from deposits in the piping, and, producing acidity with the moisture, accelerates decomposition with corrosive and erosive effects.

Further, the introduction of hot water in bulk mixed with soap and soda and alkaline constituents, the acid quality of carbon dioxide is neutralised and the life-time of the piping considerably lengthened.

Materials.—The suitable materials are limited. For large-diameter main stacks, heavy cast-iron internally and externally coated with Dr. Angus Smith's Solution by dipping in hot baths of the protective solution. The joints should be of the socket and spigot type, with the inside face of the socket corrugated or ribbed to prevent the caulking lead from working out. Alternatively stout flange joints could be used. The suitability or otherwise of a material depends to some extent also on the diameter. Branch pipes, which should be comparatively short if the scheme is to retain any advantage, can be of stout lead with wiped joints. Light-gauge copper with compression or bronze welded joints. Galvanised (steam strength) screwed iron barrel with recessed malleable fittings (see Vol. I for illustration of such a fitting). It has been stated that galvanised wrought iron used as vent above the discharging line perishes in a comparatively short while. Lead pipe is eminently suitable for branch ventilation. Special ferruled joints will be required, as previously explained, for the joint between lead and copper ; copper and iron ; lead and iron ; stoneware to copper, etc.

Access.—Bolted-on access eyes or screw eyes according to the diameter of the pipe should be provided at ends of branch runs, and at junctions on the main stack opposite the branch. Access eyes at the foot of vertical stacks and at changes of direction or any position necessary to give accessibility for clearing rods, at traps.

In high buildings, the pipes themselves must be accessible so that any moved and leaky joints caused by contraction and expansion forces can be readily caulked tight again.

The whole of the work should be planned to be fool-proof and it would really be a wise provision if only registered plumbers were engaged on the work.

Sizing of " Soil-waste " Pipes.—It is comparatively easy to find suitable diameters when a discharge is constant. The trouble in connection with sanitary fittings is from the very intermittent way the fixtures are used. The sizing will depend upon what is usually termed " peak load " times and the peak load will vary according to the number of occupants of the building, the number of fittings attached and also the character of the building, i.e. whether hotel, office or factory, etc.

One State in North America gives the following for " Soil-waste " pipes :

> 4-inch pipe, all fittings,   96 on the main.
> 5　　,,　　　,,　　　,,　　,,   192　,, ,,　　　,,
> 6　　,,　　　,,　　　,,　　,,   336　,, ,,　　　,,

If the building is six and under twelve stories high, diameter shall not be less than 5 inches. If over twelve stories, diameter shall be 6 inches.

The table is based on fixtures having a nominal diameter on the outgo. The unit is $1\frac{1}{4}$ inches or $1\frac{1}{2}$ inches, as one fixture, 2 inches counts as two fixtures, $2\frac{1}{2}$ inches counts as three and 3 inches (a W.C.) counts as four fixtures or fittings of the ordinary sanitary fitments.

The discharge from a bath is sustained over the longest period and generally speaking a number of baths discharging at the same time having 2-inch short wastes, would be the greatest tax on a main pipe to which they are connected. In America, where some of the buildings house from 2,500 to 3,000 workers, very definite calculations of the discharge over peak hours has to be made. The rule of thumb methods are not good enough when dealing with numbers on one building equivalent to the population of a small town.

It is necessary with the very high buildings having numerous fittings of the various floors discharging into one stack to graduate the diameter from large at the bottom to small at the top. The change is made at each sixth floor. The rates of discharge and quantities from sanitary fittings will vary somewhat according to type of fittings, and whether the water can be used *ad lib* or whether a metered supply is installed. In the latter case, it is used more carefully. American allowances are higher than in England, but the following discharging rates have been determined for that country : Lavatories with $1\frac{1}{4}$ outlet, 1 cu. foot of water per minute. A sink, about $2\frac{1}{2}$ cu. feet per min, on a $1\frac{1}{2}$ inch outlet ; the discharge from a bath is about 2 cu. feet per minute on a 2-inch outlet, and the discharge

from a W.C. is about 4 cu. feet per minute on a 4-inch pipe.   The above
figures were given by Mr. Francis Lorne, F.R.I.B.A., when speaking at a
meeting in London to a panel of the Advisory Council of the Building
Industry.   The writer fails to see, however, why a sink with a 1½-inch
waste discharges 2½ cu. feet against a bath with a 2-inch outlet only
2 cu. feet per minute.   The difference may be in the way they are trap-
ventilated and also the American bath trap is usually of the large bottle

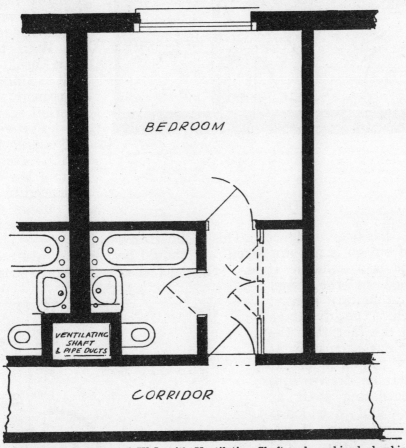

Fig. 496.—Internal Bathroom and W.C. with Ventilating Shaft and combined plumbing space.

type, which possibly retards the discharge against the typical tubular
type.[1]
      Group Planning.—It is essential in planning, to arrange the fittings
close together and preferably back to back.   A typical method is shown in
Fig. 496.   It will be noticed that the fittings and sanitary apparatus are
on an internal wall ; an arrangement which should now be possible and,
indeed, is being adopted at the Cumberland Hotel, London.   The pipes

[1] " Peak load " times for a London hotel would probably be just before dinner, due to
bath-water discharge.

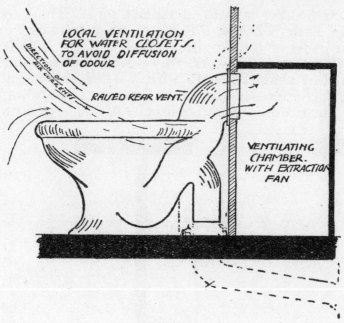

LOCAL VENTILATION FOR WATER CLOSETS. TO AVOID DIFFUSION OF ODOUR

DIRECTION OF AIR CURRENT

RAISED REAR VENT.

VENTILATING CHAMBER. WITH EXTRACTION FAN

Fig. 497.

are carried in the vertical duct which by means of an *extraction* fan forms the ventilating means for the sanitary apartment. This method is really more effective in preventing the spread of odours from the W.C. than our more usual system with window and apartment on an external wall to the air. For very difficult cases in basements, etc., where trouble has been experienced in preventing odours escaping, a very special form of W.C. has been designed. This is illustrated in Fig. 497. The hidden type of out-go is not approved. It should be clear of walls or floor. Fig. 498 is a siphonic type. The special construction referred to is contained in the large glazed stoneware arm at the back. The advantage lays in the fact that the local odour occurring at the W.C., when in use, is immediately drawn into the ventilating shaft at the back and to which it is attached before it has time to spread and escape from the apartment, possibly into adjoining room or corridor. There are distinct points in its favour where mechanical means of ventilation are provided. Fig. 499 shows a typical American lay-out of this type for back-to-back

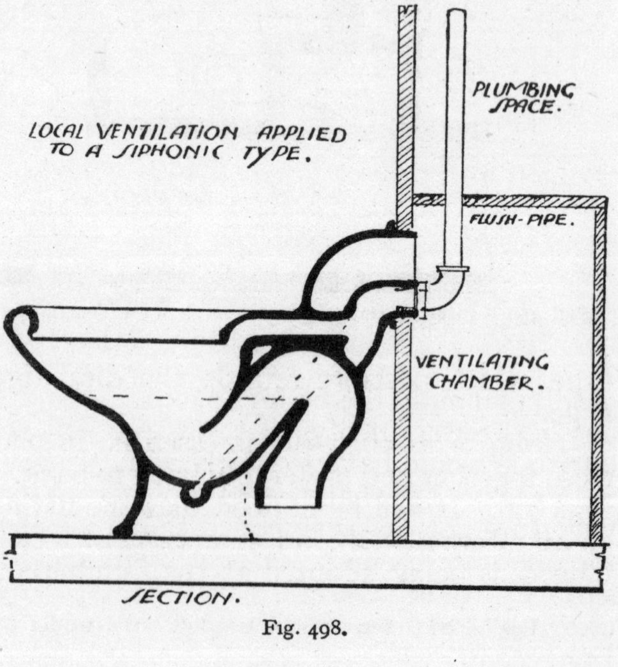

LOCAL VENTILATION APPLIED TO A SIPHONIC TYPE.

PLUMBING SPACE.

FLUSH-PIPE.

VENTILATING CHAMBER.

SECTION.

Fig. 498.

ranges with what is called a "plumbing space" between. The ventilating pipes and flushing valves or the flushing cisterns are fixed in this space. There is also a space below for horizontal runs of drain, soil and waste pipe when the latter is required. The plumbing space also is made to act as the ventilating extraction shaft, such shaft communicating with the open air.

Coming back to the ordinary circumstances for internal plumbing and

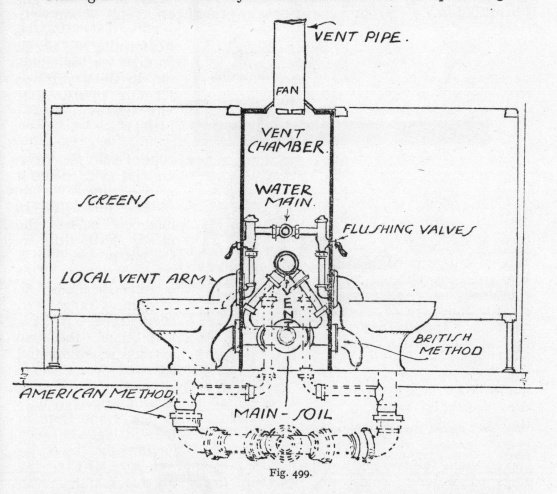

Fig. 499.

group planning, the fittings should be so arranged that there shall not be any horizontal run of piping, waste or soil exceeding 6 to 7 feet, but greater lattitude would have to be given for ranges.

Traps.—The shallow seal type of trap should not be permitted. Types which are not easily siphoned should be chosen. Fig. 500 is a good form for lavatory basins. It is in hard metal and has a chromium-plated surface. It is neat and easily fitted. It has a special feature also for clearing, it being only necessary to unscrew the cup at the bottom. Fig.

502 shows it *in situ*. They may be obtained with a long shank and wall plate as indicated. For baths Hellyer's deep seal type is an excellent form (see Fig. 503). A similar trap is made for sinks, etc., but having the access eyes on the side.

Venting.—Very thorough ventilation is essential with numerous fittings discharging into one pipe. Broadly, there are two systems. (1) Crown venting, which has been discussed thoroughly in this work and illustrated in Figs. 493 and 494 and many other figures. (2) "Loop venting." This consists of forming a circuit from the vertical stacks out to the fitting and forming by-passes to the intermediate fittings.

Fig. 501 shows a typical example of this method as carried out in the States.

Fig. 506 shows an instance where the intermediate fitments are not provided with separate vents. This is only permissible on a topmost range, and even then, if the fittings on the two extremities, right and left, of one range, happen to be flushed simultaneously, there is risk of the traps of the fittings between having the seals siphoned while the two ends of the horizontal soil are charged with moving plugs of water. There are, however, many in this country who consider it unnecessary to provide separate trap vents to each fitting for a top range of a stack of sanitary fittings. Suggestions as to necessary sizing are made on the drawing.

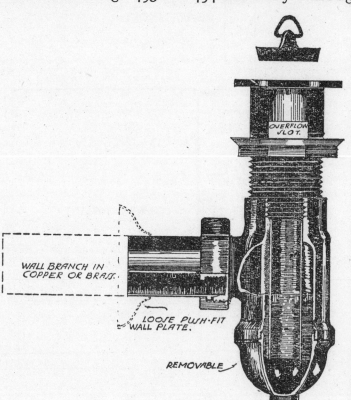

Fig. 500.—Special form of chromium-plated dip-seal trap for lavatories.

Example of Installation.—Fig. 504 shows the plan of a plumbing space and bath-rooms as being carried out now at the Cumberland Hotel, in course of construction and nearing completion. It is an outstanding job for this country, on the "One-pipe" System, or as it is sometimes termed, "Simplified Plumbing." With the basement there are eleven floors.

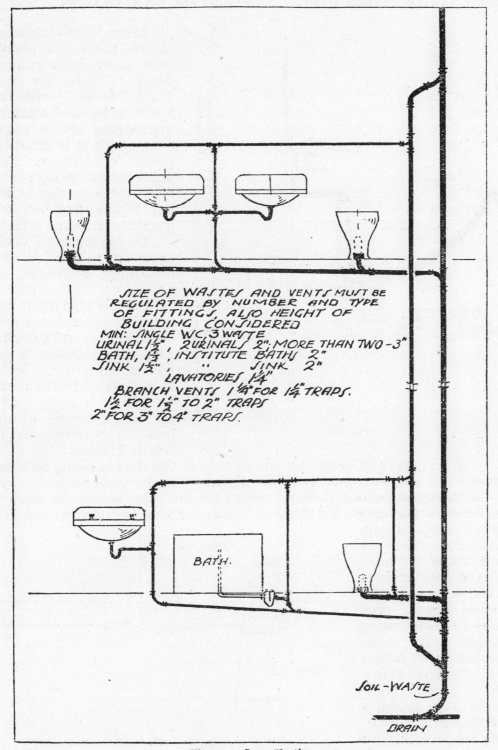

SIZE OF WASTES AND VENTS MUST BE
REGULATED BY NUMBER AND TYPE
OF FITTINGS, ALSO HEIGHT OF
BUILDING CONSIDERED
MIN: SINGLE WC, 3"WASTE
URINAL 1½", 2 URINALS 2", MORE THAN TWO - 3"
BATH, 1½", INSTITUTE BATHS 2"
SINK 1½", " " SINK 2"
LAVATORIES 1¼"
BRANCH VENTS 1¼" FOR 1¼" TRAPS.
1½" FOR 1½" TO 2" TRAPS
2" FOR 3" TO 4" TRAPS.

BATH.

SOIL-WASTE

DRAIN

Fig. 501.—Loop Venting.

There are 64 ducts as shown, but not all identically planned the same in detail. There are two drain "levels" with the lower in the sub-basement discharging into a sump from which it is lifted by pumps to the sewer. Discharging into the high-level drain there are 923 baths, 841 W.C.'s, 845 lavatory basins, 3 ranges of urinals.

To the low-level drain there are 133 W.C.'s, 218 lavatories, 88 baths, 40 urinals.

For the staff there are 135 W.C.'s, 42 baths and 60 lavatories and 50 sinks. The sub-basement is 54 feet below ground level. It can be seen by the above that the job is approaching in size some of the jobs as referred to in North America.

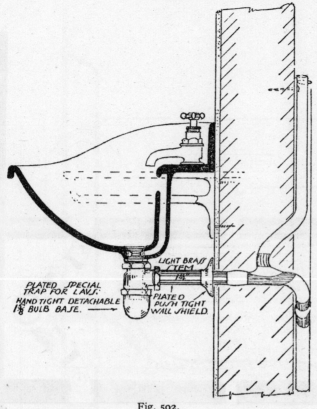

PLATED SPECIAL
TRAP FOR LAVS.
HAND TIGHT DETACHABLE
1⅝ BULB BASE. ——▸

LIGHT BRASS
STEM
1¼

PLATED
PUSH TIGHT
WALL SHIELD.

Fig. 502.

Fig. 505 gives an elevation on one side of the duct showing how the branch soil and wastes on one floor discharge to the main stack.

Although not shown in the drawing, the duct also houses the 2-gallon waste water preventers for the W.C.'s, the overflows each discharging into small hopper-heads and the cold- and hot-water pipes. The cold-water pipes and the runs of horizontal waste pipe are in light-gauge copper and connected up by means of compression joints. The high-level drain shown is carried in a plumbing space with continuous access and,

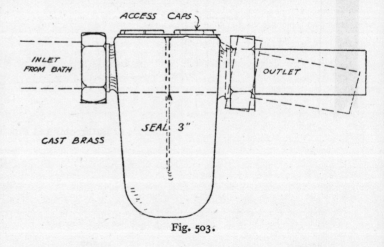

ACCESS CAPS

INLET
FROM BATH

OUTLET

CAST BRASS

SEAL 3"

Fig. 503.

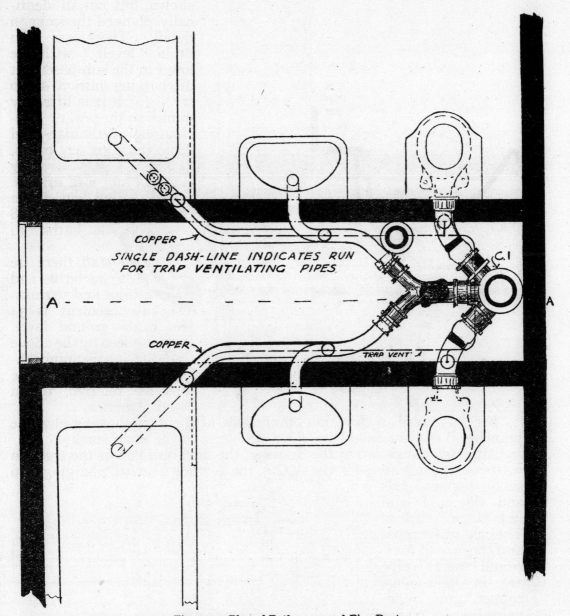

Fig. 504.—Plan of Bathrooms and Pipe Duct.

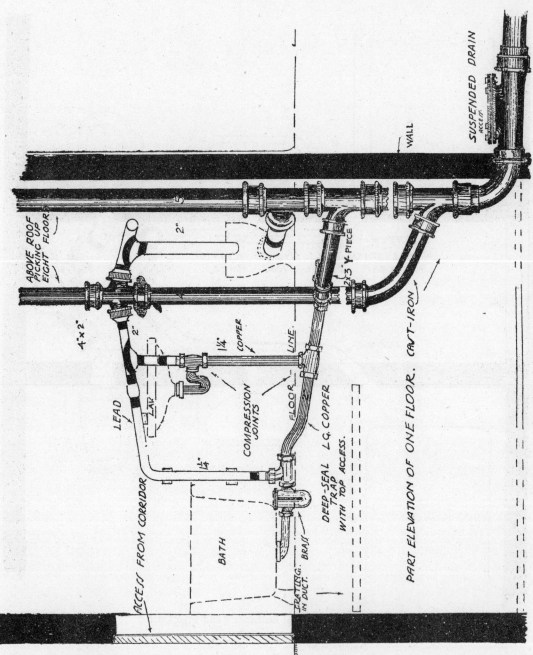

ABOVE ROOF PICKING UP EIGHT FLOORS

2"

4"×2"

2"

LEAD

TAP

1¼"

COPPER

FLOOR LINE

COMPRESSION JOINTS

1¼"

ACCESS FROM CORRIDOR

BATH

GRATING IN DUCT. BRASS

DEEP-SEAL L.G. COPPER TRAP WITH TOP ACCESS.

No. 2½ Y-PIECE

CAST-IRON

PART ELEVATION OF ONE FLOOR.

WALL

SUSPENDED DRAIN

ACCESS

Fig. 505.—In one of the Pipe Ducts at the Cumberland Hotel.

108

it will be noticed, the gully trap is cut out entirely as it should be on a combined soil-waste pipe at any rate.   In the particular case in point, there are eight floors emptying in each soil-waste stack in each duct, and there are two lavatories, two baths and two W.C.'s at each floor.

Consulting the particulars on a previous page where one bath is equal to 2 — 1¼ or 1½ connections, and a W.C. to four, the total units are 2

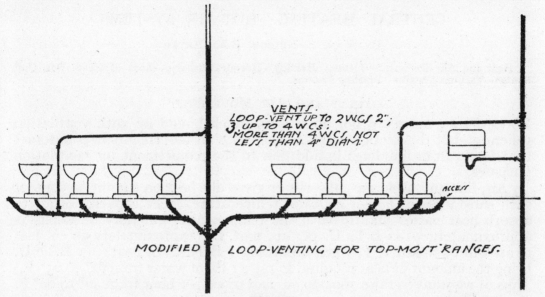

MODIFIED   LOOP-VENTING FOR TOP-MOST RANGES.

Fig. 506.

lavatories × 1 ; 2 baths × 2 ; 2 W.C.'s × 4 = 14, and 14 × 8 floors = 122 unit connections.   A 4-inch shaft from the table may take 96 and a 5-inch will take 192 fixtures, so it can be seen that according to that method the 5-inch stack is well on the safe side.   As previously stated, however, some thought must be given as to the type of building served when making a decision as to diameters.   An iron ladder is fixed the whole height of the duct and iron gratings are fixed over part of the area at each floor. Entry to the ducts is from the corridor, so it can be seen that everything is very accessible.

CHAPTER VII

CENTRAL HEATING: HOT-AIR SYSTEMS

By Stan. E. Nelson, B.A. Cantab.

Heat and Air Movement—Plenum Heating—Hot-air Furnaces—Loss of Heat—Box Unit Heater—Vacuum Systems—Pipeless Systems.

HEAT AND AIR MOVEMENT

WARMING by means of hot air is very much bound up with ventilation generally, but this section will deal only with air movements to counteract heat losses from buildings in addition to the requirement for ventilation purposes.

Air, like any other gas, absorbs or gives out heat on coming in contact with substances of higher or lower temperature. The capacity of air to absorb heat varies slightly with the temperature, but may be taken as approximately ·0182 B.Th.U. per cu. foot, i.e. approximately 55 cu. feet of air will be raised 1° F. when absorbing 1 B.Th.U. of heat. (1 B.Th.U. being the amount of heat required to raise 1 lb. of water from 62° to 63° F.) Thus, if we want to raise 360,000 cu. feet of air per hour from 40° to 60° F. we should require

$$\frac{360,000 \times (60 - 40)}{55} \text{ B.Th.U. per hour,}$$

or approximately 130,000 B.Th.U. per hour.

The computation of heat losses is the same as for direct heating systems. A list is given below of some of the common materials used in building construction together with the heat loss through them per square foot per degree Fahrenheit difference of temperature. The figures given are those usually employed by heating and ventilating engineers and designers.

4½-inch brick wall, unplastered	·5
9 ,, ,, ,, ,,	·35
14 ,, ,, ,, ,,	·27
18 ,, ,, ,, ,,	·23
4½ ,, ,, ,, plastered	·44
9 ,, ,, ,, ,,	·33
18 ,, ,, ,, ,,	·22
9 ,, ,, ,, with air space between	·29
14 ,, ,, ,, ,, ,, ,, ,,	·23
18 ,, ,, ,, ,, ,, ,, ,,	·2
6 ,, concrete wall	·48
8 ,, ,, ,,	·41
12 ,, ,, ,,	·32
18 ,, ,, ,,	·29
Timber construction, hollow wall, ¾-inch weather-boarding, 1-inch boards on 4-inch studding, lathe and plaster on the inside	·26

Cork-slab lining, 1 inch thick	·21
Wood lining, 1 inch thick	·41
Plaster lining, 1 inch thick.	·57
Cement rendering, 1 inch thick	·57
Single windows	1·03
Double windows	·48
Slate roof, on 1-inch boards	·43
Tile roof, no boards	1
,, ,, boards under	·35
,, ,, ,, ,, also ceiling under	·24
,, ,, rafters boarded both sides	·18
Flat roof, 5-inch concrete and asphalted	·15
Floor, 6-inch concrete on earth	·4
,, 6 ,, ,, ,, with air space and 1-inch boards on joists	·05

PLENUM HEATING

Air movement for warming purposes may be accomplished either by means of a centralised plant with fan and heater and a suitable duct system to convey the air to the desired points, or by Unit Heaters, a description of which is given in the chapter on " Ventilation." The latter method avoids the use of large pipes to convey the air, but requires steam or water pipes to supply the heating medium to the various points where the units are fixed, or the necessary wiring in the case of electrically-heated units.

HOT-AIR FURNACES

The Unit Heater is the more modern method of circulating warm air, but some reference might be made here to direct heating of air by furnace, although this is seldom met with in present-day practice. Briefly, the furnace took the form of a fire-box above and around which metal tubes were arranged so that the hot gases from the fire passed over them, the open ends of the tubes being connected to ducts on either side, air being allowed to pass through and so absorb some of the heat from the flue. A variation of this was for the flue gases to pass through the tubes and the air to pass over them. This method had the advantage that the tubes could be more easily cleaned out and kept free from soot and so maintain a higher rate of conductivity from the tubes to the air.

Cases may arise where use may be made of this type of apparatus, in small factories, where a furnace may be in existence or necessary for other purposes, and use may thus be made of the otherwise waste heat from the flue gases.

The rate of heat exchange from the tubes to the air, or the " emissivity " as it is called, can best be obtained from the makers of this type of apparatus, as no reliable figure can be given.

Owing to the resistance set up by the tubes against the flow of air it is usually necessary to install a fan somewhere in the duct to create adequate air movement and, provided the duct runs can be short, the Propeller type of fan is inexpensive and is suitable for this application.

As in the case of the Unit Heater, suitable arrangements can be made by means of dampers and duct connections for admitting fresh cold air to mix with the recirculated air. The main disadvantage of this type of apparatus is that unless the joints between the open ends of the tube and duct are made and kept sound there is danger of fumes getting through to the air stream. The diagram (Fig. 507) illustrates typical application of this type of apparatus.

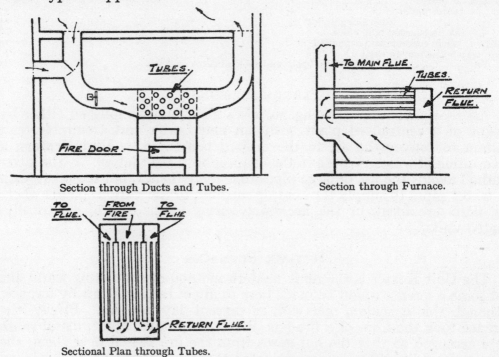

Section through Ducts and Tubes.   Section through Furnace.

Sectional Plan through Tubes.

Fig. 507.—Diagrammatic arrangement, Air-heating by Furnace.

Air on being heated becomes lighter in weight, and when it is warmed in passing through a heater its tendency would be to rise, and it is to counteract this that louvres are fitted to deflect the air downwards and at a velocity high enough to keep it moving in that direction until it reaches the working level of the occupants where the fresh and warmed air is required. Except for the floor-mounting type, Unit Heaters are usually fixed about 12 to 15 feet above the floor. At this height the air temperature leaving the Unit may be as high as 100° to 110° F. Obviously it would not be satisfactory for air at that temperature to come in direct contact with the workers in the store or workshop, but experience has shown that air at that temperature, discharged in a downward direction at 30° or 45° at velocities up to 1,000 feet per minute, has so mixed with the surrounding air that by the time it has reached the working level the mixture has settled down to a temperature of about 55° to 60° and the air velocity has dropped to a speed almost imperceptible to the human body.

In any space to be dealt with by Unit Heaters, we must first ascertain the total amount of heat necessary to maintain the desired temperature, and having obtained it, we must then decide the best method of distributing it throughout the space. Unit Heaters are obtainable in hundreds of different sizes and heat capacities. A moment's consideration will make it clear that it would be useless trying to warm a large space by means of one large unit fixed, say, at one end. The problem, therefore, is to decide on the best arrangement to obtain the best conditions at reasonable cost.

LOSS OF HEAT

The reader may already know how to obtain the amount of heat required to warm a building, but since we must understand the sources of heat loss in order to arrive at an intelligent distribution of the Unit Heaters let us consider them again.

In any building there is some source of air leakage both in and out, and, depending on the construction of the building, so will this be greater or less. In a factory workshop, often of light, inexpensive construction, with doors which will frequently be opened, we may expect the leakage to cause an air change equal to once every half-hour ; in store rooms where fewer people are employed we might allow for an air change once every hour only. Each particular case, however, will be decided on its merit and must be left to the experience of the designer.

Walls, windows, floors, and roof are direct sources of heat loss, particularly outside walls. Loss in heat units per square foot of surface varies considerably with the thickness, the materials, and the construction : the heat loss also varies directly as the temperature difference, in winter therefore the outside walls and windows are among the greater sources of heat loss.

Wind velocity will also have an appreciable effect on the heat loss, but this is such a variable quantity that it is difficult to arrive at any definite allowance to be made ; a knowledge of the direction of the prevailing winds and experience gained will give the designer some idea as to what margin to allow for this.

In this country also the northern aspect of the building needs special provision to be made for heat loss, since this has little benefit from the warming effect of the sun, which even in winter time helps to counteract heat loss due to wind and air temperature. An allowance of 10 per cent. of the total heat loss due to that side of the building is usual from this consideration, but this, of course, is quite an arbitrary figure.

Let us assume now that we have a building of one storey only to be used as a workshop of dimensions 100 feet long, 50 feet wide, and 20 feet mean height, windows on two sides, as in Fig. 507A. For such a building we may assume two air changes per hour. The walls are of 9-inch brick, the roof constructed of slates and wood joists, the floor 6 inches of concrete on solid earth ; we will suppose the temperature is to be maintained at 55° F. when the outside temperature is 30° F.

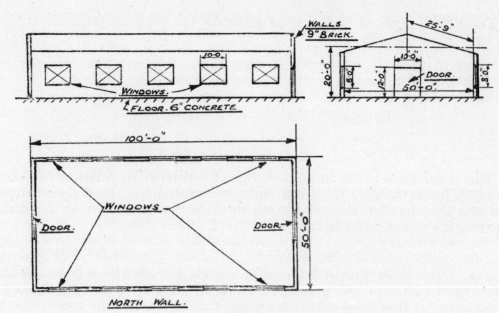

Fig. 507A.

The total cubic content of the space will be
$$= 100 \times 50 \times 20 = 100{,}000 \text{ cu. feet.}$$
For two changes per hour therefore the heat required is given by
$$\frac{200{,}000 \text{ (cu. feet per hour)} \times (55 - 30)}{55} \text{ B.Th.U. per hour}$$
$$= 91{,}000 \text{ B.Th.U. per hour.}$$
The total wall surface
$$= (2 \times 20 \times 50) + (2 \times 100 \times 18) - (10 \times 10 \times 8) - (2 \times 12 \times 10)$$
$$= 4{,}560 \text{ sq. feet.}$$
Referring back to the heat loss table we find that a 9-inch thick wall requires 0·35 B.Th.U. per hour per sq. foot ° F. to counteract the loss of heat.

Heat loss therefore due to walls $= 4{,}560 \times 0{\cdot}35 \times 25$
$$= 40{,}000 \text{ B.Th.U. per hour.}$$
Window and door surface $= 1{,}040$ sq. feet.
Coefficient $= 1{\cdot}03$ B.Th.U. per hour per sq. foot per ° F.
Heat loss due to windows $= 1{,}040 \times 1{\cdot}03 \times 25$
$$= 20{,}800 \text{ B.Th.U. per hour.}$$
The total roof surface $= 2 \times 25{\cdot}75 \times 100$
$$= 5{,}150 \text{ sq. feet.}$$
Coefficient $= 0{\cdot}83.$
Heat loss due to roof $= 5{,}150 \times 0{\cdot}83 \times 25$
$$= 107{,}000.$$
The total floor surface $= 5{,}000$
Coefficient $= 0{\cdot}25.$
Heat loss due to floor $= 5{,}000 \times 0{\cdot}25 \times 25 = 31{,}250.$

Total heat required therefore to *maintain* the required temperature is the sum of all the above.

Air	= 91,000
Walls	= 40,000
Windows	= 26,800
Roof	= 107,000
Floor	= 31,250
Allowance for north wall, say	= 2,530
Total	= 298,580

The above losses have to be made up by means of Unit Heaters. The air temperature leaving the Units must not exceed 100° F., the temperature rise therefore for normal working will be (100 — 55°) — 45° F., and the total air quantity to be moved by the Units is given by

$$\frac{298,580 \times 55}{45 \times 60} \text{ cu. feet per minute} = 6,100 \text{ cu. feet per minute.}$$

Now we have to decide on the size of the Units, and this will be determined by the number which will be considered adequate to obtain an even distribution of the air and heat.

Most good makes of this type of Unit have a range of 20 to 25 feet in which air movement is noticeable, being effective over a range of probably another 10 feet, therefore we may arrange the Units as shown in Fig. 507B.

This arrangement will ensure air movement throughout the space, and with the outside Units directed along the northern walls, where a considerable quantity of heat is lost, will tend to counteract probable down draught from that source.

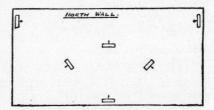

Fig. 507B.—Suggested arrangement of Unit Heaters.

The capacity of the Units is sufficient only to *maintain* 55° F. inside temperature when 30° F. outside, but since the warming of the workshop will probably only be carried out during the working time it will be necessary, especially after week-ends, to allow for probable warming up from 30° or 40° F. and to cover for this a margin of at least 20 per cent. should be allowed on the capacity of the Units. As there are six Units, each must deal with 1,020 cu. feet of air per minute approximately, and the capacity must be 60,000 B.Th.U. per hour approximately, and although the heat quantity for the Units has been based on an incoming air temperature of 30° F. the air entering the Units will probably be in the neighbourhood of the average temperature of the workshop, viz. 55° F., as the air will vary in temperature from about 45° F. at the floor to about 65° F. in the roof space; also it will be noticed that the Units are circulating more than the air change of the space and a proportion is recirculated. The outlet temperature of the air from the Units will probably therefore be a little higher than 100° F. in consequence, say 120° F. If now it is desired to ensure that definite air quantity at the rate of two changes per hour is forced into the workshop we can arrange for the Units to have definite connections to the outside air. Such an arrangement will in fact render the heater slightly more efficient, because the greater the difference of temperature between the air and the heating medium, the higher will be the rate of heat exchange. This will be more apparent when using hot water as the heating medium, e.g. assuming a mean water temperature usual in heating systems, say 170° F., and (1) air entering unit at 30° F. and leaving at 100° F. The mean air temperature $= \dfrac{100 + 30}{2} = 65°$ F. and the temperature difference between mean air temperature and heating medium is 170° F. − 65° F. = 105° F. (2) Air entering the unit at 55° F. and leaving at 120° F. The mean air temperature $= \dfrac{120 + 55}{2} = 87.5°$ F. and the temperature difference " air " to " medium " = 170° F. − 87.5° F. = 82.5° F., whence we see that (1) is about 27 per cent. greater than (2).

Now assuming steam as the heating medium at 10 lb. per sq. inch pressure, i.e. 239° F. temperature, other conditions as for (1) above. The difference between mean air temperature and heating medium is 239° F. − 65° F. = 174° F., and again with steam 239° F. and other conditions as for (2) above, the temperature difference " air " to " medium " = 239° F. − 87.5° F. = 151.5° F, whence we see that the advantage gained is only about 14 per cent.

The type of Unit Heater so far considered has been the one embodying a fan of the Propeller type, and these are very commonly installed in a number of stores and workshops throughout the country with very satisfactory results. They have, however, what some people may consider a disadvantage in that they are generally uni-directional, i.e. they discharge the air from the face of the heater in one direction only at right angles to it, and except for diffusion of the air stream, which always occurs, this type of unit is limited in its range in a lateral direction. They are seldom, if ever, fitted with deflecting duct connection, probably because such additions would render them cumbersome and unwieldy; if, however, their distribution is carefully planned there is little danger of " dead spots " being created on this account.

BOX UNIT HEATER

This leads us, however, to a consideration of the Box or Cabinet type of Unit mounted on the floor, an illustration of which is given. One, two, three, or even four fans are frequently included in one Unit and may be arranged either to draw the air over the heaters or force it through them, a suitable deflector being fitted at the top to discharge the air almost horizontally. It is also a simple matter to arrange several cowls on top of the Unit so that the air can be directed in as many different directions.

These Units, including as they do Centrifugal fans, usually discharge the air at a fairly high velocity, and in consequence have a greater range than the Propeller type. Since, however, they discharge the air just above head-level the temperature should not exceed 80 to 85° F.

It will be appreciated that there are many who favour a scheme whereby the heat losses due to the building itself are dealt with by means of direct heating. The Units then would have to provide only for the heat necessary to discharge the air at the required temperature, namely, 55°, which would mean that the Units would have a greater range, since they could be arranged to discharge in a more horizontal direction as the air would have less tendency to rise.

Next we may consider a scheme of air distribution which while producing a similar effect to that of Unit Heaters obviates the necessity for long steam or water pipe lines with valves and traps and possibly a large number of electric motors which require attention. One fan and one heater only is fixed in a central position, probably in the boiler-house or adjacent to it, and sheet-metal ducts are fixed at high level in the shop with openings provided at suitable points. These openings can either be fixed at a desired angle or fitted with swivel connections so that they can be altered as necessary.

Systems of this design are commonly adopted in workshops and usually include ducts of circular section, for reasons of economy, the air outlets being in the form of short branches from the main duct, taken off at an angle of 30° or 45°, each branch being fitted with a damper to control the air quantity. Such a scheme is illustrated diagrammatically in Fig. 507C, for a workshop similar to the one previously considered in connection with Unit Heaters.

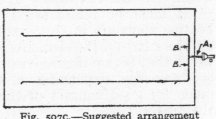

Fig. 507C.—Suggested arrangement of Ducts.

VACUUM SYSTEMS

These systems are the converse of Plenum systems, in that the latter force air into a space and the former exhaust air from the space, so tending to cause a vacuum in it.

For warming purposes the exhaust Vacuum system must be installed in conjunction with some kind of direct heating in the form of radiators or heated pipes, so that as air is exhausted from the space fresh air enters through openings so placed that it must pass over the heating elements.

Air movement from the space is brought about by means of Propeller-type fans fixed either in the roof or walls of a building, or by means of a centralised fan and a suitable duct or pipe system.

A common method adopted for warming the incoming air is to arrange air inlets immediately behind radiators situated on outside walls, as shown in Fig. 507D.

Baffles or guide plates are frequently fitted as indicated to ensure that the air is brought into more intimate contact with the heating element. Another method is to have the heater fixed actually in a duct, usually formed in brickwork or similar building construction, as Fig. 507D.

The number of air changes, and hence the air volume, is decided upon, and the heat loss from the building is computed by the method previously

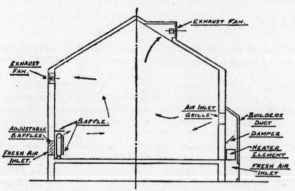

Fig. 507D.—Alternative Vacuum or Exhaust Systems.

described. Air inlets behind the radiators, or heating elements, should be made with ample free area to permit of a fairly free passage of air, and, where possible, the air speed should not be greater than 300 feet per minute. This is necessary partly from consideration of undesirable draughts and partly because too great an air speed would set up resistance to flow and there would be danger of drawing in air from sources other than through the heating elements, where it is most necessary in this type of scheme.

It must be remembered that when drawing air over radiators or heating elements in this manner, a greater rate of heat transmission is obtained than if the elements were subject only to the natural air currents which they set up themselves. As much as 30 per cent. increased emission is obtainable, depending on the type of heater and the arrangements made for good contact of the air over the available heating surface of the heater.

PIPELESS SYSTEMS

Although reference has been made in one or two instances of systems utilising ducts, this chapter has dealt primarily with systems where heating units and fans are directly connected to the space to be warmed. Such systems are generally known as " Pipeless Systems." This term is not, however, strictly true, although it serves to distinguish these types from systems incorporating long duct runs to convey the air to the desired points.

Unless electric heating is used, pipe lines are, of course, necessary to convey the heating medium to the various heaters, either gas, hot water, or steam. The term " Pipeless Systems " should be considered as referring to the conveying of the air.

The design of systems incorporating air-conveying ducts is dealt with in a later chapter on " Ventilation."

CHAPTER VIII

CENTRAL HEATING: HOT WATER

GRAVITY SYSTEM: Convection—A Typical Installation. HEAT UNITS: Heating Sense —B.Th.U.s required to Warm Air—Air Changes—Conduction Losses. TRANSMISSION TABLE OF SURFACES: Use of Tables—Top Floor Requirements—Third Floor—Ground and Other Floors—Basement—Staircase. RADIATION: Measurement of Radiating Surface— Number of Radiators—Sizes of Pipes—Force of Circulation—Travel and Height—Examples. TABLE OF PIPE SIZES. TRANSMISSION TABLE FOR PIPES: Heat Losses of Pipes— Boiler Ratings—Fixing Apparatus—Expansion and Feed Tank—Flows and Returns—Position of Radiators—Valves and Unions—Air-escape Valve—Branches—Size of Cistern—Water Capacity—Sleeve Pieces and Plates—Filling Up—Air Locks—Testing—Regulating—Finishing Off—Covering—Final Test—Firing—Two-pipe System—Warming by Cast-iron Pipes—Factory Heating—Formula—Method of Fixing—Branch Feeds—Venting—Overhead Pipes—Heat from Overhead Piping—Painting—Intermittent Heating—HIGH-PRESSURE HOT-WATER HEATING: Heating Surface—Fixing—Expansion Tank—Uses—Frost.

IT may be truly said that no branch of Sanitary Science, for that it assuredly is, has advanced more rapidly of recent years than central heating. It undoubtedly received a great impetus from the heating engineers of the United States, where central heating is practically universal. The writer well remembers the old wrought-iron saddle boilers and cast-iron pipe coils in ornamental casings, which were practically the only apparatus then in use for heating installations in his youth. But now, what with variations of the gravity system, accelerated systems, panel systems, hot-air and electric heating systems, besides rival heating fuels such as oil, gas, anthracite, ordinary coal and coke (in the old days there were only two), the owner of a large building is often perplexed as to which system to adopt. Now nearly every heating engineer has his own particular system, which in his opinion is better than those of his rivals. All push their systems to the best of their ability, so there is little wonder at the bewilderment of a non-technical client, who, to get over the difficulty, generally leaves the matter to his architect, or sometimes, and very wisely too, to his consulting engineer. They draw up a specification of what they consider to be the best system, and then tenders are obtained from three or more heating engineers for the installation as specified. In the case of smaller buildings and private houses, the heating is often left to the builder, and sometimes proves his undoing, unless he employs a qualified heating engineer, for central heating is governed by certain definite laws, which must be obeyed, which the heating engineer has made a life-study of, so that he and he alone is the only judge of what matters in all questions appertaining to the science.

A full description of the various systems would fill many volumes, but it is proposed to give as full a description of each as the extent of this work allows, so that readers may get a reliable and general knowledge of them, without having to wade through masses of mathematical and scientific data which would necessarily accompany a larger treatise.

GRAVITY SYSTEM

It may be generally stated that the natural, or gravity, system, is the one most in use. A good knowledge of this lays the foundation of the later systems, and when a client has made up his mind to install this system, he generally sends round to heating engineers to give him an estimate for installing a low-pressure, hot-water heating apparatus, which they are to guarantee will give him an internal temperature of 60° F. throughout his building when it is 30° F. outside, and the lowest tender for such an apparatus is usually accepted. In such cases each heating engineer takes his own particulars of the requirements of the building, and bases his tender on what he considers sufficient heating surface and boiler power to fulfil the conditions named : and in order to get the job, feels he is compelled to do nothing more than is absolutely necessary (so as to keep his costs down) to make a successful test. The client is satisfied if, on such a test, he sees a thermometer reading in his rooms of 60° when the outside air is at freezing-point or reasonably cold, and expects that all will be well, but a few days of working the apparatus generally disillusion him. For while it is quite possible to get up a desired temperature, it is quite another matter to maintain it, and soon his satisfaction is turned to irritation and complaint. There can be no question but that the temperature test alone is most unfair and unreasonable, for the heating engineer who calculates his installation on really effective lines would never be successful in obtaining such a competitive job. The only fair way is for each heating engineer to tender for the same heating surface, boiler power, and pipe sizes, so that all are on the same footing and each has an equal chance. The writer well remembers being called in to inspect an installation which had fulfilled the foregoing test, but he found it necessary to have four more sections added to the boiler before it could maintain the 60° all over the building. Examples such as this are quite common.

The main principle underlying all heating work on the low-pressure gravity system, or any other system, is the change produced in the density of the water by the introduction of heat, as the water gets warmer so its density decreases, and expansion takes place, making it lighter.

Convection.—The method by which heat is transmitted in water and gases is termed convection. The minute particles move amongst themselves, owing to their difference in density on being warmed, for the heated particles, being in direct contact with a heated surface, first become heated by conduction ; they then expand and so occupy more space, and thus become lighter or of reduced density, and by the law of gravity

PLATE II

Fig. 508.—Classic Wall Radiators.   Fig. 509.—Wall Radiator.   Fig. 510.—Classic Radiator.

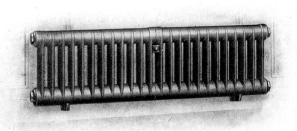

Fig. 511.—Wall Radiator.   Fig. 512.—Hospital Radiator.

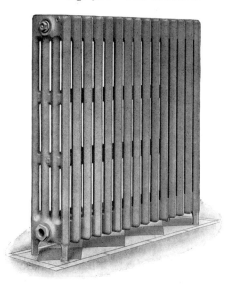

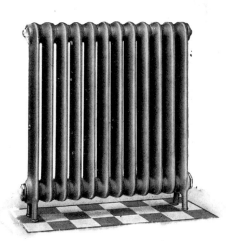

Fig. 513.—Royal Radiator.   Fig. 514.—Narrow Pattern Hospital Radiator.

TYPES OF RADIATORS.

rise, their place being taken by the cooler or denser particles. As the heat increases, so these movements become more rapid and heat is transmitted by this convection.

The circulation of water in a gravity system is due to this convection, and it will be clear from the foregoing that the success of the system depends entirely on giving full play, without hindrance, to the convection of the water particles, and the following simple illustration shows the circulation of the water, due to convection in a hot-water apparatus.

As the water gets heated, becoming less in density, it rises in the vertical pipe, on top of the boiler, called the flow pipe, and its place is taken by the cooler and denser water in the vertical dropping or return pipe, on side of boiler near the bottom, and thus a circulation is set up.

This principle being thoroughly mastered, so that pipe lines, however

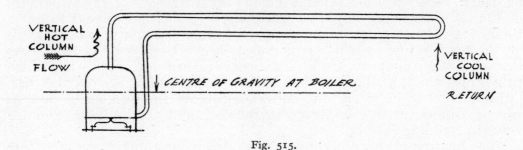

Fig. 515.

long and numerous, do not depart from it, success is assured. On the other hand, however slight a fall there may be in a flow pipe, or rise in a return pipe, failure is inevitable, and when the direction of the pipe line is altered, say by a wall, to a right angle, as easy a bend as possible should be used, and never elbows, or any fitting which might impede the easy flow of the water particles (Fig. 515).

A Typical Installation.—We will now proceed with the fitting and fixing in detail of a typical installation of low-pressure, hot-water heating apparatus, using radiators as the heating medium, on the gravity system, of medium size. For our example we will select a building having a frontage of 100 feet and depth of 30 feet, with six floors, viz. basement, ground, first, second, third, and fourth floors, to be let out as suites of offices, with an average height of 11 feet per floor, and with a sub-basement for the boiler room, and storage of fuel, and machinery, if any, required. If the basement itself is proposed to be heated by radiators, then a sub-basement is absolutely necessary, in order to get the necessary fall back to the boiler. On calculation, we find the cubical contents of each floor to be 33,000 cu. feet. When absolute accuracy is required, each room should be measured separately, because of the partitioning of the floor space and varying thicknesses of main walls. In such case the sum of the contents of the various rooms will give the total required, but in our building, the floors are not partitioned off until the space is let, and then this is done to suit the incoming tenant's requirements, but the variation mentioned is so slight that for all practical purposes we can ignore it. We have, however, not only the cubical contents to deal with, but also the loss of heat that will take place from conduction through the walls, windows, floors, and ceilings, roof and skylights (if any), for every foot of surface in a building loses a definite quantity of heat per hour, according to the difference in temperature between the inner and outer air, and the greater the difference the more heat will be lost. There will be also heat required for ventilation purposes, two changes of air per hour at least being necessary for this. The amount of heat required to be supplied to a building can only be calculated definitely when the conditions to be fulfilled are exactly known. The old method of calculating the amount of radiation required by allowing so many feet of radiation per 1,000 cu. feet of contents is not reliable, chiefly for two reasons : (1) Two rooms of the same size may require very different quantities of heat to warm them. (2) The amount of heat given off from a radiator or pipe depends on the temperature at which it is maintained. Besides the regular heat losses mentioned above, additional loss will arise from the air which passes into or out of the room per hour, whether by leakage or otherwise. Other factors to be taken into consideration are the number of persons who will be ordinarily employed in the rooms of the building, and the way the building is to be used.

The heating of any building, water, air, or anything else, consists in the communication to it of that form of " energy " known as heat.

Heat Units

Quantities of heat may be measured in several different units, but to the heating engineer there are only two in ordinary use ; these are :

(1) The British thermal unit, known as the B.Th.U.

(2) The Continental thermal unit, known as the " calorie."

The British thermal unit is the amount of heat which will warm 1 lb. of water 1° F., say from 42° F. to 43° F., or from 121° F. to 122° F. ; while the calorie is the amount of heat which will warm 1 kilogram of water (2·205 lb.) through 1° C. = 1·8° F. or approximately 4 B.Th.U.s.

Now our problem resolves itself into finding the number of B.Th.U.s required to warm all the floors of our building. We must ascertain first the cubical contents or air to be warmed ; secondly, for the losses due to conduction from walls, windows, floors and ceilings, roof, etc., together with any portions more exposed than the others, such as corners. In this case there are six floors, each of approximately the same cubical contents, viz. 33,000 cu. feet, giving in all 198,000 cu. feet, and it will be fairly obvious, even to non-technical readers, that the top floor will have more, and the basement less, heat losses than the other floors.

For those who have the requisite mathematical ability to work out the scientific theories and necessary equations for the exact determination of the required heating surface, pipe sizes, and boiler power, the writer would refer to Barker on *Heating*, as, in his opinion, no better book could possibly be found, and several years of reference to it have not altered this opinion, but it is hoped, for the benefit of those who do not possess such knowledge, that the practical figures given in this chapter, based on many years of experience and from proved results, may enable them to obtain a good insight into the science, and sufficient knowledge to secure practical results.

Heating Sense.—The reader must be careful in giving due weight to the many factors that have to be taken into account in determining the exact, or approximately exact, amount of heat required. These may appear confusing at first, but practice soon makes perfect, and after a time the hot-water engineer acquires a sort of heating sense, and quickly " sizes " a building up, taking note of its exposed parts, and making mental notes, as it were, as to what extra heat would be required for this or that as the case may be, for no two buildings are exactly alike, and so no general rule, as mentioned previously, is applicable, consequently each must be worked out in accordance with its position, materials used in construction, number of people working in it, and use to which it is put.

B.Th.U.s required to Warm Air.—Now, it will be found that every cubic foot of air requires approximately ·018 B.Th.U.s to raise it 1° F., so that 1,000 cu. feet will require 18 B.Th.U.s, and if it be raised 28°, say from freezing point, 32°, to 60° approximately 500 B.Th.U.s would be necessary. It is well to remember this particular calculation, for in working out changes of air for ventilation, we have only to divide the cubical amount required by 2, and it will be gathered from the foregoing, that we obtain the amount of the additional B.Th.U.s required for the fresh air. The writer stresses this temperature rise for the reason that it is the one usually asked for in most architects' specifications for heating work, and variations can be easily worked out by taking the B.Th.U.s for 1° rise or fall, and adding or subtracting as the case may be.

Air Changes.—In our calculations for ventilation, two changes of air per hour will be included.

Conduction Losses.—Next, the B.Th.U.s required to make good the losses by conduction, and these can be found by reference to the following conduction or, as it is generally termed, " transmission " table, and the figures given in this table are based on the assumption that the outside air is still, and that all walls and windows face south, and percentages are given, which must be added, when the exposed wall surfaces face in any other direction.

Use of Table.—By reference to the table on p. 124 we can proceed with our calculations. It has already been ascertained that the cubical contents or air to be warmed amount to 198,000 cu. feet, or approximately 200,000 cu. feet, and that the B.Th.U.s required for this duty to raise the air through 28° (32° to 60°) will be $\dfrac{200,000}{2} = 100,000$, and,

TABLE LX
TRANSMISSION OF SURFACES

	B.Th.U. loss per hour per sq. foot for 1° difference in internal and external temperatures.
Windows, single	1·08
„ double	0·45
Skylight, single	1·04
„ double	0·48
Walls, 9 inch-brickwork, plaster covered	0·41
„ 14 „ „ „ „	0·33
„ 18 „ „ „ „	0·28
„ 24 „ „ „ „	0·23
„ 9 „ „ wood lined	0·25
„ 14 „ „ „ „	0·22
„ 9 „ „ with air space and 4½-inch brick wall inside . . .	0·29
„ 14 „ „ „ „ „ „ „ . .	0·25
„ 18 „ „ „ „ „ „ „ . .	0·22
„ 12 „ Portland stone	0·47
„ 16 „ „ „	0·42
„ 20 „ „ „	0·37
„ 24 „ „ „	0·34
„ 6 „ concrete	0·57
„ 8 „ „	0·53
„ 10 „ „	0·49
„ 12 „ „	0·45
Roof of Tiles, with rafters boarded on one side	0·35
„ „ „ „ both sides	0·18
„ „ bare, but tight	0·99
„ „ with lath and plaster	0·33
„ Flat of wood joists, boarded and covered with lead and with lath and plaster ceiling underneath	0·17
„ „ Reinforced concrete covered with asphalt 5 inches thick . .	0·30
„ „ „ „ „ „ 12 „ . .	0·20
Floor of wood on joists, with lath and plaster ceiling under (floor side) . .	0·07
„ „ „ „ „ „ (ceiling side) . .	0·17
„ concrete and steel, with wood blocks and plaster ceiling, 7 inches thick .	0·19
„ „ „ „ „ „ „ 9 „ „ .	0·18
„ „ „ „ „ „ „ 11 „ „ .	0·17
„ „ „ „ „ „ „ 13 „ „ .	0·16
„ wood on joists, with air space and 6-inch concrete	0·05
„ „ „ „ pugging and lath and plaster ceiling under (floor side)	0·06
„ „ „ „ „ „ „ „ „ (ceiling side)	0·11

	per cent.
Add, for walls and windows facing north	20
„ „ „ „ east	15
„ „ „ „ west	5
„ building heated during the day only	15
„ a corner building	10
„ buildings heated occasionally, such as churches and chapels from	40 to 75

allowing for two changes of air per hour for ventilation, we allow a similar amount for this duty or 200,000 B.Th.U.s for the air only, or 33,333 B.Th.U.s for each floor approximately.

Top Floor Requirements.—Proceeding with the top floor, we will commence at the roof, say a lead flat one with lath and plaster ceiling underneath. Now, this is 100 feet long by 30 feet wide, which amounts to 3,000 square feet of this kind of surface. Turning to the transmission table it will be found that the B.Th.U. loss for such a roof is 0·17, which for the temperature rise specified must be multiplied by 28, so that the total loss is 3,000 × 0·17 × 28 = 14,280 B.Th.U.s for the roof.

The walls, the two long ones, 100 feet × 11 feet high, or 2 (100 × 11) = 2,200 sq. feet, and the two short ones 30 feet × 11 feet high, or 2 (30 × 11) = 660 sq. feet; adding these together, 2,860 sq. feet is the sum of the wall surfaces on this floor. It will not be all wall surface, however, for we have to reckon on the extra transmission of the windows, and assuming these to measure altogether 400 sq. feet, we must deduct this amount from the wall surface, which gives us 2,460 actual wall surface, and 400 sq. feet of glass in windows. Again referring to transmission table for brick walls, and being a top floor, a 9-inch one, with plaster layer, it will be found that the B.Th.U. loss is 0·41. A 10 per cent. addition must be made to this, however, for only one of the walls can face south, which averages the B.Th.U. loss at 0·45. Therefore, our total wall loss will be 2,460 × 0·45 × 28 = 30,996 B.Th.U.s. To this must be added the window loss, which the table gives as 1·08, but as some of the windows will probably face north at least 1·21 should be allowed, so that the loss from these is 400 × 1·21 × 28 = 13,552 B.Th.U.s, so that walls and windows together take 44,548 B.Th.U.s.

Next would be the floor, but as the whole building is to be warmed, no heat will be lost to any of the floors except the basement, which will be dealt with subsequently.

Summarising the heat losses and heat required to warm the air, allowing for two changes per hour, we get a total for this floor as follows :

TABLE LXI

B.Th.U.s to warm the air	33,333
„ lost through roof	14,280
„ „ „ walls and windows . .	44,548
	92,161

Third Floor.—It will be obvious that one cannot "six times" the remaining floors, for these have no roof, and the ceilings have no cold air above, also the walls are thicker on the lower floors, so for the next or third floor there is only a ceiling loss, as per transmission table of 0·07 = 3,000 square feet × 0.07 × 28 = 5,880 B.Th.U.s, instead of the 14,250 loss of the top floor ; the wall and window losses will, however, be practically the same, and air to be warmed also, so that the total for the third floor will be :

TABLE LXII

B.Th.U.s to warm the air	33,333
„ lost through ceiling . . .	5,880
„ „ „ walls and windows . .	44,548
Total . .	83,761

Ground, First, and Second Floors.—Now, the second, first, and ground floors will be practically the same, for although the walls may be thicker, the windows are usually larger, which more or less equalises the losses, so that these can be added together, the sum being 251,283 B.Th.U.s required for these three floors.

Basement.—The basement next claims attention. There will probably be an area to the front of the building to provide as much light as possible, and, should the building be a corner one, to each front. In some instances pavement lights are used, and in other, bulkhead lights, so that no particular figures are possible, unless one has the exact plan and elevation of the building. The air space will be practically the same as that of the other floors, viz. 33,333, so that we get the same number of B.Th.U.s required for it, while for the walls and windows the loss will be much less, and half the loss of the other floors will be ample for it, that is, 22,748 B.Th.U.s ; while for the floor, which in this instance must be taken into our calculation, and assuming that it is a wooden one, on joists with air space, on 6 inches of concrete, it will be found by transmission table that 0·05 is the B.Th.U. loss for this, in all 3,000 sq. feet × 0·05 × 28 = 4,200 B.Th.U.s. Summarising, we get for this floor :

TABLE LXIII

B.Th.U.s to warm the air		33,333
,, lost through walls and windows .		22,748
,, ,, ,, floor . . .		4,200
Total for basement .		60,281

By adding up all the floors the following total is obtained :

TABLE LXIV

Top floor	92,161	B.Th.U.s
Third floor	83,761	,,
Second, first, and ground floors .	251,283	,,
Basement	60,281	,,
	487,486	,,

Staircase.—As part of the space of the building will be taken up by a staircase in which the air is constantly changing, additional B.Th.U.s must be allowed for this, which will increase our B.Th.U.s required to approximately 500,000.

RADIATION

The next step will be the amount of radiation required to emit this amount of heat, choosing radiators of either the " Classic " or " Royal " type, as these, being of lighter castings, have greater air space between the sections, and thus give a better rating, or emit more heat, than the ordinary type, some makers claiming an additional 12 to 15 per cent. advantage for this type.

Measurement of Radiating Surface.—To ascertain the square feet of radiating surface, in this case radiators, it is usual to divide the B.Th.U.s by 144, as most boilers are rated on this mean emission, that is, allow for each foot of radiator surface to be capable of emitting 144 B.Th.U.s

Fig. 516.—" Classic " Radiator.

Fig. 517.—" Royal " Radiator.

per hour, when the water in radiator is 160° and air in room 60°, so that the amount of radiator surface required works out at $\dfrac{500,000}{144} = 3,472$ sq. feet for the building ; but as the B.Th.U.s required for the various floors vary, these must be taken separately, viz. :

TABLE LXV

Top floor	.	.	.	.	$\dfrac{92,161}{144}$ = 640	sq. feet.
Third floor	.	.	.	.	$\dfrac{83,761}{144}$ = 581	,,
Second floor	.	.	.	.	Do. = 581	,,
First floor	.	.	.	.	Do. = 581	,,
Ground floor	.	.	.	.	Do. = 581	,,
Basement	.	.	.	.	$\dfrac{60,281}{144}$ = 418	,,
Staircase (additional)	.	.	.		90	,,
Total	.	.	.		3,472	,,

Number of Radiators.—Dividing the above results up for radiators, it will be seen that 12 radiators, each of approximately 54 sq. feet of heating surface, will be required for the top floor, while 12 of approximately 48 sq. feet will do for the other floors excepting basement, and here 12 of approximately 36 sq. feet will be ample for rooms and staircase, while 1 of 60 sq. feet of radiating surface will be necessary for entrance hall, and 1 of 30 feet on staircase first floor. The next task will be the placing of these radiators in the most advantageous positions, against the outside walls wherever possible, and as nearly in line above each other on each floor as circumstances will permit.

Sizes of Pipes.—This alignment of radiators is a very important point as regards the cost of the piping feeding the radiators, as a reference to Fig. 518, Plate III, will show ; and this brings us to our next calculation, the quantity and proper sizes of the steam barrel required for our feeder and rising mains, and the efficiency of a heating installation practically depends on the correct design and fixing of the pipes circulating the water from the boiler to the radiators. One may ask, how shall I know when the piping has been properly designed ? and the answer is, when the temperature in all the radiators is the same. There are no simple rules which will give the correct diameter for all pipes in a large installation, for they depend not only on the radiator to be supplied but also on the arrangement of other radiators connected to the same system.

Force of Circulation.—The size of pipe required to supply a radiator having a given heat emission depends on the force circulating the water through the system, and this varies in different parts of the apparatus according to the height of the various radiators above the boiler. The table on next page shows how an approximation to the required size of pipe may be made without any great amount of calculation, but it must be remembered, that to determine the pipe sizes accurately, in order that each radiator should receive its proper flow of water, needs a considerable amount of calculation.

Rule for Use with Table of Pipe Sizes.—Divide the total distance which the water has to travel in passing from the boiler through the pipe to be calculated, and back to the boiler again, by the height above the centre of the boiler, is the centre of the lowest radiator served by the pipe, that is $\dfrac{\text{distance or travel}}{\text{height}}$.

Travel and Height.—In measuring the distance or travel, take the most remote radiator, that is, the end one on the circuit in question, through which the water can travel from the boiler and back to it again. The height to be measured is the least height (nearest radiator on this circuit to boiler) of any radiator served by the pipe (see Plate III).

On dividing the travel by the height, the table will give the corresponding approximate size of pipe required, which will be ample for the work.

PLATE III

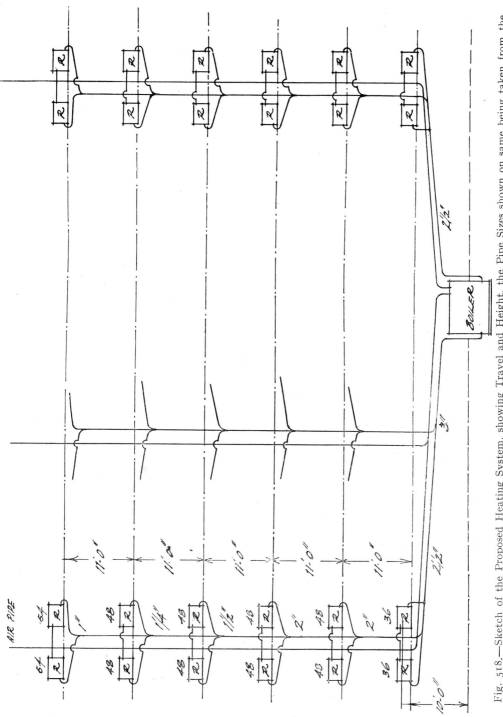

Fig. 518.—Sketch of the Proposed Heating System, showing Travel and Height, the Pipe Sizes shown on same being taken from the Table on page 129.

Examples.—Examples can be worked out from the sketch, but as an independent one, suppose the travel to be 300 feet and the height of the centre of the lowest radiator connected to the pipe to be 10 feet above the centre of the boiler, and the radiating surface carried by the pipe to be 200 sq. feet. The approximate size of the pipe required will be found from table to be $\frac{300}{10} = 30$, and pipe $1\frac{1}{2}$ inch as carrying 200 sq. feet. See Fig. 518, Plate III.

TABLE LXVI

PIPE SIZES ON THE TWO-PIPE SYSTEM

(In low-pressure hot-water systems for 40° F. difference between flow and return pipes.)

Travel.			Diameter of Pipe.							
Height.			$\frac{3}{4}$ inch.	1 inch.	$1\frac{1}{4}$ inch.	$1\frac{1}{2}$ inch.	2 inch.	$2\frac{1}{2}$ inch.	3 inch.	4 inch.
			Sq. Feet of Heating Surface at 175° F.							
2 .	.	.	166	354	625	990	2,100	3,615	5,670	12,090
3 .	.	.	130	280	498	787	1,672	2,895	4,832	9,675
4 .	.	.	110	234	417	666	1,307	2,475	3,915	8,235
5 .	.	.	96	208	364	583	1,230	2,160	3,390	7,185
6 .	.	.	88	183	327	523	1,120	1,935	3,090	6,645
7 .	.	.	78	170	292	480	999	1,755	2,775	5,770
10 .	.	.	63	140	240	390	823	1,450	2,295	4,890
12 .	.	.	56	120	210	343	738	1,282	2,025	4,320
17 .	.	.	46	104	180	288	610	1,084	1,710	3,652
20 .	.	.	40	90	160	260	552	968	1,545	3,315
25 .	.	.	33	80	140	226	480	855	1,356	2,910
30 .	.	.	28	66	123	200	420	756	1,200	2,580
40 .	.	.	25	57	104	172	356	647	1,015	2,205
50 .	.	.	21	51	90	149	308	562	897	1,935
60 .	.	.	18	44	80	130	271	484	782	1,695
70 .	.	.	16	40	72	120	248	450	720	1,560
80 .	.	.	—	36	66	110	224	406	657	1,428
100 .	.	.	—	31	58	88	200	364	588	1,282

With these particulars, not only the pipes size, but the total run of all the piping can be figured out, and this is necessary before we can calculate the full requirement in B.Th.U.s from the boiler. In some buildings the rising mains are fixed by distance clips about $1\frac{1}{2}$ inches from the walls, in which case they help in the heating of the rooms through which they pass ; but in others, chases are left in the brick walls by the builder for them to be fixed in, and so their B.Th.U. emission is mostly lost ; and assuming this to be the case in this installation, we must add this B.Th.U. loss to our previous total to determine the size of the boiler, and the following B.Th.U. emission tables of pipes from 1 inch to 4 inches will enable this calculation also to be made.

TABLE LXVII

TRANSMISSION FOR PIPES

(B.Th.U.s per Lineal Foot per Hour.)

Size of Pipe. Inches.	Water 160°, Air 60°.	Water 170°, Air 60°	Water 180°, Air 60°.
1	76	83	91
1¼	93	103	112
1½	105	116	126
2	129	142	155
2½	155	170	185
3	188	207	226
4	232	255	279

Heat Losses of Pipes.—As we are figuring on a temperature of 175° from our radiators, the water in the pipes feeding them will be higher, so the third column 180° should be used ; and it will be found that the various sized pipes as shown on sketch approximately measure the following lineal feet.

TABLE LXVIII

1-inch pipes	180 feet, B.Th.U. loss	= 16,380
1¼ ,, ,,	180 ,, ,, ,,	= 20,160
1½ ,, ,,	180 ,, ,, ,,	= 22,680
2 ,, ,,	360 ,, ,, ,,	= 55,800
2½ ,, ,,	130 ,, ,, ,,	= 24,050
3 ,, ,,	50 ,, ,, ,,	= 11,300
Total		150,370

Boiler Rating.—Adding previous total of 500,000 B.Th.U.s, we get in round figures 650,000 B.Th.U.s required from boiler, and are now in a position to select one capable of giving this duty. Most boiler makers recommend that their boilers should not be worked to their full capacity, and as a matter of fact many heating engineers advocate a margin of 25 per cent. This allows for the stoker not being in constant attention, slow draught, and, as sometimes happens, bad fuel ; so that one of a heating power of over 800,000 B.Th.U.s should be selected. On Plate IV will be found illustrations of the boilers of several well-known manufacturers with the capacities given below.

Fig. 519.—The Robin Hood Series of Boilers (by the Beeston Boiler Co. Ltd.). These boilers range from the Junior " Robin Hood," rated from 58,000 B.Th.U. per hour, the Robin Hood General rated from 122,300 B.Th.U. per hour, the Robin Hood " C " Pattern rated from 232,900 B.Th.U. per hour. The Robin Hood Senior Boiler rated from 411,400 B.Th.U. per hour, and the Robin Hood Major Boiler, rated from 587,900 B.Th.U. per hour, up to 1,290,200. For places where a very low boiler is required this Company manufacture the Robin Hood " Mona " Boiler, rated from 112,400 B.Th.U. per hour, which is very suitable for horticultural work.

PLATE IV

Fig. 519.—Robin Hood Boiler, Beeston Co.

Fig. 520.—Ideal Britannia, National Radiator Co.

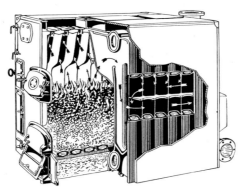

Fig. 521.—Ideal H Boiler, National Radiator Co.

Fig. 522.—White Rose Boiler, Hartley & Sugden.

Fig. 523.—Section of White Rose Boiler.

TYPES OF BOILERS.

TABLE LXIX
"ROBIN HOOD" BOILER

Number and type of Boiler.	To heat feet of 4 in. pipe.	To heat square feet of Radiation.	Heating Power British Thermal Units.	Number and type of Boiler.	To heat feet of 4-in. pipe.	To heat square feet of Radiation.	Heating Power British Thermal Units.
No. 3 B Junior	310	400	58,000	No. 5 C pattern	1,260	1,620	232,900
,, 4 B ,,	415	530	76,500	,, 6 ,,	1,515	1,940	279,600
,, 5 B ,,	515	660	95,500	,, 7 ,,	1,765	2,260	326,300
,, 6 B ,,	600	770	110,600	,, 8 ,,	2,100	2,690	387,500
,, 7 B ,,	720	920	132,900	,, 9 ,,	2,350	3,015	434,200
,, 8 B ,,	820	1,050	151,900	,, 10 ,,	2,600	3,340	481,000
				,, 11 ,,	2,860	3,665	527,700
No. 4 H General	660	850	122,300	,, 12 ,,	3,110	3,990	574,400
,, 5 H ,,	810	1,040	150,300				
,, 6 H ,,	960	1,230	176,700				
,, 7 H ,,	1,130	1,460	209,900	No. 6 A Senior	2,220	2,850	411,400
,, 8 H ,,	1,290	1,650	238,000	,, 7 A ,,	2,650	3,400	490,700
,, 9 H ,,	1,470	1,880	271,200	,, 8 A ,,	3,090	3,970	572,200
,, 10 H ,,	1,620	2,070	299,200	,, 9 A ,,	3,520	4,520	651,500
				,, 10 A ,,	3,950	5,070	730,800
No. 5 Mona	600	780	112,400	,, 11 A ,,	4,380	5,620	810,200
,, 6 ,,	800	1,020	147,200	,, 12 A ,,	4,820	6,180	889,500
,, 7 ,,	960	1,240	178,500				
,, 8 ,,	1,200	1,540	221,600				
,, 9 ,,	1,400	1,790	258,500	No. 6 M Major	3,190	4,080	587,900
,, 10 ,,	1,600	2,050	295,500	,, 7 M ,,	3,820	4,880	704,000
				,, 8 M ,,	4,460	5,700	821,900
No. 5 F pattern	900	1,160	167,700	,, 9 M ,,	5,090	6,510	938,100
,, 6 ,,	1,100	1,420	204,600	,, 10 M ,,	5,730	7,330	1,056,000
,, 7 ,,	1,300	1,670	241,600	,, 11 M ,,	6,365	8,140	1,173,100
,, 8 ,,	1,500	1,930	278,600	,, 12 M ,,	7,000	8,960	1,290,200
,, 9 ,,	1,700	2,190	315,500				
,, 10 ,,	1,900	2,440	352,500				

TABLE LXX
IDEAL "BRITANNIA" BOILER

No.	Heating Surface.	Ratings.			No.	Heating Surface.	Ratings.		
		B.Th.U. per hour.	Direct Radiation.	Lineal Feet of 4-inch Pipe.			B.Th.U. per hour.	Direct Radiation.	Lineal Feet of 4-inch Pipe.
	Sq. feet.		Sq. feet.			Sq. feet.		Sq. feet.	
03	9·0	40,000	280	215	24	35·5	159,000	1,100	860
04	11·5	51,000	355	275	25	45·0	200,000	1,385	1,080
05	14·0	62,000	430	335	26	54·5	241,000	1,670	1,300
06	16·5	73,000	505	395	27	64·0	282,000	1,955	1,520
07	19·0	84,000	580	455	28	73·5	323,000	2,240	1,740
†14	21·0	93,000	650	500	29	83·0	364,000	2,525	1,960
†15	26·5	117,000	815	630					
†16	32·0	141,000	980	760					
†17	37·5	165,000	1,145	890					
†18	43·0	189,000	1,310	1,020					

Fixing Apparatus.—Having ascertained the essential requirements of the installation, we can proceed with the remaining ones and the assembling together and fitting up of radiators, boiler, and piping. The position of the boiler will be determined by the brick flue, which is generally built to the size given by the heating engineer, in this case to suit

TABLE LXXI
IDEAL "BRITANNIA" BOILER

No.	Heating surface.	Ratings.			No.	Heating surface.	Ratings.		
		B.Th.U. per hour.	Direct Radiation.	Lineal Feet of 4-inch Pipe.			B.Th.U. per hour.	Direct Radiation.	Lineal Feet of 4-inch Pipe.
	Sq. feet.		Sq. feet.			Sq. feet.		Sq. feet.	
35	70·5	313,000	2,170	1,695	47	141	625,000	4,340	3,370
36	85·5	379,000	2,630	2,050	48	162	718,000	4,985	3,875
37	100·5	445,000	3,090	2,405	49	183	811,000	5,630	4,380
38	115·5	511,000	3,550	2,760	410	204	904,000	6,275	4,885
39	130·5	577,000	4,010	3,115	411	225	997,000	6,920	5,390
310	145·5	643,000	4,470	3,470	412	246	1,090,000	7,565	5,895
					413	267	1,183,000	8,210	6,400

TABLE LXXII
IDEAL H BOILER

WATER   STEAM

No.	Water Capacity.	Ratings.			No.	Water Capacity.	Ratings.	
		B.Th.U. per hour.	Direct Radiation.	Lineal Feet of 4-in. Pipe.			B.Th.U. per hour.	Direct Radiation.
	Gals.		Sq. feet.			Gals.		Sq. feet.
1-H-4	22	108,000	750	580	1-H-40	14	108,000	420
1-H-5	27	151,000	1,050	815	1-H-50	17	151,000	590
1-H-6	33	194,000	1,350	1,050	1-H-60	20	194,000	760
1-H-7	38	237,000	1,650	1,285	1-H-70	23	237,000	930
1-H-8	44	280,000	1,950	1,520	1-H-80	26	280,000	1,100
2-H-6	53	293,000	2,000	1,580	2-H-60	34·5	293,000	1,145
2-H-7	62	348,000	2,400	1,880	2-H-70	40·0	348,000	1,360
2-H-8	71	403,000	2,800	2,180	2-H-80	45·5	403,000	1,575
2-H-9	80	458,000	3,200	2,480	2-H-90	51·0	458,000	1,790
2-H-10	89	513,000	3,600	2,780	2-H-100	56·5	513,000	2,005
2-H-11	98	568,000	4,000	3,080	2-H-110	62·0	568,000	2,220
3-H-8	115·0	629,000	4,370	3,400	3-H-80	72·8	629,000	2,455
3-H-9	129·2	710,400	4,935	3,840	3-H-90	81·6	710,400	2,775
3-H-10	143·4	791,800	5,500	4,280	3-H-100	90·4	791,800	3,095
3-H-11	157·6	873,200	6,065	4,720	3-H-110	99·2	873,200	3,415
3-H-12	171·8	954,600	6,630	5,160	3-H-120	108·0	954,600	3,735
4-H-8	161·0	870,000	6,000	4,700	4-H-80	104	870,000	3,395
4-H-9	179·5	989,000	6,825	5,345	4-H-90	116	989,000	3,860
4-H-10	198·0	1,108,000	7,650	5,990	4-H-100	128	1,108,000	4,325
4-H-11	216·5	1,227,000	8,475	6,635	4-H-110	140	1,227,000	4,790
4-H-12	235·0	1,346,000	9,300	7,280	4-H-120	152	1,346,000	5,255
4-H-13	253·5	1,465,000	10,125	7,925	4-H-130	164	1,465,000	5,720
4-H-14	272·0	1,584,000	10,950	8,570	4-H-140	176	1,584,000	6,185

a 14-inch outlet from boiler, and provision must be made for a suitable soot door and frame for keeping the flue clean ; which is most essential, as heating boilers must have a good draught. Instructions as to fixing are sent out by all the boiler makers and so are not necessary here, but

TABLE LXXIII
"WHITE ROSE" BOILER

Type and Number of Boiler.	Boiler Heating Surface.	Heating Power 4-inch Pipes.	Heating Power Direct Radiation.	Heating Capacity B.Th.U.	Type and Number of Boiler.	Boiler Heating Surface.	Heating Power 4-inch Pipes.	Heating Power Direct Radiation.	Heating Capacity B.Th.U.
	Sq. ft.	Lineal ft.	Sq. ft.	Per hour.		Sq. ft.	Lineal ft.	Sq. ft.	Per hour.
613-A1	301	7,850	9,200	1,324,400	39 County 3	84·6	2,215	2,595	372,240
612-A1	277	7,225	8,465	1,218,800	38 County 3	74·85	1,960	2,295	329,340
611-A1	253	6,600	7,730	1,113,200	37 County 3	65·1	1,700	1,995	286,440
610-A1	229	5,975	7,000	1,007,600	36 County 3	55·35	1,450	1,695	243,540
609-A1	205	5,350	6,265	902,000	35 County 3	45·6	1,192	1,395	200,640
608-A1	181	4,725	5,530	796,400	34 County 3	35·85	935	1,095	157,740
607-A1	157	4,100	4,800	690,800					
606-A1	133	3,475	4,065	585,200					
					29 County 2	52	1,350	1,590	228,800
					28 County 2	46	1,200	1,410	202,400
512-B2	188·0	4,920	5,745	827,200	27 County 2	40	1,040	1,225	176,000
511-B2	172·0	4,500	5,255	756,800	26 County 2	34	885	1,040	149,600
510-B2	156·0	4,080	4,765	686,400	25 County 2	28	730	860	123,200
509-B2	140·0	3,660	4,275	616,000	24 County 2	22	575	675	96,800
508-B2	124·0	3,240	3,785	545,600					
507-B2	108·0	2,820	3,300	475,200					
506-B2	92·0	2,400	2,810	404,800	17 County 1	22	575	675	96,800
505-B2	76·0	1,985	2,320	334,400	16 County 1	19	504	580	83,600
					15 County 1	16	423	490	70,400
					14 County 1	13	342	400	57,200
					13 County 1	10	261	310	44,000

the writer would like to stress one, and that is, be sure the boiler base is dead level ; before putting the sections on, use a spirit-level and make certain of it, and so save a lot of unnecessary trouble. After fixing the boiler, it is as well to test it, before any pipes are connected to it.

Expansion and Feed Tank or Cistern.—The permanent feed and expansion tank, temporarily connected, will do for this, for the boiler will not have to stand a greater pressure in ordinary use, but more often a pressure pump is used, as by its means the full pressure guaranteed by the makers can be tested, and one knows there is a good margin of safety when this is done. The reader may query why, when the permanent feed is used, a temporary connection should be used. The reason is that a cold feed should never be taken direct into a cast-iron boiler, for should the apparatus get very hot and water bubble over the expansion pipe or pipes, the cold water entering direct into the boiler would probably cause a fracture in the cast-iron due to the sudden check to its expansion. The cold-water feed should be taken into a return pipe a few feet away from boiler, sufficient to warm the feed water before entering the boiler. Assuming the boiler to have stood its test, the piping may be proceeded with. Only steam-quality tubes or barrel should be used for this work, with long sweep fittings, bends, and not elbows, so that the freest passage is made for the water.

Flows and Returns.—It will be noticed that the head of water in the building is about 80 feet, which means a pressure of about 40 lb. per square inch, so that all joints will have to be carefully made and screwed right home, whatever jointing material may be used. A reference to the sketch shows that there are 4 main flow pipes with similar returns, 2 sets of 3-inch size, and 2 of $2\frac{1}{2}$-inch, feeding in all 6 sets of risers, the risers being of 2-inch above basement floor to first-floor level, thence $1\frac{1}{2}$-inch to second floor, $1\frac{1}{4}$-inch to third floor, and 1-inch to top floor, with $\frac{3}{4}$-inch branches (right and left hand) to the various radiators. Now, in order to make sure that the water will flow into all these radiator branches, so that all the radiators may get equally hot, either the riser is reduced in size or a tongued tee is inserted which forces part of the water flowing through it, to pass through its outlet to the branch. Thus, it will be noticed from the sketch that all the floors have reduced risers except ground floor, and here tongued tees will be used to secure the same distribution. After making connection for top-floor radiators, the riser should be continued to above feed-tank level as vent pipe, reducing to $\frac{1}{2}$-inch pipe for this purpose. Having finished fixing the risers, it will be better to leave the branches until the radiators are placed in position.

Position of Radiators.—As a rule, the heating engineer consults the architect concerned, or the client, before deciding on the exact position of the radiators, but wherever possible the shortest distance from the rising main is naturally the better position.

Valves and Unions.—The radiators should be fitted with gunmetal union control valves on the flow inlet, and similar valves for regulating the temperature on the return outlet, as shown on Plate V, Figs. 524-5. The reason union valves are chosen is because, should any repair be necessary to a radiator, such as a leak in a section, the valves can be shut off, and the radiator disconnected and taken away for repair, without interfering with the working of the installation, except so far as that particular radiator is concerned. Without them, the whole installation has to be emptied down, and the building left without heat until the repair has been effected ; then the apparatus has to be refilled—always a lengthy job—and the fire re-kindled in furnace, thus rendering the repair a very tedious and costly matter. Moreover, the union does away with the otherwise necessary connector and nut, which is never a very sightly fitting in an office and is frequently a source of leakage.

Air-escape Valves.—Air-escape valves must also be fitted to each radiator, and as air is about 820 times lighter than water, at the top of the same.

Branches.—Returning to the branches, these will be $\frac{3}{4}$ inch, and require very careful setting out and fixing, as not only are they run on the surface in most buildings, but they frequently have to be set round piers and window recesses, in which case the pipe itself should be bent in the forge in one piece, and not made up with fittings which impede the easy flow of the water ; and these pipes need a connector and nut as well as the union, for they cannot be turned when thus set. The radiators can now be made fast with their top stays, and permanent feed pipe connected up to the 50-gallon galvanised iron feed and expansion tank,

PLATE V

Fig. 524.　　　　　　　　Fig. 525.

GUN-METAL UNION CONTROL VALVES.

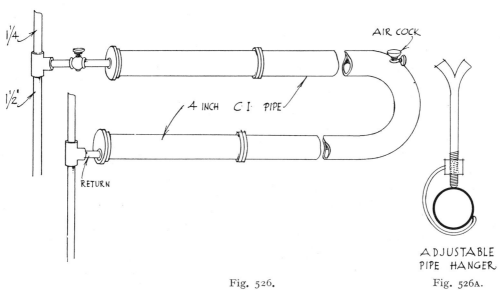

Fig. 526.　　　　　Fig. 526A.

VALVES AND PIPE FITTINGS.

fitted with ball valve and overflow pipe by the hot-water fitter, but with the cold-water supply connection usually laid on by the builder.

Size of Cistern.—To allow for the proper expansion of the water, feed cisterns should be sufficiently large to hold about one-twentieth part of the whole of the water contained in the apparatus.

Water Capacity.—The boiler and radiator manufacturers now give the water capacity of their boilers and radiators, so that there will be no need to give these here ; but for pipes the capacities are as follow :

TABLE LXXIV

1-inch barrel ·0340 of a gallon per foot run, weight ·340 lb. do.

1¼ ,,	,,	·0531 ,,	,,	,,	,,	·531 ,,
1½ ,,	,,	·0764 ,,	,,	,,	,,	·764 ,,
2 ,,	,,	·1360 ,,	,,	,,	,,	1·360 ,,
2½ ,,	,,	·2124 ,,	,,	,,	,,	2·124 ,,
3 ,,	,,	·3060 ,,	,,	,,	,,	3·060 ,,
4 ,,	,,	·5440 ,,	,,	,,	,,	5·440 ,,

Sleeve Pieces and Plates.—A gunmetal stop-valve should be inserted in feed pipe, near point of entry into return. It will be noticed that in our building the pipe risers, flow and return, are fixed in chases, also that the radiator branches, both flow and return, are above the floors, but this is not possible in all cases, or expedient in others, and in these buildings the pipes pass through floors and often walls, and where they do this, sleeve pieces should be fitted round them, with plates for floors and ceilings.

Filling up.—Everything is now ready for filling up the apparatus, for which every air vent on radiators and boiler must be open, as an air lock will prevent the water filling up properly and cause a lot of trouble, and absolutely prevent hot water circulating in the pipe or radiator in which it is present, so each radiator is carefully watched until nothing but water issues from the air valve, and then, and then only, should it be shut off.

Air Locks.—It sometimes happens that five out of six circuits may be working well and uniformly hot, while the sixth is stone cold, and that because air is hidden somewhere or other in it, and unfortunately cannot be detected until the whole system is hot, and there is nothing for it but emptying down again and refilling. With good or uniform venting this should be impossible, but carelessness and the neglect of the required precautions nearly always bring it about.

Testing.—Assuming that the apparatus is filled, the hot-water fitter now goes carefully over the whole of the piping to see if all the joints are standing, and he is a very lucky man if he has no leakages at all in them. Next the radiators, radiator valves, and boiler claim his attention for the same reason, and if all is well the furnace fire may be lighted for yet another test when the whole installation is fairly hot, and this because many joints which appear perfectly sound when the apparatus is cold, start leaking when these joints expand with the heat. It is the same with boiler, radiators, and all fittings used, and not until the apparatus has been working for several days can the fitter be sure of his work being absolutely free from such leakages.

Regulating.—The next step will be the regulating of the radiator valves, to ensure an even distribution of the heat, for, however carefully the pipe sizes are worked out, some radiators will get more than their share of the heat, and consequently others will suffer, so that these must be regulated until the emission is fairly even, and to prevent valves being altered or perhaps accidentally shut off by unauthorised persons, it is usual in public buildings to use a lock-shield valve (Figs. 524, 525, Plate V), and this valve, being operated by a detachable tee handle, cannot be altered, when once set, except by the heating engineer in charge or other person entrusted by the management with a key-handle.

Finishing Off.—Having satisfied himself that the installation is in proper working order, the hot-water fitter now attends to the finishing off necessary to hand the installation over as complete, such as the painting of the radiators and pipes (sometimes left to the builder), cleaning of valves, etc. Where paint is used, it should be as thin as possible with very little oil, because a dull surface gives the highest efficiency, while a thick enamel, also metallic paints, give a very low efficiency.

Covering.—The boiler should always be covered with non-conducting composition, or a steel-covered insulating jacket, which adds about 10 per cent. to its efficiency, with a corresponding saving in fuel cost, and so is true economy in the long run ; also the flow and return feeder mains, unless used as part of the heating medium, which are generally run in either brick or concrete conduits below floor level, as here it saves the heat from being emitted where it is not wanted, which also adds to the fuel saving.

In the old days most fitters did their own covering, but now certain firms specialise in non-conducting covering, and thus can do the work more quickly and give it a better finish than the hot-water fitter could ever hope to do, and the value of " lagging," as it is often called, is now more fully appreciated, and very few large installations are without it.

Final Test.—On the final or " handing-over " test there need be no apprehension as regards the capability of our installation to fully satisfy the temperature conditions imposed by the client or his architect, for the apparatus as described will fulfil all such conditions easily, and, what is more, maintain the stipulated temperature for any length of time, and in very severe weather without forcing the boiler.

Firing.—Although it may not appear on the surface, it is real economy to install a really adequate apparatus, especially with regard to the boiler, for when a boiler has ample furnace space, it is not necessary to heap up the fuel and make what is called a " thick fire," for such a fire loses a certain proportion of its carbon. through lack of proper combustion, but a medium or " thin fire " which gives perfect combustion, and therefore parts with every fraction of its heat.

Two-pipe System : Warming by Cast-iron Pipes.—It will be ascertained from the foregoing that our installation has been calculated on the " two-pipe " system, and before going on to describe the " one-pipe " system, it may be well to mention that other heating media, such as cast-iron pipes and pipe coils, can be equally well served by it ; and as many public buildings and most factories use cast-iron pipes for their warming, owing to their lower installation cost, a short description of the layout is given. The rising mains and boiler power will follow the same lines as for radiators, but as cast-iron pipes generally run the whole, or nearly the whole, length of a building, two sets, and in some cases probably only one, of risers only will be required ; and again, the conditions obtaining in factories are different, for while in offices the occupation of the inmates is mostly sedentary, in factories the workpeople are mostly moving about, consequently they do not require the same amount of heat.

Factory Heating.—The temperature usually asked for in factories is 55° F., when it is 32° F. outside, so in making calculations for cast-iron pipes, the reader must note that the temperature difference is 23°, and not 28°, as for radiators. It is well to point out here that 1 sq. foot of pipe surface gives off more heat than 1 sq. foot of radiator surface, because it is more exposed to the air.

Formula for Cast-iron Piping.—The following simple formula, derived from practice, may be used to calculate the length of pipe, all the other conditions being known, required to give the stipulated temperature.

Let P = temperature of pipes in degrees F., say 165°
 T = temperature required in factory, say 55°
 t = temperature of outer air, say 32°
 C = cubic feet of air to be warmed per minute, say 1,500
 D = diameter of pipe in inches, say 4 inches
 L = length of pipe in feet

Then :

$$L = \frac{\cdot018C\,(P - t)\,(T - t)}{D\,(P - T)}$$

or :

$$L = \frac{(\cdot018 \times 1,500) \times (165 - 32) \times (55 - 32)}{4 \times (165 - 55)}$$

or :

$$L = \frac{27 \times 133 \times 23}{4 \times 110} = \text{approx. 190 feet.}$$

Example.—The figures referred to in the formula, giving the conditions used, are taken as an example of a factory floor, having a cubical capacity of 30,000 cu. feet, with three air changes per hour, that is, 90,000 cu. feet per hour, which makes 1,500 per minute, the hot water circulating in the pipes at 165°, inside temperature to be 55° F., and taking the outside temperature at 32° F., or freezing point, and 4-inch cast-iron piping as the heating medium.

Another Rule.—An easier way is simply to take the cubical contents of any factory floor and divide by 158, which in this case gives approximately the same result, and if 60° inside is asked for, divide by 150, and it will be found that the difference between the result so obtained, and that of the formula is practically negligible.

Should 3-inch cast-iron pipes be used as the heating medium, they would require to be one-third greater in extent than the 4-inch, while 2-inch cast-iron pipes would have to be doubled.

Having calculated the total heating surface required, the pipe sizes

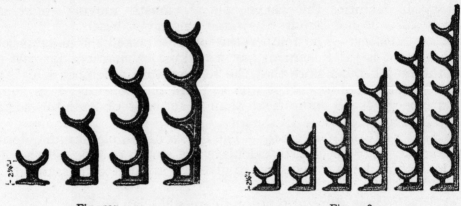

Fig. 527.   Fig. 528.

Pipe Stands for C.I. Pipes and Coils.

and boiler rating can easily be found from the examples given in the radiator installation.

Method of Fixing.—Cast-iron heating pipes are usually run along part, and in some cases the whole, length of the walls of the factory, a few inches above floor level, with just sufficient rise in the flow and corresponding fall in the return to ensure an easy circulation, as shown in illustration.

The wrought iron flow and return feeder mains and risers are calculated in the same way as those for radiators, as the cast-iron piping or coil takes the place of a radiator, and the lowest coil is taken as the equivalent of the lowest radiator. Each coil is controlled by a wheelvalve on its flow feeder pipe, and while the position of this feeder pipe as it enters the cap on the coil is not of great importance, that of the return branch must come from the bottom of the cap of the return end of the coil, where the coolest water is, so that no obstruction is offered to the natural fall or return of such water. The pipes are fixed on brackets or stands as shown (Figs. 527, 528).

Venting.—The venting of the pipes is most important, there being such a large amount of air to displace, venting valves or air pipes being taken from the top end of flow pipe, generally on the socket of the siphon

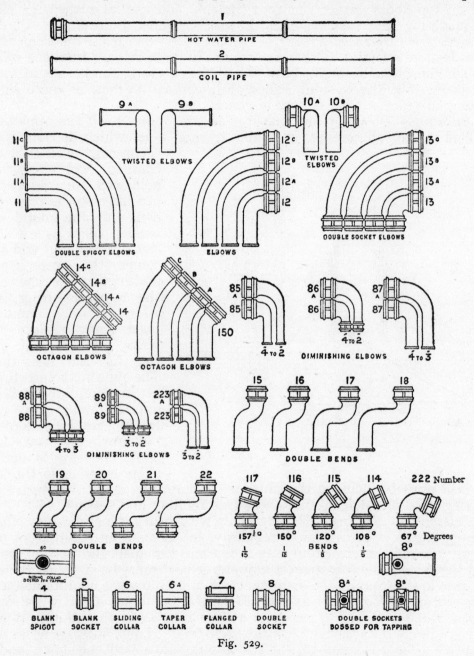

Fig. 529.

return bend as shown, and air pipes somewhat larger than in a radiator installation must be taken from each flow riser.

Overhead Pipes.—In some factories, owing to all the floor space along the walls being required for machinery, the pipes cannot be fixed to the walls at all ; in this case it is usual to suspend them from the ceilings, and on top floors, girders, or roof timbers, and special suspension clips are made for their suspension as shown (Fig. 526A, Plate V).

Heat from Overhead Piping.—The heat emission from the suspended pipes is more effective as they are generally farther away from the walls, though the diffusion of the heat takes longer owing to the height from the floor ; but this system, called the overhead system, is quite satisfactory in practice, and is now in general use.

Painting.—Do not paint cast-iron heating pipes until the apparatus is filled up, for all castings are liable to sand holes which do not reveal themselves until they are charged, and often then hold with the cold water, but directly the pipes get hot, and the metal expands, away goes the grit or stopping, and out comes the water, and nothing is more trying to the hotwater fitter, for although the manufacturers may replace the faulty pipe, they do not pay for the lost time. The pipe may sometimes be repaired by drilling out the weak stop, and tapping and fixing a plug; but in whatever way it is done, the cost is out of all proportion to the job, for in it must be included the time lost in emptying down the apparatus, making good the defect, and afterwards refilling and testing.

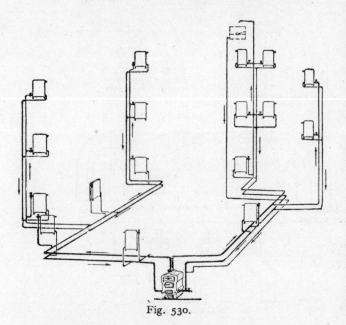

Fig. 530.

Intermittent Heating.—Having dealt with heating installations where the apparatus is in use fairly regularly, let us take an example of one where it is only intermittent, say a church or chapel, and here we shall find that a considerably greater amount of heat must be supplied than in our previous examples. For instance, if a church when maintained at a temperature of 60° loses 250,000 B.Th.U.s per hour, then if we only supply 250,000 B.Th.U.s per hour to the interior of the church, it will only gradually raise the temperature up to 60°. If only the bare necessary quantity of heat is supplied, the rise in temperature will be slow ; and it will take days before the temperature is attained if the building is heated from cold. The reason for this is that before the temperature can be raised, the whole structure must be warmed. If we only allow for the building as much heat as the structure will lose when it is already warmed, there will not be enough heat both to warm the structure itself rapidly and at the same time to provide for the losses from the outside. From which the reader will note that it is absolutely necessary to provide much more heat than before, and an excess of 50 per cent. more at least should be calculated for, and in some cases 75 per cent. or more. Another point to be borne in mind in this class of heating is that the feeder mains must be ample, for there is very little rise, and reference to the pipe-sizes table shows that with a long travel and very small

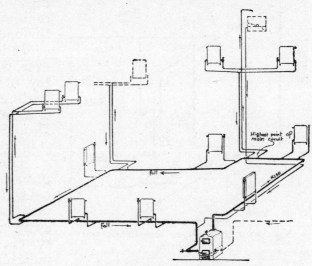

Fig. 531.—Single-pipe System.

height together with a large radiating surface a very much larger pipe size than with an ordinary installation is required.

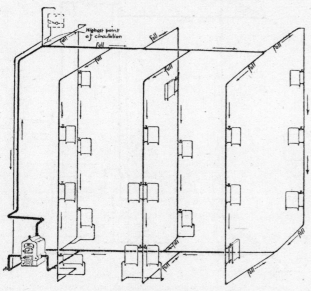

Fig. 532.—Overhead or Drop System.

We will now pass on to the one-pipe system, or single-pipe system, and Fig. 531 shows the general arrangement.

It will be noticed at once that the circulation of this system is essentially different from that of the two-pipe system, because in it one pipe constitutes both the return from one radiator and the flow for the next succeeding radiators, the flow branches taken from the top side of the feeder main, and the return branches into the bottom, along a pipe, therefore, which carries a number of radiators connected to it. In this way there is a continual drop of temperature from the end where it leaves the flow main to the end where it joins the return main, and to correct this as far as possible the flow of water through the radiators must be carefully regulated, each succeeding radiator getting a little more than the one preceding it.

It is more often installed, however, with the flow pipe taken to the top of the building, with branches feeding the various dropping circuits, and this variation is called the Drop System, or Overhead System (Fig. 532).

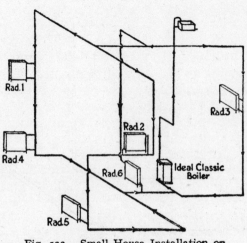

Fig. 533.—Small House Installation on Drop System.

This system is very suitable for private houses, one pipe naturally being less unsightly than two and practically halving the "cutting away and making good." In this system the centre of the lowest radiator is not to be taken in figuring out the $\frac{\text{height}}{\text{travel}}$ rule for pipe sizes, but the height of the centre of gravity of all the radiators connected to the pipe, from which it will be found that the feeder or drop pipe is somewhat larger, and this pipe should not be diminished or reduced; and to prevent short-circuiting, a tongued tee is generally used for the flow outlet, which ensures that part of the water in the drop pipe must go through the radiator, the amount being regulated by the valves, as in the other systems (Fig. 533).

HIGH-PRESSURE HOT-WATER HEATING

The principle on which high-pressure heating systems work is similar to that for low pressure, for the circulating power is caused by the difference in weight between the hot water in the flow pipe and the cold or cooler water in the return pipe; but owing to the

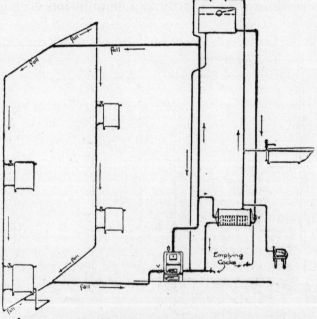

Fig. 534.—Combined Heating with Domestic System.

water being raised to a very high temperature, the circulating power is very much greater, and the hot-water fitter need not be so careful as to the rise and fall, which he is bound to be with the low-pressure system.

Name.—The name " high-pressure " is given to this system because, instead of being open to the atmospheric pressure, it is sealed off from it, by means of a loaded safety valve, as much as 1,000 lb. per square inch pressure being sometimes obtained. Owing to the existence of such high pressures the danger of explosion is greatly increased, and it speaks well for the construction of these apparati that accidents are very rare.

Heating Surface.—The form of heating surface used is heavy hydraulic tubing of great strength, far stronger than that used in low-pressure systems, and the piping is continuous throughout the installation, the boiler being made up of coils of the same pipe, fixed in a firebrick-lined furnace. The interior diameter of the pipes used is about $\frac{7}{8}$ inch, and the outside diameter is nearly $1\frac{3}{8}$ inch, with about 1 sq. foot of heating surface to every $2\frac{3}{4}$ feet of piping, and to get the necessary amount of heating surface in a room, the pipe is coiled to get the exact quantity required ; but it must be remembered that the amount of heat obtained is much greater than in a low-pressure system, so much so that particles of dust coming in contact with the pipe are burnt, and the pipes cannot be touched, which to many people, combined with the smell of the burnt effect, is a great objection.

Fixing.—The pipes are put together by means of a special hydraulic joint, whereby the end of one of the pipes is sharpened, the other pipe being left flat, and the two ends are drawn together by right- and left-handed screwed sockets ; by this means a metal-to-metal joint is made, rendering the employment of jointing material unnecessary. Great care is required to see that the apparatus is completely filled with water, and that no air is left in the pipes. Much trouble is frequently caused in high-pressure systems through neglect of this precaution, and a pump should be used to fill the apparatus which forces the water into the pipes and drives the air before it.

Expansion Tank.—The upper or top end of the system is taken into a very strong expansion tank, which is fitted with a safety valve as before mentioned, and this is loaded to the pressure at which it is decided the apparatus should work.

Uses.—This system is often used for baking and enamelling ovens, where temperatures of between 500° and 600° are required, and its one great advantage is the overcoming of level difficulties, and the quickness, owing to the small water contents of the pipes, in which the heat can be raised. The regulation of the heat, however, is impossible, there being a regular drop the farther away the coils are from the boiler, so that the system is best adapted to halls, or wherever a quantity of heat is wanted in one place.

Frost.—Care must also be taken to protect the pipes from frost. Although they are so strong, the frost is stronger, and serious results happen from a burst.

Accelerated Circulation.—Where it is not possible to get the necessary rise and fall for the flow and return pipes respectively, the difficulty may be overcome by the use of an accelerator, which is usually a water circulator or centrifugal pump, directly coupled to an electric motor, and mounted together on a cast-iron bedplate.

The accelerator is best fixed as close to the boiler as possible, and above the floor level, on account of its liability to damage from dirt and water, and should be connected to the main return pipe, after the returns of all the circuits have been merged into it, so that it can effectively deal with them all and pump their contents back into the boiler. The method of calculation of pipe sizes is essentially the same in principle as that of the low-pressure system, but smaller pipes may safely be used, if kept in their proper proportions, and the hot-water fitter has no need to worry over variations in the circulating head which the pump does for him, but which in the low-pressure system constitutes the only motive force. Its advantages are very obvious when dealing with the heating of an old building, especially where there is no basement, as it saves all cutting through floors and forming conduits to get a fall for the return back to boiler. It also solves the difficulty of doorways, the great bugbear of return pipes, quite easily, for with the accelerator the return pipe may be taken above doorways, or above the flow pipe, and an otherwise impracticable job successfully overcome. If necessary, the radiators or other heating medium can be fixed below the level of the boiler. Another advantage lies in the fact that directly the water in the boiler gets hot, it is circulated by means of the pump all through the installation, and the building is being warmed long before it would find its way round by the natural circulation, which means a saving in fuel, almost sufficient to pay for the electric energy consumed by the motor driving the pump which in a medium-sized installation, say up to 3,000 or 4,000 superficial feet of heating surface, should not exceed from 200 to 300 watts. With a pump circulation, if desired, it would be quite possible to place the boiler at the highest point of the installation, without prejudice to the effective working of the apparatus.

FUELS FOR HEATING APPARATUS AND METHOD OF ESTIMATING AMOUNT REQUIRED

Calculations for fuel for heating installations are usually based on an outside temperature of 30°, but from the official meteorological record it will be seen that the mean record is much higher than that, viz. 42° for the autumn and winter months, so that on the average the heating installation is only required to raise the inside temperature through about 60 per cent. of the maximum requirements. Again, the furnace fire is usually " banked " at night, and the air temperature allowed to fall a few degrees, thus affecting a further saving in fuel.

Practical experience has shown that the average demand for 14 hours per day is 60 per cent., and for the remaining 10 hours 40 per cent. of the maximum, equivalent to an average over the whole period of about half the maximum. As an example let us take an installation of say 2,000 sq. feet of radiation, and the flow and return mains and branches to radiators, and working under maximum conditions with a mean water temperature of 160° in radiators and air temperature of 60°.

TABLE LXXV

		B Th.U.s
2,000 sq. feet of radiation × 156 (see " Radiator Transmission ")	=	312,000
300 feet run of 3-inch pipe (uncovered) × 188 (see " Pipe Transmission ")	=	56,400
100 ,, ,, 2-inch ,, ,, × 129 ,, ,, ,,	=	12,900
200 ,, ,, 1¼-inch ,, ,, × 93 ,, ,, ,,	=	18,600
200 ,, ,, 1-inch ,, ,, × 76 ,, ,, ,,	=	15,200
100 ,, ,, ¾-inch ,, ,, × 62 ,, ,, ,,	=	6,200
		421,300

Taking coke as the fuel used and its calorific value at 8,500 B.Th.U.s per lb. (a table of the calorific value of various fuels will be found a little farther on), to determine the maximum hourly fuel consumption we divide the total transmission loss of 421,300 B.Th.U.s by 8,500 B.Th.U.s from 1 lb. of coke, which shows that 50 lb. of coke per hour are required for full or maximum working. It is very rarely that an installation is worked to its full capacity all day long, so that we will assume the average mentioned above holds good, that is, 14 hours at 60 per cent. and 10 hours at 40 per cent., and this gives an approximate average fuel consumption as follows :

TABLE LXXVI

14 hours × 50 lb. ÷ 60 per cent. = 420 lb.
10 hours × 50 lb. ÷ 40 per cent. = 200 lb.

620 lb. for 24 hours

or $\frac{620}{24} = 26$ lb. of coke per hour, which is practically half the maximum amount required. As the heating engineer is nearly always asked what a given heating installation will cost for fuel maintenance, he will find it useful to memorise the above, which holds good whatever fuel may be used. The other fuel calorific values will be found in the table, and these divided into the installation transmission loss give the hourly amount required for maximum working, half that amount only being required for average daily use, and it is the latter figure which is nearly always given for the cost of maintenance.

In considering the question of fuel values, the carbon and hydrogen may be taken as the " heating substance," these elements providing practically all the heat produced by the combustion of the fuels. Sulphur is present as either sulphates or pyrites or both, but only the latter has any combustible value, and even that is very small, as the sulphates remain in the ash. The following is the heat combustion value : Hydrogen, 52,200 B.Th.U.s per lb. when forming steam and 62,100 B.Th.U.s when forming water; carbon forming carbon monoxide, 4,450 B.Th.U.s, and 14,540 B.Th.U.s when forming carbon dioxide; sulphur, 3,895 B.Th.U.s when forming sulphur dioxide, so that on determining the use of any particular fuel which may be recommended, the heating engineer would only select those having at least 50 per cent. of the above, excluding the carbon monoxide and sulphur (the carbon monoxide arises from incomplete combustion, and as being supplied with the necessary oxygen, further burns to form carbon dioxide, thus 1 lb. of carbon uniting with $1\frac{1}{3}$ lb. of oxygen forms carbon monoxide CO, but 1 lb. of carbon uniting with $2\frac{2}{3}$ lb. of oxygen forms carbon dioxide CO_2). In the first stage 4,450 B.Th.U.s are evolved, while in the second 10,150 are evolved, making together the 14,540 B.Th.U.s per lb. mentioned.

We now pass on to the ordinary fuels in daily use for heating installations (there are many others, but these are not in general use and can be traced in works on chemical values, giving the theoretical and practical calorific values, as follows:

TABLE LXXVII

Fuel.	Total B.Th.U.s from 1 lb.	Boiler Efficiency Value.
Anthracite	14,700	11,000 B.Th.U.s
Coal	13,000	9,000 ,,
Coke	12,500	8,500 ,,
Fuel oil	19,000	18,000 ,,
Ordinary gas	17,500	16,000 ,,
Gas and air burnt in patent burner	52,000	46,000 ,,

As gas is sold in cubic feet, it may be noted that about 35 cu. feet of gas weighs 1 lb. and the B.Th.U. value per cu. foot is usually taken at 500—three times that amount being obtained from the patent mixing burner.

Of the solid fuels, anthracite is the most useful on account of its density, heat value, and clean burning properties, and the advantage thus gained more or less compensates for its higher price per ton. Coke is so well known to every heating engineer that little need be said here concerning it, except that wherever possible furnace coke should be used in preference to gas coke, as the former more nearly approximates to anthracite, being heavier than the gas coke and having a more consistent heat and purity; and another important consideration is that it generally contains less combustible sulphur than gas coke. The latter, as previously mentioned, burns to form sulphur dioxide, and this in combustion with water and oxygen forms sulphuric acid, which attacks the metal of the boiler and causes jutting and helps to shorten the life of the boiler. A favourable condition for forming sulphuric acid is when the boiler is banked up for a night run or working at a reduced output, for the temperature of the flue gases would probably be less than 212° F., and so condensation takes place; and care must be taken, whatever fuel may be used, to ensure that the chimney used for the boiler is sufficiently large to allow enough air to be drawn through the ashpit and fire to maintain perfect combustion, viz. to ensure that each pound of carbon is burnt to carbon dioxide (CO_2).

On account of their cleanliness, oil and gas are now coming into favour as fuels for central heating installations. When petroleum has had the lighter constituents, such as naphtha, petrol, and paraffin extracted from it, the residuum constitutes crude or fuel oil, which consists primarily of carbon and hydrogen, and is sold by the ton and delivered in the same way as coke. Ordinary gas is far too dear for general use, but with the new patent mixing burner it is rapidly gaining ground, its many advantages being obvious.

CHAPTER IX

CENTRAL HEATING; CONCEALED CENTRAL HEATING

Advantages of the System—Planning a System—Covering Pipes with Plaster—Calculating Heating Surface—Two Boilers Required—Accelerators—Electrical Panel Heating.

DURING the last few years the warming of buildings by coils of pipes concealed in ceilings, or walls, also by cast-iron sections made in the form of plates of various designs and sizes, having a number of waterways and connected together with right- and left-hand threaded nipples, has made very rapid progress, many of the most modern buildings being warmed in this way, as shown in Fig. 535. The sections either have moulded edges for fixing on the face of a plastered wall or ceiling, or other wall, or are made with flanged beads at the back so that the radiator, termed the Rayrad, as a whole can be fixed flush (see Fig. 536, Plate VI).

Advantages of the System.—It is by no means a cheap system of heating, but on the other hand is in many ways a very pleasing one. On entering a building a comfortable sensation of warmth is experienced without any heating apparatus being visible, or the inconvenience of any movement of warmed air from ducts and gratings. Of course the air itself eventually becomes warmed, but one of the advantages of radiant heat is that the occupants of a building are directly made comfortable by the heat rays emitted by this method without regard to the actual air temperature. Experience has proved that comfort point is reached even though the air temperature is only about 60° F. with this system, whereas 63° to 67° F. is generally needed where the comfort condition is being sought by the more common method of warming the air. Where pipe coils are used as the heating medium, $\frac{1}{2}$-inch steam barrel of special strength, made by our leading tube manufacturers for this purpose, is the general practice, though copper tubing is also used by some heating engineers. Needless to say, no screwed joints are employed, for leakage is a serious matter; joints must be welded, and these have to stand a severe hydraulic test before they are covered in. As a rule, individual coils do not exceed 200 feet in length, and the only joints in the whole of this piping are those of the control valve. Ample provision must be made for expansion and venting.

Planning a System.—In planning out an installation, the coils are calculated in the same way as radiators would be, but with this difference, that a certain amount of heat is lost by conduction to the floor above, or wall, as the case may be, though most of this heat is eventually transmitted to the surroundings by convection and radiation. In order that as much of the total heat as possible should be given off from the front

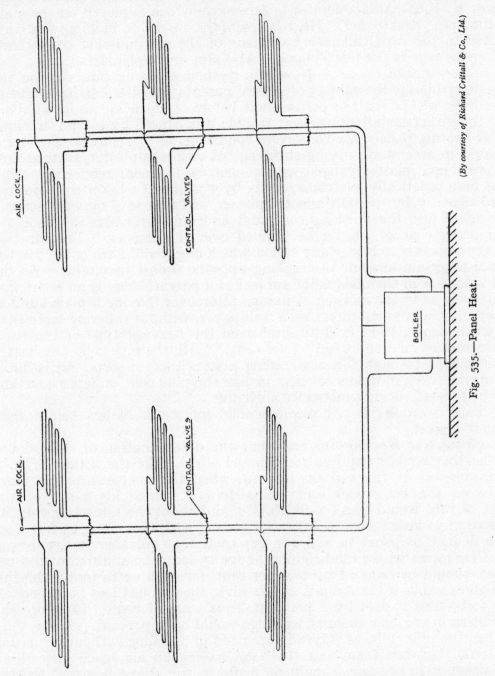

AIR COCK.

CONTROL VALVES

AIR COCK.

CONTROL VALVES

BOILER

(By courtesy of Richard Crittall & Co., Ltd.)

Fig. 535.—Panel Heat.

of the coils, they should be packed on the top or back, as the case may require, with slag wool or other effective non-conductor. The heating emission is generally taken at 100 B.Th.U.'s per square foot of heating surface. To overcome the friction set up by the long runs of small-diameter tubes, an accelerator is necessary, which is placed on the main return pipe near boiler. Heat losses of the rooms or building are computed in the usual manner by means of the transmission co-efficients given on page 124 of this Volume. Also pipe and boiler sizes.

Covering with Plaster.—Now, the method of fixing pipe coils in the plaster panels is the subject of several patents, and the heating engineer would be well advised to peruse these before commencing an installation. In the earlier installations great trouble was caused by plaster cracking over heating panels, for the severe conditions of exposure would be expected to accentuate drying shrinkage of ordinary plaster, such as lime plaster, lime plaster gauged with cement and cement rendering. This has been practically overcome, firstly by working at a lower temperature, and secondly, by specially selected plaster, and the use of canvas " scrim," trowelled into the finishing coat, and under no circumstances should a skimming coat of plaster be applied over the canvas. The function of the canvas is to bridge any cracks which might still form in the plaster, since a certain amount of cracking appears almost inevitable. As the Rayrads are in themselves the subject of a patent, there is no restriction whatever as to the method of fixing. Moreover, having a plain surface, they may be covered direct with wall paper, without suffering more than a small depreciation in duty, and even the heaviest type of Lincrusta reduces the emission by only 3 per cent. With the pipe coils, the heat is transmitted through the surrounding plaster and supports, but is direct from the Rayrad, unless covered in like the pipe coils, a paper covering, as just stated, being practically negligible.

Panel warming is not recommended for rooms of less height than about 10 feet.

Calculating Heating Surface.—For the determination of the amount of heating surface required for comfort effect, take the actual B.Th.U. transmission of the coil or Rayrad, when the temperature difference between the hot water and air is 100° F. which for a coil of 100 feet of tube would be 5,600 B.Th.U.'s, and about the same transmission for 10 to 30-inch Rayrads ; then for a room with the ceiling 15 feet from the floor, it is usual to add 100 per cent. for equivalent transmission. But for rooms where the height is above 15 feet, the addition of 100 per cent. should be reduced by two per cent. for each extra foot in height. As an example, if the room is 25 feet high, then 25 feet less 15 feet equals 10 feet ; and 10 feet by 2 per cent. equals 20 per cent. Therefore the addition figure for a room 25 feet high would be 80 per cent. (see Fig. 539). When the pipe coils, as Rayrads, are fixed in a ceiling without insulating material between them and the floor, having an air space instead, an addition of 10 per cent. should be made to the above figures. Neither pipe coils nor Rayrads should be fixed in the ceiling on concrete roofs, unless the roof is either covered or lined with insulating board.

PLATE **VI**

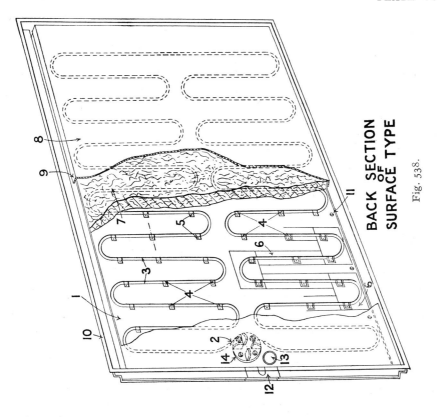

BACK SECTION
OF
SURFACE TYPE

Fig. 538.

Fig. 536.

Fig. 537.

CONCEALED RAYRAD AND ELECTRIC CONCEALED PANEL HEATER.

As a working example assume a small public hall 50 feet long by 20 feet wide and 25 feet high, with a calculated heat loss of 66,000 B.Th.U.'s per hour, which it is intended to warm with pipe coils or Rayrads for comfort effect. As the ceiling is 25 feet from the floor, the addition figure of 100 per cent. must be reduced to 80 per cent., so to find the total length of pipe coils required we divide 66,000 by 5,600, plus 80 per cent. 66,000 divided by 10,080 which gives about 6½ pipe coils of 100 feet ½-inch tube

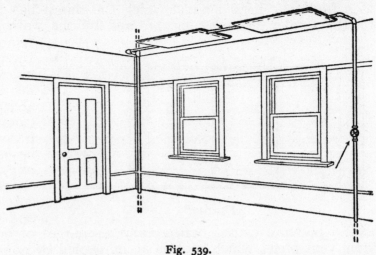

Fig. 539.

or 650 feet ½-inch tube. For the Rayrads, as ten 30-inch Rayrads gave an equivalent to the 100-feet coil of ½-inch tube, it follows that sixty-five 30-inch Rayrads would be required for the same duty. For all practical purposes the same rules apply to walls as for ceilings (see Fig. 537 on Plate VI, showing recessed Rayrads in ceiling).

Two Boilers Required.—For economical running, and also as a standby in case of necessity, two boilers are usually installed, coupled up so that one, or the two, may be used as required, the B.Th.U. capacity of each being sufficient to easily maintain for the whole installation a temperature difference of 100 degrees between the internal and external air. Then, with the two boilers in use, the building will still be kept uniformly comfortable during the most severe cold spell.

Accelerators.—It will be evident to the heating engineer why an accelerator is required, because except for say very small installations, such as private houses, long coils of ½-inch tubing, or large numbers of Rayrads, the ½-inch tubing often running into many thousands of feet, to which must be added the feeder circuits, and main flows and returns, while with the Rayrads a corresponding number would be required, with feeder circuits and main flows and returns. The Rayrads have a number of narrow waterways as will be seen in Fig. 540. The hot water circulating through these waterways warms the plate throughout by conduction. Now the ½-inch tubing bent into coils to suit the panelling, sets up friction, and so do the narrow waterways of the Rayrads, to a greater extent than the natural circulating head in a gravity system can overcome, hence a mechanical circulator is necessary. The accelerator system has its coil or Rayrad index circuit and circuit length as in a gravity system. The force producing circulation is derived from the power transmitted to the pump, which may be driven by electric, steam, oil or other motive power. It is necessary to determine the allowable frictional head against which the pump has to work, which will be the total resistances encountered by the water in flowing through

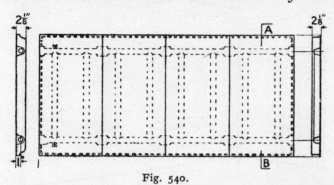

Fig. 540.

the pump and coils or Rayrads comprising the index circuit. For small installations the frictional head allowable varies from 1 to 5 feet, and from 6 to 10 feet or higher on large installations. It is important that the pump should be set to the actual frictional head and no more, as any excess pressure causes unnecessary discharges of hot water and steam from vent pipes, which is often accompanied by noise and vibration. It is advisable also to take a safety pipe of ample size direct from top of boiler to deliver over feed cistern, to prevent water being forced out by the pump. The open end of this pipe above the level of the water in the feed cistern, should be at least 5 feet more than the frictional head. For a small installation, in order to diminish the frictional head, $\frac{3}{4}$-inch tubing is used on a gravity drop system, the emission value being about 25 per cent. greater than the $\frac{1}{2}$-inch figures given.

Electrical Panel Heating.—Panel warming is not confined to hot water or steam heating systems. Electrical science has been making rapid strides in this direction, and whereas a few years ago the price of electric energy made electrical heating of any form prohibitive, this has now been so reduced, as to bring it within practical reach, many electrical undertakings now supplying at a fraction of a penny per unit.

Any scheme of radiant heating should be prepared by a heating engineer, owing to his special knowledge of all the factors concerned, the wiring up of the electrical heating panels being left to the electrical engineer. While the greatest care has to be taken with hot-water heated panels that there should be no leakage, causing damage by water, equal care must be taken in the wiring up of the electrical heating panels, when a leakage would cause fire. The construction of the latest electrical panel heater (Fig. 538, Plate VI) consists (in all its different sizes and shapes) of a rolled steel plate, specially flattened, its edges being turned back to retain stiffness, with the heating element of nickel chromium wire encased in a flexible refractory material, fastened to it by clips of untarnishable steel by small rivets. Extra insulation between the element and the plate is obtained by means of thin mica strips placed in all positions where contact is made. To prevent loss of heat from the back of the panel, a mattress of special insulating, and particularly non-hygrometic material, is laid over the whole of the heated surface and held in position by a galvanised back plate with its edges turned over on to the front plate, in box form as shown in (9) thus rendering it water and air tight. These plates are fastened into a frame (10) of steel moulding (wood may be used with suitable types).

Electrical entry to the panel is made either through the removable moulding (12) in the case of surface fixing and wiring, or by the back entry hole (13) to meet recessed requirements. The points of entry are arranged for a $\frac{5}{8}$-inch conduit. Wire connections are made to a porcelain block of approved pattern (14) by means of porcelain connectors arranged with flexible leads covered with material which is fire and heat proof.

It is claimed that an electrical heating panel of 5 square feet of surface consuming 500 watts ($\frac{1}{2}$ unit) comfortably warms 1,000 cubic feet of room space, the B.Th.U. emission being 1,702, so that a room 30 feet by 20 feet by 10 feet high would consume three units per hour, and with thermostatic control a little less.

CHAPTER X

CENTRAL HEATING : STEAM

General Principles—Roof—Air—Skylights—Walls—Floors—Transmission Table—Steam Boilers for Low-pressure Steam Heating. VACUUM STEAM HEATING. HIGH-PRESSURE STEAM INSTALLATION : Limitations of the System—Steam Traps—Vacuum Pumps—The Unit System.

Heating by Steam : Low-pressure Gravity System

Low-pressure steam heating is a very suitable system for warming factories, but is not so suitable for ordinary and public buildings, owing to the fact that there is no satisfactory method of regulating the amount of heat. In periods of milder weather you must have all or none with steam heating, except by shutting off or turning on steam in the radiators at more or less frequent intervals as may be required, which, being a sort of nobody's job, is generally left undone.

Owing to the higher temperature of steam, less heating surface is required in radiators and pipes, though this is somewhat discounted by the extra cost of the steam mountings on the boiler and the constant attention required for the stoking.

Steam heating with pipes, especially long lines of pipes having few fittings, is very economical in cost both as regards labour and materials. These pipes are generally fixed overhead, (1) because the whole of the floor-space is then available, (2) because they are then out of reach and thus prevent people touching them and getting burned or scalded, (3) the height allows an easy return of the condensed water back to the boiler.

General Principles.—The general principle according to which heat is distributed from a boiler to heating surface of whatever kind (radiators, cast-iron pipes, wrought-iron pipes) by means of steam is similar to that already described in " Hot-water Heating," but the great differences between the properties of water and steam introduce such variations into the principle by which the circulation is effected that the two are for all practical purposes quite distinct.

In both cases, though in a different sense, the circulation may be said to be affected by differences in density between the flow and return (condense in steam) pipes, which in the hot-water circulation makes little difference in the static head. With the steam, however, the case is quite different. The pressure in a steam system has practically no relation to the static head, or height of the hot-water pipe. In the hot-water system the pressure is almost entirely determined by that height, but in steam systems the water sinks back to the boiler by its own weight or gravity, that is, greater density.

In a hot-water system the circulating pressure is generated in the piping, in a steam system always in the boiler, and the movement of the steam by its drop in pressure, which drop in pressure is caused by the loss of heat through the radiating surface, and it is a necessary condition of continued circulation in a steam system that this continuous drop of absolute pressure all along the circuit should exist.

As an illustration (see Fig. 541), let us take a one-story factory building 100 feet long by 50 feet wide, and an average height of 12 feet, to be warmed to 55° F. inside when it is 32° F. outside, with a two-bay roof of the " Northern Light " type, as it is called, these lights being generally placed looking north, so that at no time are they facing the sun, the direct rays from which might interfere with the workers or damage the materials being manufactured.

It will first be necessary to calculate the amount of heat required to warm the air, and then the heat losses from skylights, roof, walls, and floor. This should be done as described in Chapter VIII, as the calculation of heat losses is always the same, whatever heating system may be installed.

Let us assume that the materials used in the structure of the building are as follow :

Roof.—Tiles with rafters boarded on one side.

Northern lights—single skylight.

Walls of 14-inch brickwork, plaster covered.

Floor, wood on joists with air space and 6-inch concrete.

The amount of heat required may now be calculated as follows :

Air.

55° F. raised from 32° F.	= 23° F. rise.
100 feet by 50 feet by 12 feet average height	= 60,000 cu. feet.
Allow for at least two changes per hour	= 60,000 + 60,000 = 120,000 cu. feet.
Therefore the B.Th.U.s required for the air will be 120,000 × ·018 × 23	= approximately 50,000 B.Th.U.s.

Skylights.

2 lines, each 100 feet by 5 feet	= 1,000 sq. feet.
1,000 sq. feet by 1·30 (20 per cent. for facing north) × 23	= approximately 29,900 B.Th.U.s.

Roof.

2 lines, each 100 feet by 25 feet	= 5,000 sq. feet.
5,000 sq. feet by 0·42 (20 per cent. for facing north) × 23	= 48,300 B.Th.U.s.

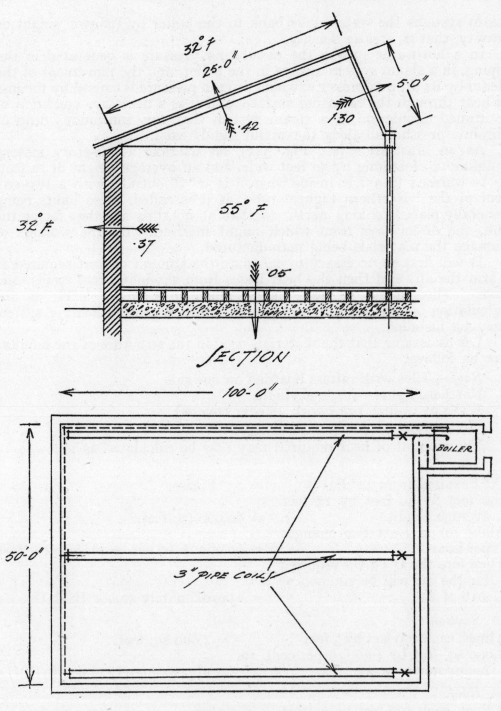

32° F

25'-0"

32° F

5'-0"

·42

1·30

55° F.

32° F.

·37

·05

SECTION

100'-0"

BOILER

50'-0"

3" PIPE COILS

PLAN

Fig. 541.

156

Walls.

Side walls, 200 feet by 12 feet average height	= 2,400 sq. feet
End walls, 100 feet by 12 feet	= 1,200 „
	3,600

3,600 sq. feet by 0·37 (10 per cent. for average
   percentage) × 23   = 30,636 B.Th.U.s.

Floor.

100 feet by 50 feet	= 5,000 sq. feet
5,000 sq. feet by 0·05 × 23	= 5,750 B.Th.U.s.

Summary.

B.Th.U.s required for warming air			= 50,000
„	loss through	skylights	= 29,900
„	„	roof	= 48,300
„	„	walls	= 30,636
„	„	floor	= 5,750
	Total B.Th.U.s required		164,586

Assuming that 3-inch diameter cast-iron or steam piping has been chosen for the heating medium, to be fixed overhead on detachable clips, it will be found from the following Emission Table that approximately 458 feet of pipe would be required, that is $\frac{164,586}{360} = 458$ approx.

TABLE LXXVIII

PIPE TRANSMISSION TABLE

B.Th.U. per Lineal Foot per Hour

Size of Pipes.	Steam 215° – 55° Air.	Size of Pipes.	Steam 215° – 55° Air.	Size of Pipes.	Steam 215° – 55° Air.
½ inch	92	1½ inch	200	4 inch	445
¾ „	118	2 „	246	5 „	540
1 „	145	2½ „	295	6 „	632
1¼ „	178	3 „	360		

We will now turn to the plan to determine the most advantageous way of disposing this piping, and take 3 lines as shown, which with the heat given from the feed and condense mains will give the temperature required. So as to allow for the effective draining of the condense water, the pipe lines should fall slightly from the feed inlet to the condense outlet, the feed inlets and main being on the wall nearest to boiler, assuming it is fixed as shown on plan, and the condense water carried along the far or opposite wall, and brought along the side wall, slightly dropping all the way back to boiler. The size of the steam main and branches should next be calculated, and the emission from the 3 pipe coils of 3-inch piping, which can be taken as 148 feet long, just leaving room enough for the inlet and outlet connections and valves. It will be seen that each line takes 53,280 B.Th.U.s or 159,840 in all, so that B.Th.U.s required are :

TABLE LXXIX

	B.Th.U.s.
Heating medium	159,840
Allowance for starting cold, more steam being required for this, say 20 per cent. .	31,968
Emission from mains, 10 per cent.	10,500
Total . .	202,308

As explained before, the steam condenses directly it enters the piping and consequently loses its initial pressure, the pressure drop increasing as the feed pipe is lengthened. In this case, assuming the boiler pressure to be 2 lb. (a low pressure is more economical to maintain and more satisfactory in working), it will be found that the pressure at the valve to the third or last line of 3-inch pipe will have dropped to $1\frac{1}{2}$ lb., a drop of $\frac{1}{2}$ lb. in about 50 feet from the boiler, so that the average drop per foot of pipe works out ·01 lb. This pressure is, however, generally worked out in 10-feet lengths, which would be ·1 lb. and in inches of water gauge instead of lb., in this instance 2·77 inches water gauge per 10-foot length. At this pressure our main feed to first valve should be 2 inches in diameter, as this diameter pipe will carry up to 300,000 B.Th.U.s, and the branch $1\frac{1}{4}$ inch, which will carry up to 100,000 B.Th.U.s. The feed pipe can now be reduced to $1\frac{1}{2}$ inch, as there are under 175,000 B.Th.U.s to be carried to the three remaining 3-inch pipe lines and after the next $1\frac{1}{4}$-inch branch, $1\frac{1}{4}$-inch can be continued to the last pipe line, the condense can generally be accommodated with a size smaller pipe than the feed, so that, starting with the last pipe line, 1-inch diameter steam pipe will be quite sufficient with $1\frac{1}{4}$ inch after the junction of the second 3-inch pipe, and $1\frac{1}{2}$ inch after the third and back to boiler. It is now possible to calculate the total emission of heat into the factory, from the heating medium and feed and condense piping :

TABLE LXXX

3-inch Pipe lines as previously given		= 159,840	B.Th.U.s	
2-inch steam feeder main, say	8 feet × 240 =	1,920	,,	
$1\frac{1}{2}$-inch ,, ,,	24 feet × 200 =	4,800	,,	approx.
$1\frac{1}{4}$-inch ,, ,,	24 feet × 178 =	4,270	,,	
$\frac{3}{4}$-inch condense pipe	24 feet × 110 =	2,640	,,	
1-inch ,,	24 feet × 140 =	3,360	,,	
$1\frac{1}{4}$-inch ,,	24 feet × 170 =	8,500	,,	
		185,330		

and allowing for the warming-up of the circuits from cold and a margin over all requirements on the boiler rating, we find the size of the boiler required to be 250,000 B.Th.U.s.

Steam Boilers for Low-pressure Steam Heating.—Before steam is raised, the piping is full of air, and the pressure of the air will be as great

PLATE VII

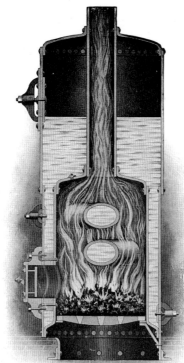

Fig. 542

Fig. 543.

Fig 544.

TYPES OF BOILERS.

as that of the steam, so that the first essential is to allow the air to escape ; but as steam is lighter than air, the outlets should not be taken from the top, or highest point in the pipe line, as in hot-water systems, nor at the bottom of the pipe, which will have the water of the condensation running along it, but about half-way up (in line with a horizontal line taken through the centre of the pipe to be vented). In this position it does not get all the air out but it does remove most of it, quite sufficient for all practical purposes. For types of boilers see Figs. 542–4, Plate VII.

For an ordinary building with radiators, the piping would follow the same lines as a two-pipe hot-water system, the radiators being tapped for air vents about half-way down as shown. Care must be taken that the condense water has a free run back to boiler. Long sweep fittings should be used instead of tees, or any fitting that would cause friction, for where there is friction the equilibrium between the water in the boiler and condense pipe is upset and the water backs up the condense pipe, which causes a lot of trouble.

VACUUM STEAM HEATING

When water is heated in a closed system absolutely cut off from the atmosphere, the atmospheric pressure has no influence on the boiling point. The circulation will proceed on exactly the same principle below as well as above the atmosphere, for the atmospheric pressure has only an influence when there are leakages ; by this system, the temperature of the steam may be reduced below 212°. A leakage of air occurring in such a system upsets everything, as the entering air will drive back the whole of the low-pressure steam before it, and gradually spread over the whole system, rendering it cold and inoperative, so that it is absolutely necessary in such a system that there should be no leakages whatever, if a satisfactory distribution of heat is to be maintained, and this is a condition which it is very difficult to maintain.

HIGH-PRESSURE STEAM INSTALLATIONS

In our large institutions high-pressure steam is required for the production of motive power for electric lighting, sterilising, cooking, and laundry work from which all the water of condensation cannot be returned to the boiler. In these installations a continual supply of fresh water is necessary for feeding purposes, and this renders the use of cast-iron sectional boilers undesirable, on account of the impossibility of cleaning out the fur or deposit, which results from the evaporisation of hard water, from the interior of the sections. No really satisfactory method has yet been devised, in the writer's opinion, for removing scale from a sectional boiler ; therefore, where the boiler must be fed continuously with hard water, a wrought-iron boiler should be used, provided with manholes, the interior of which can be periodically inspected and cleaned, and for really high pressures are essential.

Where high-pressure steam is employed, the size of the pipe necessary to convey a given quantity of heat to a distant point is considerably reduced, owing to the increased density of high-pressure steam. Great care must be taken, in fixing long runs of steam pipes, that free expansion and contraction are in all cases possible : this is generally done by inserting expansion joints. The best kind are undoubtedly annealed bent copper pipes (Fig. 551, Plate IX), but as these are very expensive a sliding sleeve type of expansion joint is often used, as it is much cheaper, but these require constant attention, for if bolted up too tight they do not allow expansion to take place, and when loosened generally drip water more or less continuously. A long length of steam pipe usually expands 1½ inch in every hundred feet, and this amount of expansion must be allowed for in all cases. With long ranges of high-pressure steam pipes the best non-conducting covering procurable should be used. It is also of great importance in installations of this kind that the pipes should be fixed in such a way that they can easily clear themselves of condensed water, which is bound to be formed in them ; the usual method is to fix the pipes with a gradual fall in the direction in which the water has to flow, and the steam traps used should be such that no steam can escape into the water pipe. The deterioration of condensed water pipes is a very serious matter, they have been known to rust through in one or two seasons, the reason being that they are partly filled with air, as only rarely do they run full, and the greatest corrosion takes place at the level where the water and air are in contact ; and as cast-iron does not rust so easily as wrought, it should be used where possible. The layout of these installations, sizes of boilers, pipe sizes, method of fixing, are always specified by consulting engineers, who also superintend the work during erection, and are responsible for its satisfactory working.

Limitations of the System.—High-pressure steam cannot be used advantageously for heating buildings owing to the temperature of the steam being too great, but it may be used when a reducing valve is fixed on the end of the pipe, thus reducing the steam pressure to that of a low-pressure system, or (1) by tubular water heaters, called calorifiers, from which water circulates by ordinary low-pressure gravity circulation, (2) by batteries of pipes, or indirect radiators, over which air is blown for heating buildings, as described in the Plenum system.

Most of our large institutions are fitted up with calorifiers both for heating and hot-water supply, one for each purpose. This is a very economical way when exhaust steam from engines and pumps is utilised, for although the steam has lost its pressure, it contains practically its full amount of heating value, and when passed into the calorifier where it condenses it parts with 1,000 B.Th.U.s for every lb. condensed to water. There are numerous types of calorifiers on the market, and the following illustrations give a good idea of their general arrangement.

The heating or tube surface required in calorifiers to carry out certain duties is calculated as follows :

Assume a calorifier is required to work as a boiler would for a low-

PLATE VIII

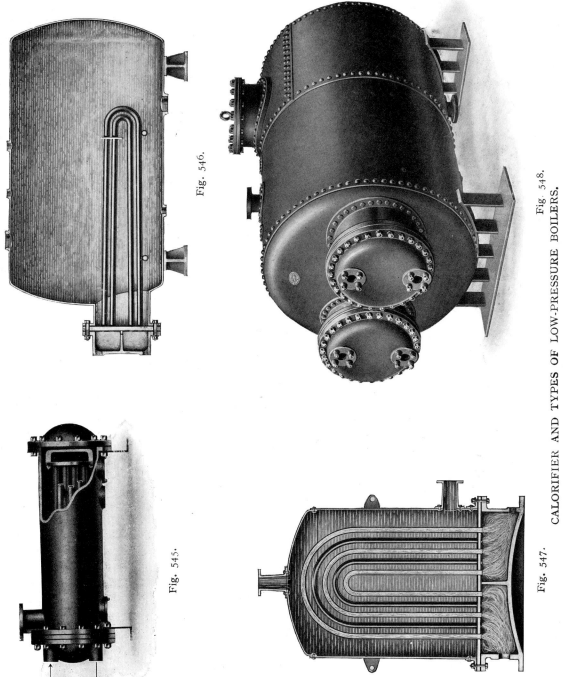

Fig. 546.

Fig. 548.

Fig. 545.

Fig. 547.

STEAM

CONDENSE

CALORIFIER AND TYPES OF LOW-PRESSURE BOILERS.

pressure heating apparatus, and that 500,000 B.Th.U.s per hour are required from it, then the heating surface in the calorifier must be sufficient to give a transmission of 500,000 B.Th.U.s per hour from the steam (or hot water) in the tubes to the surrounding water. After starting, the water in the cylinder from the return pipes at 140° F. would have to be raised to 180° F. before leaving as flow or flows, consequently the mean temperature of the water surrounding the tubes would be 160° F., and supposing the steam entered the tubes at a pressure of 10 lb., its temperature would be 240° F., condensing at 212° F. as it leaves the tubes of the calorifiers as water. The mean steam temperature in the tubes will be 226° F. and as the mean temperature is 160° F., the temperature difference is 66° F. The tubes of a calorifier are generally of copper, though the writer has used iron quite satisfactorily, and the heat transmission for copper pipes per square foot per degree F. per hour is 200 B.Th.U.s. Thus for calculating the tube surface we get :

$$= \frac{500,000 \text{ B.Th.U.s}}{200 \text{ B.Th.U.s per sq. foot} \times 66° \text{ F.}} \quad \frac{\text{heat required.}}{\text{temperature difference.}}$$

$$= \frac{500,000}{13,200} \quad 37.84 \text{ sq. feet of heating surface required.}$$

With wrought-iron tubes the heat transmission is 10 B.Th.U.s less per square foot per degree F. per hour.

As hot water when entering a calorifier for heating purposes, instead of steam, has only about half the heating power of steam, with a lower temperature degree difference, quite a lot of heating surface is required in the calorifier, when used for hot-water heating ; but for hot-water supply where the temperature degree difference is much greater, the results are more satisfactory. Automatic regulators are sometimes utilised with steam calorifiers and so adjusted that when the temperature of the water in the calorifier reaches the prescribed temperature they close the steam valve, but the calorifiers to a great extent regulate themselves, as when the water in the calorifier attains a very high temperature, the condensation of the steam in the tube surface becomes very small, and the steam trap at the outlet of the tubes prevents the steam from escaping, so that very little steam is used even if the steam-control valve should be left open.

It sometimes happens that it is not possible to place a steam boiler in such a position that all the condense water is able to fall by gravity back to it ; and where this obtains and there are many instances of it, the condense water is collected in steam traps, which in turn deliver into a condense pipe connected to a condense tank or sump, from which it is pumped into the boiler. There are also occasions where the necessary fall for the condense water into a tank or sump cannot be obtained, and artificial help is given by means of a vacuum pump, and the vacuum so created ensures the return of the condense water from what would otherwise be impossible positions. The vacuum finishes at the outlets of the steam traps fitted to the radiators or pipe coils. (See Plate VIII, Figs. 545–548.)

Steam Traps.—The function of the steam trap, in low-pressure, vacuum, or vapour heating systems, is to save heat, and thus fuel, by keeping the heating medium, radiators or pipe coils, at their maximum efficiency. The steam enters the radiators or pipe coils through the inlet valve, but no steam can pass out of the radiator pipe or coil until condensation has taken place. The action is as follows : When steam passes into a cold radiator or pipe coil, it forces the cold air which is in the radiator or pipe coil into the trap and thence through the return or condense piping. In warming the radiator or pipe coil the steam parts with its heat at about the rate of 1,000 B.Th.U.s per lb. of water condensed, and in so doing turns into water again. The water, being heavier than the steam, falls to the bottom of the radiator, and fills up the trap, through which it passes into the return or condense piping. As soon as the air is entirely forced out, the steam completely fills the radiator or pipe coil, and follows after the water into the trap ; here, owing to its being many degrees hotter than either the air or the water, it automatically closes the trap, thus causing the steam to be trapped within the radiator or pipe coil. After the radiator is completely filled with steam, condensation takes place at a uniform rate, and the water of the condensation, being many degrees cooler than the steam, opens the trap again, through which it flows in a steady stream and passes out into the return or condense piping (Fig 549, Plate IX).

As a matter of fact it will be found, after the apparatus has got properly going, that the trap adjusts itself to a condition corresponding to the water of condensation temperature, just in the same way that the thermometer does in registering the temperature of a room, and so allows a continuous flow of water from the radiator or pipe coil, just sufficient to keep the radiating surface free from water and air, and at the same time full of steam without any waste.

It will be noticed from the foregoing that in addition to the ordinary valves, radiators, and pipe coils, a steam trap should be fitted to each radiator or pipe coil in the system ; further, automatic air-vent outlet valves should be fitted at the top of each vertical condense pipe, and where a vacuum pump is used, a strainer should be inserted in the condense main before it reaches the pump, so as to keep any grit or dirt from getting into it, and the strainer basket should be frequently emptied.

Vacuum Pumps.—The vacuum pump, of which there are many makes, may be driven by either steam or electric motor. It should be as compact as possible and designed for handling water from the condense mains of a low-pressure steam heating system.

The pump is usually rated for a condensation of a ¼ lb. of water for each square foot of radiating surface, which it has to lift from the return or condense mains to condense tank, or to boiler, as the case may be.

A steam " drier " is often fixed to the main steam feeder, before any branches are taken from it, so as to keep the feeder mains as " dry " as possible. This consists of an iron chamber fitted with baffle plates, on

PLATE IX

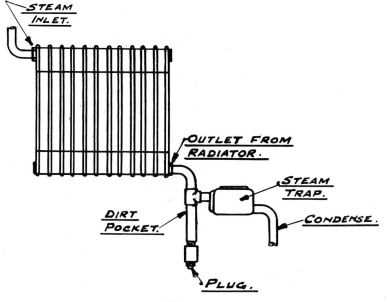

Fig. 549.

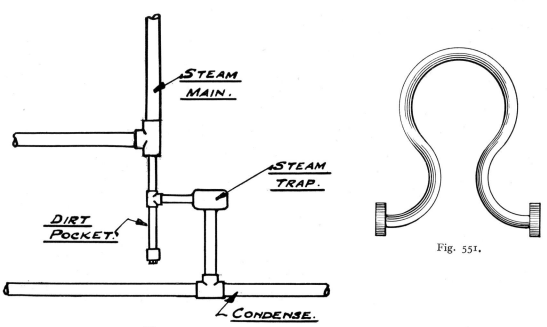

Fig. 550.

Fig. 551.

STEAM HEATING APPARATUS.

which the steam impinges, and any suspended water is caught by these baffle plates, from which it falls or drips to the bottom of the baffler, or " drier," and is connected up by pipe to the nearest drain.

In all gravity condense mains, that is, where the boiler is below the lowest radiator or pipe coil, a vertical pipe about 3 feet high should be fitted to the return or condense main at the point where it drops to enter the boiler (see illustration), an automatic air relief valve being fixed on the top end ; and just before the connection of the return or condense main into boiler, a swing check or non-return valve should be fitted. Many engineers also fix what is termed a balancing pipe, that is, a branch from the main feed pipe, just above boiler, vented as described previously for the condense, down to the level of the condense inlet, and connected to same as shown and fitted with non-return valve.

As dirt and grit would damage and thus interfere with the working of the steam traps to radiators or pipe coils, and they are extremely sensitive, they should be protected from any chance of such interference by inserting a dirt pocket between the radiator or pipe coil and the trap ; this can be done by fixing an ordinary tee-piece, short, and cap, or socket and plug, as shown (Figs. 549 and 550, Plate IX).

The Unit System.—This is a system, not a standardised apparatus, though it comprises certain essential components, such as a boiler or other steam-raising appliance, a battery of pipes, and a fan. All these parts, with the exception of the steam-raising appliance, are housed in a metal box, so as to form a complete unit. The merits of the system are that it is a practical, simplified application of current practice, compact, easily managed, and capable of drastic modifications to meet particular requirements. The steam is used to heat the battery of pipes, and thereby the air contained in the metal box, which is then distributed by the action of the fan. Although details of planning and construction vary with different manufacturers, briefly the principles on which the system is based are these : The metal box, usually rectangular in form, stands on the floor, and has an outlet grid round the base ; the body of the box contains the battery of steam pipes, disposed horizontally ; on this is a hood containing a propeller fan. Air is drawn in by the fan through a louvred chamber (which commonly contains a mixing damper), which is forced down over the steam-pipe battery, downward and outwards through the outlet grid at the base. Thus complete circulation is secured, and if the unit is properly placed, a uniform distribution of warmth. While in a big, well-ventilated factory or other building the air may be drawn from the building itself, it will be readily understood that the mixing chamber above the fan can be connected with the outer air through a duct or tubing. Naturally the determining factors in an installation of this character are the area of the heating surface (the battery of steam pipes), the size and rate of revolution of the fan, as compared with the cubic space to be warmed. Calculations based on these factors have already been discussed in connection with ventilation and heating systems, Volume II, and also in relation to air propellers in Chapter XI of this volume.

It will be seen that the installation of such a system presents no exceptional difficulties. If the air is to be drawn from outside, it is well to have the " unit " placed as near an outer wall as possible, to avoid undue lengthening of the air-duct. In some positions (near a wooden partition, for instance) it may be advisable to provide asbestos sheet insulation ; but this is rarely necessary. The unit system is specially adapted to the heating of a factory, a garage, or similar building. It is claimed to be efficient, moderate in first outlay, and economical in working, this last, as in other hot-water and steam-heating systems, depending largely on the cost of fuel, though here there is conservation of heat and even distribution.

CHAPTER XI

VENTILATION

BY STAN. E. NELSON, B.A. CANTAB.

Composition of Air—Natural Ventilation—Air Volume—Testing Air Velocity—Propeller and Centrifugal Fans—Systems of Ventilation—Heating Units—Special Type of Unit Heater—Exhaust Systems—Air Conditioning—Filters—Air Washers—Humidifier—Miscellaneous.

CLOSE attention is now being paid to the ventilation and conditioning of air, not only in workshops, offices, and public buildings, but also in private dwellings, in order to assure the comfort and well-being of occupants.

It is necessary to understand the essentials of ventilation and warming, and for this purpose the elementary principles of the subject are dealt with in this chapter in a way that the men who actually install or supervise the installation of ventilation plant may realise what the designer has in mind and how their contribution to the apparatus affects the ultimate success of it.

First we must all realise that fresh air is necessary in enclosed spaces for the comfort and health of occupants, and the supplying of suitable conditions involve not merely an adequate quantity of air but the control of its direction and condition.

COMPOSITION OF AIR

Air is, of course, purer in country districts than in large cities and factory towns, but generally speaking its chief constituents are oxygen and nitrogen in the approximate proportions of 21 per cent. and 79 per cent. by volume respectively, the former being the essential constituent for breathing, and this combining with carbon in the body is exhaled as CO_2 (carbon dioxide). Although only about 5 per cent. of the oxygen in the air is used up when we breathe, 4 per cent. CO_2 is added and it will be appreciated that an inadequately ventilated room will in time become heavily charged with CO_2, since the oxygen will gradually be used up and replaced by CO_2, and although air may contain the latter up to 30 parts in 10,000 without being actually injurious (outside air containing approximately 4 parts in 10,000) it gives a feeling of lassitude or drowsiness which is unpleasant and a serious hindrance where work of any kind must be carried out. Concentration of CO_2 to the extent referred to is unlikely to be met with, however, in modern buildings, and mention of it at all is only made to emphasise the desirability of air change to maintain freshness.

In this country air at 65° F. with the barometer at 30 inches of mercury weighs approximately ·075 lb. per cu. foot, and this figure will be used in calculations throughout this chapter. Actually the weight varies with barometric pressure, temperature, and water vapour content, but except for the more important calculations for air conditioning the working margins normally allowed render the variations due to barometer and water vapour content relatively unimportant.

NATURAL VENTILATION

The term "natural ventilation" depends on two things: motive power or difference of pressure in an air column brought about by difference of temperature and wind pressure. The latter is actually also occasioned by the former, but this is too big a subject to be gone into here, so for the purpose of present considerations we will consider them as two separate items.

In ventilation calculations it is convenient to refer to motive power or pressure in terms of height or head of water column. It can be shown that a depth of 1 inch of water creates a pressure of 5·2 lb. per square foot.

Now consider a chimney or vertical duct 100 feet high, the surrounding air being at 65° F. and the air in the chimney raised by some heating medium to an average temperature of 140° F. The weight of the surrounding air is ·075 lb. per cu. foot. The weight of the heated air is given by $·075 \times \dfrac{459 + 65}{459 + 140} = ·0655,$

the weight varying inversely as the absolute temperature, absolute zero temperature being 459° below 0° F. Thus it is clear that the heated air is lighter than the outside air, and if the latter is allowed to enter the base of the chimney it will tend to push the lighter air and so cause an upward current in the chimney.

The difference in weight of a column of air on one square foot inside and outside chimney is $100\left(1 - \dfrac{524}{599}\right).0751 \text{ lb.} = 0·9375 \text{ lb.}$

and since 1 inch of water column = 5·2 lb. per square foot the pressure of motive power is equivalent to $\dfrac{·9375}{5·2}$ inches of water = ·18 inches.

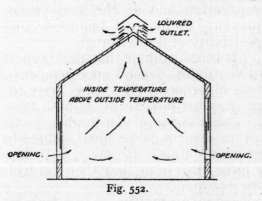

LOUVRED OUTLET.

INSIDE TEMPERATURE ABOVE OUTSIDE TEMPERATURE

OPENING.

OPENING.

Fig. 552.

From the foregoing it will be seen that in an enclosed space or building with openings arranged at the top and bottom there will be an upward or downward current of air within the space according as the outside temperature is above or below that inside, and also that the strength of the air current can be varied by varying the height "h" between the inlets and outlets for the air.

It will be observed that given certain inside and outside air temperatures the conditions inside a space depend to a large extent on intelligent manipulation of the available openings.

Greater air movement, however, is possible by the use of one of the many " ventilators " obtainable, which assist the natural draught, being so designed that when a wind passes through them, past them, under or over them, an induced effect is obtained which increases the flow of air through them. This type of outlet is usually fixed on the ridge of the roof of single-storey buildings, and although there are many types obtainable, the author calls one to mind in particular which will serve to illustrate their use. It is called the "Patent Honeyman Ventilator" and particulars of it are obtainable from Messrs. R. Crittall & Co. Ltd. A diagrammatic sketch, Fig. 553, shows this fitting, "A" being a sheet metal or wooden box fitted on

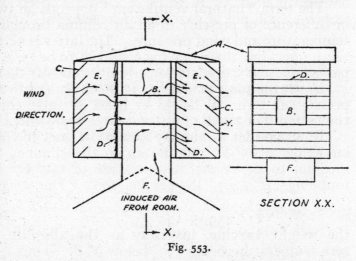

Fig. 553.

either two or four sides with weathering louvres " C," inside these louvres is a frame on which is mounted a number of silk flaps " D," through the centre of which a tube " B " passes. Wind coming from the direction " Y " passes through this tube, at the same time closing the silk flaps on that side and causing an injector effect in the space " E," thus inducing air up through the opening from the room " F " and out via the silk flaps as indicated. A variation of this fitting is also shown for adaptation to a hip roof with ceiling below, Fig. 553A. There are a number of other designs on the market, most of which give similar assistance to natural ventilation and at the same time prevent, or at least minimise, the possibility of down draught.

It is unfortunate that these types of ventilators depend upon temperature differences and wind velocity to produce air movement, as both factors are most in evidence when least air movement is required, namely, in winter time. However, with intelligent adjustment of opening they have their uses, but their control must be left to the common sense of the occupants.

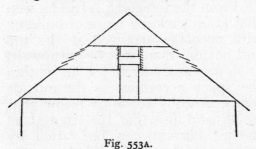

Fig. 553A.

In regard to the statement above regarding air movement in reference to winter time it is a matter of common knowledge from experience that in colder weather the more we keep out of a wind the more comfortable we feel, whereas in hot summer days we welcome a breeze to keep us cool. The speed of air, therefore, over the body has a very definite effect on our feeling of comfort. A good deal of research work has been done in connection therewith, covering a great variety of temperatures and conditions, but for normal ventilation considerations for most occupations temperatures of 55° F. to 70° F. and air speed of three to five feet per second should not be exceeded if a feeling of " draught " is to be avoided.

AIR VOLUME

Before proceeding further some reference must be made to the air quantities adopted nowadays as being good practice in ventilation work in this country. It should be borne in mind, however, that the figures given are approximate only and may be modified to suit a particular case at the discretion of the designer in accordance with his experience and knowledge of requirements.

Private Houses
    Living-rooms   .   .   .   .   .   .   1– 2 air changes per hour.
    Bedrooms   1   ,,   ,,   ,,   ,,
    Kitchens .   .   .   .   .   .   5–10 ,,   ,,   ,,   ,,

Public Buildings
    Offices   .   .   .   .   .   .   1– 2 ,,   ,,   ,,   ,,
    Board Rooms .   .   .   .   3– 6 ,,   ,,   ,,   ,,
    Banking Halls .   .   .   .   1– 2 ,,   ,,   ,,   ,,
    Theatre Auditoriums }
    Lecture Halls   .   .   .   5–10 ,,   ,,   ,,   ,,
    Assembly Halls, etc. }
    Saloons or Lounges .   .   .   5   ,,   ,,   ,,   ,,
    Restaurants   5   ,,   ,,   ,,   ,,
    Dance Halls   5   ,,   ,,   ,,   ,,
    Smoke Rooms .   .   .   5–10 ,,   ,,   ,,   ,,
    Indoor Sports Rooms, Squash Racquets, Gym., etc.   5–10 ,,   ,,   ,,   ,,
    Closed Swimming Pools .   .   1– 2 ,,   ,,   ,,   ,,
    Kitchens .   .   .   .   20–30 ,,   ,,   ,,   ,,
    Boiler Rooms .   .   .   .   Usually determined by air requirements of boilers.
    Lavatories .   .   .   .   5–10 air changes per hour.

Workshops
    Generally .   .   .   .   .   1– 2 ,,   ,,   ,,   ,,
         but require special consideration for particular processes.

For rooms or halls where a large number of occupants are assembled a good plan is to base the requirements on the number of occupants, allowing 750–1,500 cu. feet of air per person per hour, and for this purpose the following tables might be used.

    Theatres, Assembly Halls, etc.   .   .   .   6 sq. feet per person
    Dance Halls .   .   .   .   10–15 ,,   ,,   ,,   ,,
    Restaurants .   .   .   .   20–30 ,,   ,,   ,,   ,,
    Retail Stores }
    Bargain Basements } .   .   .   8–10 ,,   ,,   ,,   ,,

The requirements for ventilation of public buildings are frequently governed by local councils, e.g. the L.C.C. stipulate not less than 1,000 cu. feet per person for new buildings with a concession of 750 cu. feet per hour per person for existing buildings that are reconstructed. For internal lavatories which have not an outside wall, the ventilation must be entirely separate from any other system in the building, must be by mechanical exhaust and in duplicate, ample air inlets to be provided and exhaust at a minimum rate of 750 cu. feet per hour per soil pan, the air to be changed at least three times per hour.

TESTING AIR VELOCITY

To understand the application of mechanical systems of ventilation it is necessary to have some knowledge of the relation between air speed or velocity and the resistance set up against the power supplied to force air into the space to be ventilated. Except in the case of the open type of case-less fan, air is directed by means of ducts, which may be in brickwork, wood, or metal, and the resistance to flow will vary according as the surface is rough or smooth, the extent of the surface, the number of times the air is made to change direction, and how it is buffeted about generally before it arrives at its destination.

First let us consider the roughness of the surface. When air passes over any surface friction tends to prevent, or at least retard, its doing so, and a pressure is necessary to force the air along and keep it in motion. The amount of friction varies with the area and the nature of the surface; it also varies as the square of the air speed. Many tests have been made of passing air over similar materials, and the results given by different authorities vary very much, but for general ventilation purposes it may be assumed that for air passing over a smooth metal surface the coefficient of friction, as it is called, is about ·003 inch water gauge when the velocity is 1,000 feet per minute.

The force tending to push the air through the ducts will be $(H \times A)$ where H = total pressure in inches water gauge and A the cross section of the duct in square feet.

The frictional resistance of the ducts will be K.P.L. $\left(\dfrac{V}{1000}\right)^2$ where K = ·003, P = Perimeter, L = Length, V = Velocity, the perimeter and length being in feet and velocity in feet per minute. Thus we may write

$$H \times A = K.P.L. \left(\frac{V}{1000}\right)^2 \text{ or } H = \frac{K.P.L.}{A} \frac{V^2}{(1000)^2}$$

which gives the pressure in inches water gauge to overcome surface friction in a straight duct.

Force or pressure is also necessary to create velocity and this is best understood by reference to the hydraulic formula $v = \sqrt{2.g.H.}$
where H is head of water in feet, g = 32·2 (acceleration due to gravity) v = velocity of water in feet per second.

Now the density of water is approximately 62·4 lb. per cu. foot and the density of air is ·075 lb. per cu. foot. If now H is the head in feet of air and W.G. = Water Gauge $H = \dfrac{62·4}{·075} \times \dfrac{W.G.}{12}$

Then substituting in the above hydraulic formula we get

$$v = \sqrt{2g.\ 69·3\ W.G.}$$

Whence $W.G. = \dfrac{v^2}{64·4 \times 69·3} = \dfrac{v^2}{4,460}$

and since it is more convenient to deal with velocities in feet per minute

$$= V\ W.G. = \dfrac{V^2}{4,460} \times 3,600 = \left(\dfrac{V}{4,000}\right)^2 \text{ approx.}$$

Resistance to air flow is also set up by changes of direction and eddies in the air stream due to sudden enlargements or contractions sometimes necessary or unavoidable in the design of the duct system for a building. Losses of this nature are conveniently expressed in terms of the velocity of the duct, the necessary head in inches of water gauge to overcome them varying as the square of the velocity. For duct work of circular section having a right-angle bend, the bigger the radius of the bend the less will be the loss, but for radii greater than twice the diameter of the duct the advantage gained is negligible. For an elbow, that is a sharp junction, of two ducts at right angles with no radius in the throat at all, the resistance coefficient may be taken as 1, thus the loss in inches water gauge will be $\left(\dfrac{V}{4,000}\right)^2$

The resistance coefficient for other radii being as follows :

Radius = 2 diameters, coefficient ·15
,,   1·5   ,,   ,,   ·2
,,   1   ,,   ,,   ·25
,, $\frac{1}{2}$,,   ,,   ·75

For a junction of three ducts, that is a Tee connection, each radius equal to twice the diameter of the duct the coefficient is ·15 and for a square T the coefficient is 1.

For junctions branching out at various angles to the duct, coefficients are as follows :

Branch at 15 degs. to the axis of the main duct coefficient ·1
,,   30 ,,   ,,   ,,   ,,   ,,   ,,   ·15
,,   45 ,,   ,,   ,,   ,,   ,,   ,,   ·25
,,   60 ,,   ,,   ,,   ,,   ,,   ,,   ·45

Sudden enlargements or contractions in ducts are occasionally met with and the loss sustained is given by the difference in the velocity pressure in the two ducts, that is, if V_1 is the velocity in, say, the smaller duct and V_2 velocity in the larger duct, the pressure loss in inches water gauge is given by $\left(\dfrac{V_1^2 - V_2^2}{4,000^2}\right)$

From this it will be seen that when the larger duct is three or more times the diameter of the smaller, the velocity in it will be a small proportion of the velocity in the smaller and the pressure loss may then be expressed in terms of velocity of the smaller duct with a resistance coefficient of 1.

A considerable reduction in loss can be effected by putting a gradual slope on the length of duct which connects two different sizes, a diffuser piece, and it has been found by experiment that the most efficient connecting piece for this purpose is one which has a total included angle of 7°. Such a connecting piece has an efficiency of 80 per cent., thus, expressing the friction loss in terms of the velocity in the smaller duct, the resistance coefficient is ·2. For a similar connecting piece with an included angle of 25° a coefficient of ·5 should be allowed, and for 50° coefficient ·75.

For open grilles or gratings, usually met with at the termination of the ducts, gratings having a free area of not less than 50 per cent. of the gross area coefficient of 1·5 should be allowed, the loss being expressed in terms of the velocity in the duct.

For a converging piece the loss is so small as to be neglected even when the included angle is as much as 30°.

The coefficients given

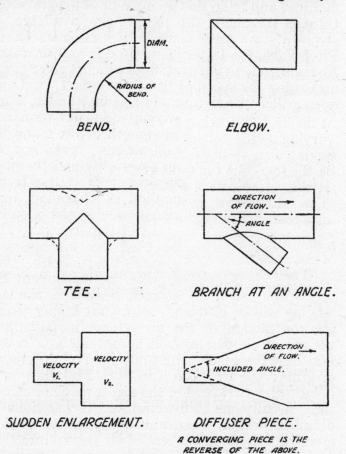

BEND.   ELBOW.

TEE.   BRANCH AT AN ANGLE.

SUDDEN ENLARGEMENT.   DIFFUSER PIECE.
A CONVERGING PIECE IS THE
REVERSE OF THE ABOVE.

Fig. 554.

above, as already mentioned, are for circular section duct work; it is, however, frequently necessary to use ducts of rectangular section, but a little consideration will show that circular ducts are the more efficient and least expensive to adopt, since for the same cross-sectional area the circular duct has the least perimeter, less metal therefore is used to make these ducts, also the area of surface causing friction is consequently less. When using rectangular duct work it should be kept as nearly square as possible, as wide shallow ducts are even less efficient than the square.

A duct system designed with square section ducts would require about 10 per cent. more pressure than circular ducts to pass the same volume of air at the same speed, flatter ducts being of course proportionately greater

So far we have considered only information necessary for the design of a new duct system; it is, however, frequently necessary to add to or alter existing systems, and before this can be done we must have some knowledge of how to ascertain the conditions existing in the system to be modified and to do this we must be able to measure the air quantity passing through the ducts, also the pressure available. For this purpose two instruments are most commonly used, namely, the Anemometer and the Pitot Tube, the latter being used in conjunction with a " U " tube. The Anemometer, an illustration of which is given (Fig. 555), is an instrument for measuring the speed of the air in a duct, or the speed of the air leaving an open grille. Unfortunately this instrument is rather delicate and on that account does not remain particularly accurate for any length of time, and therefore requires frequent calibrations ; even so, it is not safe to assume readings obtained thereby as being correct within 10 or 15 per cent. It is, however, a convenient method of obtaining approximate air quantities, and is widely used in cases where extreme accuracy is not of importance. This instrument should not be used for air speeds in excess of 1,500 to 2,000 feet per minute. When taking readings over a grille the instrument should be held about half an inch away from the face of the grille or a false reading will be obtained, somewhat higher than the actual speed, due to the contraction of the air stream in passing through the grille. The volume of air passing will be obtained, of course, from the velocity obtained by this instrument multiplied by the cross sectional area of the duct or grille ; the air speed is indicated by dials on the instrument, and since it measures the speed of the air, tests will need to be made over a space of time, usually one to five minutes, thence the velocity in feet per minute is obtained, which, when multiplied by the duct area in square feet, will give the volume in cu. feet of air per minute.

Fig. 555.—Anemometer.

The Pitot Tube, Fig. 555A, is an instrument by means of which the pressure in inches of water gauge in a duct can be obtained. It is actually a combination of two tubes, one having an open end which can be inserted in the duct to face the air stream, thus being subject to a pressure due to the velocity of the air, the other tube, which will be seen has a number of small holes drilled in the side of it, is subject only to the effect of the static pressure, the holes being at right angles to the direction of air flow. Thus it will be appreciated that the velocity pressure is the difference between the pressure obtained by means of the open-ended tube, called the facing gauge, and the tube with side holes, called the side gauge. Reference to Fig. 555A will show that the end of the instrument which is inserted in the duct is " L " shaped, so that when the facing gauge is towards the air stream the main stem of the instrument is at right angles,

and to the free ends of the tubes rubber piping is connected, the other ends of this being fitted to the two open ends of a " U " tube, also illustrated. Water is placed in the " U " tube to a suitable height, a scale being fitted between the two legs of the " U " graduated in inches marked off from a central zero, this scale being capable of a slight adjustment up and down so that the zero mark can be set opposite the level of the water before the Pitot Tube is placed in the duct, when, of course, the height of the

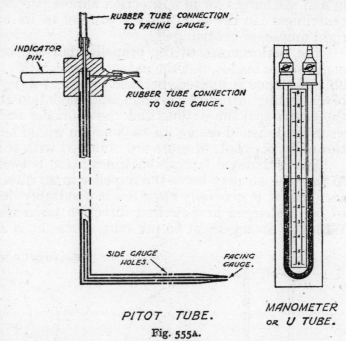

PITOT TUBE.

Fig. 555A.

MANOMETER OR U TUBE.

water in each leg will be exactly the same, since the pressure down each leg of the " U " tube will be the same.

The instrument with its rubber tubes connected up as described above may then be inserted in the duct, choosing a point if possible in a straight length of duct five to six diameters length away from a bend or change section, thus ensuring a steady air stream. With the facing gauge pointing against the direction of air flow there will then be a different pressure in each leg of the " U " tube and the amount by which the one exceeds the other will be shown by the difference of level of water in the two legs. If the total head, that

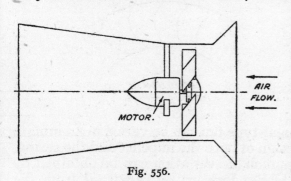

Fig. 556.

is, facing-gauge reading only, is required, the side-gauge connections may be taken off, leaving that end of the " U " tube open to atmosphere, and in a similar manner side-gauge or static readings can be obtained if required.

PROPELLER AND CENTRIFUGAL FANS

Now let us consider the behaviour or characteristics of the main type of fans used in ventilation work. These are the propeller fan and the centrifugal fan. The chief difference between them is that the former draws in and discharges air in a direction almost parallel to its axis, whereas the centrifugal fan draws in the air parallel to its axis and discharges it at right angles, or centrifugally.

The performance of the propeller fan can be varied by altering the angle of the blades, but the extent to which this can be done with reasonable efficiency is limited, because too great a deviation below the normal blade setting introduces air slip, and deviation the other way approaches the centrifugal fan action, and the propeller type fan not mounted in a suitably designed casing for such action would be less efficient. Efficiencies of 65 per cent. or more are obtained with this type of fan.

The centrifugal fan is sometimes fitted between suitable guide plates, so that the air may leave the impeller in all directions from its circumference, but it is generally mounted in a suitably designed casing for the air to be discharged in a desired direction tangential to the circumference. With this arrangement 80 per cent. efficiency is not unusual.

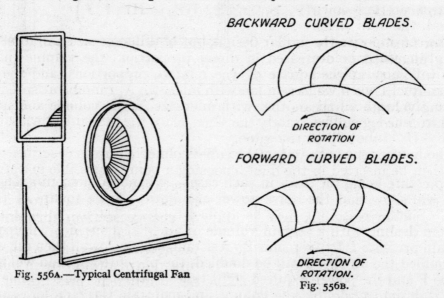

BACKWARD CURVED BLADES.

DIRECTION OF ROTATION

FORWARD CURVED BLADES.

DIRECTION OF ROTATION.

Fig. 556A.—Typical Centrifugal Fan

Fig. 556B.

The performance of the centrifugal-type fan can be varied in an infinite number of ways by differences in design of both the impeller and the casing, but other things being equal an appreciable variation can be obtained by merely altering the angle of the blades forward or backward from the simple straight radial blade. It is useful to remember that for a given design of centrifugal fan running at constant speed, one with a forward curved blade will set up the greatest pressure within the normal range, the capacity for setting up pressure diminishing as the blade angle is turned back through the radial position to a backward slope, i.e. sloping away from the direction of rotation of the impeller.

The following facts concerning all types of fans should be thoroughly understood for application to ventilation scheme designs :

The volume passed through a fan varies in direct proportion to its speed of rotation. The pressure set up varies as the square of speed. The horse power required to drive it includes both pressure and volume and varies therefore as the cube of the speed, assuming that it is connected to the same system of resistance to air flow, or putting the above in symbols :

V = Volume	V varies as S	HP varies as $S.V^2$
P = Pressure	P „ „ S^2	HP „ „ S^3
HP = Horse Power or	P „ „ V^2 or	HP „ „ V^3

E.g.—If a fan passes volume V_1 at speed S_1 the volume V_2 at speed S_2 is given by $V_2 = V^1 \dfrac{S_2}{S_1}$

Similarly to find Pressure P_2 given P_1, S_1, and S_2, $P_2 = P_1 \left(\dfrac{S_2}{S_1}\right)^2$

and to find HP_2 given HP_1, S_1, and S_2, $HP_2 = HP_1 \left(\dfrac{S_2}{S_1}\right)^3$

For fans of exactly similar design, but of different sizes, all dimensions being increased or decreased in direct proportion, the volume that will pass will vary as the square of the relative proportions and the speed inversely. Thus if we have a fan with inlet size A_1 running at speed S and passing volume V and another with inlet size A_2 the volume and speed of the latter are given by

$$V_2 = \left(\frac{A_2}{A_1}\right)^2 V_1 \text{ and } S_2 = \frac{A_1}{A_2} S_1$$

the pressure being the same in each case. Whence a moment's consideration will show that the horse power also varies as the square of the fan size. Similar reasoning may be applied to duct systems, in that a given system dealing with a certain volume of air V at a speed S will require a certain pressure P to overcome its resistance to air flow, if then the volume is doubled the air speed will be doubled, the pressure required will be four times P and the power required eight times that for passing volume V_1, or if it is desired to double the volume and maintain the same pressure, the air speed must be the same and therefore the area of the ducts must be doubled. Whence it will be seen that the area varies inversely as the speed, and since we have already stated that pressure varies as the square of the speed, it also varies inversely as the square of the area. Thus if A_1 and A_2 are duct areas corresponding to pressures P_1 and P_2 :

$$P_2 = \left(\frac{A_1}{A_2}\right)^2 P_1$$

To choose the best fan to use for a particular application the various characteristics of the different types should be considered. These are best understood by reference to graphs which are obtained from a test of a particular fan type ; the fan running at constant speed, the pressure is plotted on a vertical scale and the volume horizontally. Efficiency is also plotted to a vertical scale. Such graphs of characteristic fan curves are shown in Figs. 557, 557A, and 557B for three common fan types : the propeller fan, the forward curved centrifugal fan, and the backward curved centrifugal fan.

Study curve Fig. 557 for the propeller-type fan ; this will make clear that this type of fan is at maximum efficiency when working at quite a low pressure, in fact very little more than at free air conditions. It will also be noted that from maximum efficiency point the volume falls off fairly rapidly as the total water-gauge pressure is increased and, at the same time, the efficiency also falling off, the horse power required mounts up quickly. The available water-gauge pressure to overcome resistance is of course given by the difference between the total water-gauge curve and the velocity head curve, the latter being the pressure required to set up velocity through the fan. Two efficiency curves are shown which indicate the difference for this type of fan when blowing into a restricted space under most unfavourable conditions and when exhausting from the same space under favourable conditions.

The curve, Fig. 557A, is typical of a forward blade centrifugal fan. This type, it will be seen, is comparatively inefficient under free air conditions and reaches maximum efficiency a little to the left of the maximum pressure attained ; this type of fan is therefore more suitable for working against resistance and should be so chosen that its working point is never below say 55 per cent. to 60 per cent. efficiency. It should be noted also that the power absorbed is the converse of the propeller type, i.e. as the pressure curve rises to a maximum the horse power falls and continues to fall back to the closed condition when the impeller is merely setting up pressure in its own casing and passing no volume. Here again the pressure available for overcoming resistance, i.e. the static water gauge, is given by the difference between the total water-gauge curve and the velocity head curve. It should be noted that the peak of the pressure curve is fairly flat, a characteristic which is sometimes very useful when two spaces of approximately equal volume require to be ventilated intermittently, when nothing whatever need be altered at the fan, a damper only requiring to be closed on the circuit which is not required. The power absorbed will automatically drop to that necessary to deal with the reduced volume at practically the same pressure.

Lastly, we have the curve for the backward sloping blade, Fig. 557B. This is similar to Fig. 557A except that the pressure curve rises more rapidly from free air condition and reaches a maximum at zero volume.

It should also be noted that the power consumption is practically a maximum at free air condition, falling very gradually to almost maximum efficiency point and thence falling more rapidly. This characteristic is an advantage when, if for some reason the resistance of the system is relieved, the pressure falls and the fan passes a greater volume of air in consequence, the power consumption is limited and there is no danger of overloading the driving motor.

Another advantage of this type of fan for certain application is due to its rapidly rising pressure characteristic, which means that the volume will not be reduced to any great extent as the result of an increase of resistance which may be set up when a system includes air heaters or filters, the resistances of which rapidly increase if not kept clean and free from obstruction.

Referring to Fig. 557A, a curve is shown superimposed on the fan curve which represents the resistance of the system; this is called the System or Job Characteristic and represents the resistance which will be set up in any given system corresponding to the volume passing through it and illustrates the statement made earlier that the pressure P varies as V^2. It will be seen that this line passes through the total water-gauge curve at a point where it has been recommended the fan should be chosen for that particular system. If this same system had been designed to pass half the volume indicated by the point of intersection of the two curves, the same fan would have the same efficiency but would require to run at half the speed, the total water-gauge or pressure curve being shown dotted in Fig. 557A.

Suppose now that the Job Characteristic curve, when superimposed on a fan curve, intersected it at a point approaching free air condition of the fan, as indicated on Fig. 557C, it would mean that a fan of that size was too small and inefficient for that particular job. In order, therefore, to find a more suitable fan we must find what the volume should be at the required pressure in order that the Job Characteristic may intersect this fan curve between the points of reasonable efficiency previously referred to. In order to do this we must refer back to the statement that $V_2 = \left(\dfrac{A_2}{A_1}\right)^2 V_1$. The curve, Fig. 557C, let us suppose is a typical fan curve for size 1 fan at 1,000 R.P.M. and there is a point in the higher efficiency range at a volume $= 4$, the required volume being given $= 7$ at pressure 3·3. The pressure, it will be seen, at volume 4 on this constant speed curve is 4·1, hence since the pressure varies as the square of the volume, the volume which will pass at the required pressure is given by $\sqrt{\left(\dfrac{3·3}{4·1}\right)} \times 4 = 3·58$ and the speed will be ·897. The size of fan, therefore, to give the required volume at the same efficiency point as chosen on the curve for fan size 1 is given by $7 = \left(\dfrac{\text{Required size}}{1}\right)^2 \times 4$

$$\text{Required size} = \sqrt{\dfrac{7}{4}} = 1·322$$

and the speed of the required fans is given by $\dfrac{1}{1\cdot322} \times 897 = \cdot678$ R.P.M.

Thus the fan should have been chosen in the case considered $1\cdot322$ times the size of the fan for which the curve was made and would run at a speed $\cdot678$ times that of fan size 1.

Similar reasoning to the above can be adopted to find the particular fan size for any system given the volume and the pressure required and the characteristic curves of any fan size.

SYSTEMS OF VENTILATION

We will now proceed with a survey of the various systems of mechanical ventilation which are in practice. The simplest form is that in which air movement in a room or building is assisted by means of a propeller-type fan. This usually takes one of the two forms illustrated in Fig. 558, one of which may be called the " closed type " and the other the " open-bladed " type. Either of these, when suitably designed, will give a positive displacement of air when caused to rotate, driven by means of an engine, belt, or electric motor. These propeller-type fans when used for ventilation purposes are only to be recommended for working against resistances of not more than, say, half an inch water gauge, as they usually have to run at exceptionally high speeds when required to overcome higher pressure. This is undesirable chiefly from the point of view of noise and vibration. In view of the above it is apparent that long duct runs should be avoided in conjunction with this type of fan, but

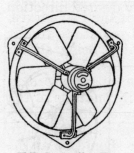 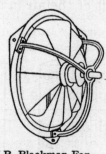

K.B. Streamline Fan,　　K.B. Blackman Fan,
Motor Drive.　　　　　Belt Drive.

Fig. 558.—Open and Closed Propeller-type Fans by
James Keith and Blackman Co. Ltd.

the efficiency can be appreciably improved, particularly with the open-bladed type, by fitting properly shaped entry and discharge ducts, a fact which will be appreciated by reference to the resistance coefficient table mentioned earlier, since we are in effect providing diffusers where sudden contraction and enlargement would otherwise take place. The two efficiency curves shown in Fig. 557 illustrate also the advantage gained by proper diffusion, the higher curve being typical of a fan with correctly designed inlet and outlet cones taken into account.

The diffusers referred to are also illustrated in the sketch. Circumstances may prevent the use of the most efficient type of diffuser, but where possible at least an approximation to it should be fitted, as even a short coned inlet and outlet will improve matters. Properly designed diffusers will make as much as 10 per cent. to 15 per cent. difference to the efficiency of this type of fan.

It should also be mentioned that propeller-type fans are as much as

20 per cent. to 30 per cent. more efficient when exhausting from a room than when blowing into it ; this is a fact which is often overlooked when enquiries are sent to manufacturers, and it is to the customer's benefit that the manufacturer should know the exact conditions under which the fan is intended to work.

HEATING UNITS

The propeller fan is also commonly used in conjunction with a heating unit, the latter usually being placed on the discharge side of the fan, cold air being drawn through the fan and discharged over or through the heating elements to obtain a circulation of warm air in winter time or for special manufacturing processes. The fan and heater are assembled together and called a Unit Heater (see Fig. 558A). The Unit shown is a tubular type for use with hot water or steam as a heating medium. Electric heating elements are also commonly used.

These Unit Heaters are sometimes fitted with fixed or adjustable louvres on the air discharge side to deflect the air in any desired direction. They are sometimes suspended in the middle of rooms and workshops merely to recirculate and warm the air. By means of suitable short duct connections, however, they can, and are, sometimes fixed on an outside wall so that fresh air is drawn through and forced into the space to be ventilated, a further modification being the arrangement of suitable dampers so that air may either be admitted from outside or from the room, or a mixture of both as desired.

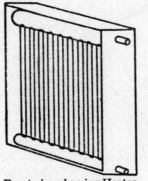 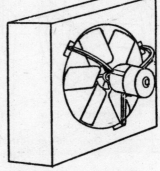

Front view showing Heater.   Reverse view showing Fan.
Fig. 558A.—Typical Unit Heater.

SPECIAL TYPE OF UNIT HEATER

Another type of Unit Heater which is commonly used is one which is usually mounted in a sheet-metal casing and incorporating one or more small centrifugal fans and is arranged to stand on the floor, the air being discharged at a height of about seven to ten feet above the floor line. They are also frequently fitted with cowls to discharge the air in various directions (see Fig. 558B).

The application of Unit Heaters to buildings for ventilation purposes has already been dealt with in the chapter on Hot-air Heating. They are most commonly used in workshops or large store rooms, since they depend on fairly high air velocities to carry the air across the space, the discharged air gradually mixing with that in the space and thence returning by gravity or levitation to the Unit to be recirculated.

Let us consider now the design of a scheme for dealing with the air only, by means of a centralised plant and system of duct-work, to convey it to desired points in a workshop (see Fig. 507C, on page 117).

We will again assume we have a space 100 feet × 50 feet in plan and of 200,000 cu. feet volume, and hence for two air changes per hour 3,333 cu. feet of air will be required per minute.

In a workshop where air noise is not of too great importance it is usual to adopt an air speed in the main ducts up to 2,000 feet per minute ; it should be borne in mind that too high a speed, while requiring smaller ducts and hence a lower first cost for the duct-work, the power required to overcome the friction set up may involve considerable running costs. An air speed in the main duct, therefore, of 2,000 feet per minute should be considered a maximum compatible with reasonable economy. Some installations are designed to maintain this velocity throughout, but an appreciable saving in power can be obtained by reducing the speed in the duct after each outlet and so reducing the power necessary to overcome the

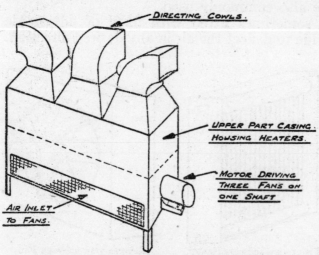

Fig. 558B.—Typical Cabinet-type Unit Heater.

resistance set up. The former method reduces the initial cost of the duct-work, whereas the latter reduces maintenance costs. The system adopted must be decided by the designer. It is usual to arrange a coned diffuser on the outlet branches to reduce the air speed efficiently, down to about half the main duct speed.

Let us consider both methods. First, maintaining constant speed in the main ducts. The plant is to deal with the air for the two changes only, viz. 3,333 cu. feet per minute. Main duct A, leaving the fan, will pass the total volume. Each of the main branches 1,667 cu. feet per minute approximately and at 2,000 feet per minute the areas will be 1·67 sq. feet respectively, and continuing along each branch after each outlet is taken off, there being five outlets to each duct, the duct areas will be :

$$\frac{4}{5} \times \frac{1,667}{2,000} = \cdot667 \text{ sq. feet} \qquad \frac{2}{5} \times \frac{1,667}{2,000} = \cdot333$$

$$\frac{3}{5} \times \frac{1,667}{2,000} = \cdot5 \qquad\qquad \frac{1}{5} \times \frac{1,667}{2,000} = \cdot16$$

and the diameters will be :

Main duct $= 17\frac{1}{2}$ inches.

Each main branch $= 12\frac{1}{4}$ inches.

and after each outlet in succession $11\frac{1}{4}$ inches, $9\frac{3}{4}$ inches, $7\frac{3}{4}$ inches and terminating at $5\frac{1}{2}$ inches with diameters to the nearest quarter of an inch.

Each outlet to be at 45° to the main branch duct and to leave it with a diameter $5\frac{1}{2}$ inches for a short length with a sliding damper fitted as shown in Fig. 558c and then open out to twice the area in a suitable length to about twice the latter diameter, i.e. $7\frac{3}{4}$ inches.

Now let us consider the resistance of such a system. We will assume that from the fan we open out to the heater, the resistance of which with its duct connections is, say, ·25 inch water gauge, thence we will assume a run of main duct of 30 feet with one right-angle bend and a Tee connection to the main branches, the remainder of the system being as tabulated below.

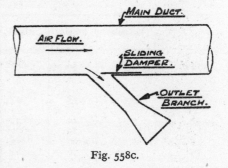

Fig. 558c.

In any system it is, of course, only necessary to compute the pressure required to overcome the resistance in the worst run of duct from the point of view of friction, etc., as it is obvious that if we have sufficient pressure available to overcome that circuit there will be sufficient for any other.

In this particular case the two branches are identical and we need therefore only consider the losses in one of them.

Diameter of duct.	Perimeter.	Length.	Area.	$\cdot003 \frac{P.L.}{A}\left(\frac{V}{1000}\right)^2$	Coefficient.	Total losses.
$17\frac{1}{2}$ inches	4·58	30	1·67	·988		·988
					1 Bend = ·25	·0623
					1 Tee = ·15	·0375
$12\frac{1}{4}$,,	3·20	23	·835	1·08		1·08
					1 Bend = ·25	·0625
$11\frac{1}{4}$,,	2·94	20	·69	·97		·97
$9\frac{3}{4}$,,	2·55	20	·52	1·09		1·09
$7\frac{3}{4}$,,	2·03	20	·328	1·53		1·53
$5\frac{1}{2}$,,	1·44	20	·165	2·15		2·15
					45° set = ·25	·0625
					Diffuser = ·5	·125
					V.H. loss at outlet $=$ $\left(\frac{1000}{4000}\right)^2$	0625

Total pressure for losses in duct $= 8\cdot2205$

Add to this ·25 for heater and we get Total static water-gauge loss $= 8\cdot4705$

To arrive at the total head for the fan we must know approximately the size of fan we propose to employ and thence obtain the velocity head at the fan outlet.

We will assume that the fan has an area at outlet of 1·25 sq. feet, thus accounting for ·45 inch water gauge in velocity head. The total water gauge against which the fan has to work is Static Water Gauge + Velocity Head = 8·92 inches, and assuming an efficiency of 60 per cent., the power required is given by $\dfrac{3,333 \text{ c.f.m.} \times 8·92}{60 \text{ per cent.}} \times \dfrac{1}{6,370} = 7·77$ H.P. since it will be remembered that 1 inch water gauge = 5·2 lb. per sq. foot, and hence 5·2 foot pounds per minute are required to force each cu. foot of air against 1 inch water-gauge pressure, the horse power required $= \dfrac{5·2}{33,000} = \dfrac{1}{6,370}$ per cu. foot.

Now let us turn to the alternative case, the velocities in the ducts being as given in the table below.

Diameter of duct.	Perimeter.	Length.	Area.	Velocity F.P.M.	$·003 \dfrac{P.L.}{A}\left(\dfrac{V}{1000}\right)^2$	Coefficient.	Total losses.
17½ inches	4·58	30	1·67	2000	·988		·988
						1 Bend = ·25	·0625
						1 Tee = ·15	·0375
13 ,,	3·4	23	·927	1800	·825		·825
						1 Bend = ·25	·05
12½ ,,	3·27	20	·835	1600	·588		·588
11 ,,	2·88	20	·667	1500	·59		·59
9¾ ,,	2·55	20	·512	1300	·5		·5
7½ ,,	1·96	20	·304	1100	·465		·465
						45° set = ·25	·019
						V.H. loss at outlet = $\left(\dfrac{1000}{4000}\right)^2$	·0625

Total pressure for losses in duct   = 4·1875
Add to this ·25 for heater and we get Total static water-gauge loss = 4·4375

Assuming the same fan size as before we have a total water gauge = 4·44 + ·45 = 4·89 inches water gauge approximately. Thus it will be seen that the power required for the latter system is only 4¼ H.P., showing a saving in running cost to the extent of 3½ H.P., which is considerable.

Now consider the same duct system as the latter case and let us assume that it is required to add a third leg of ducting in the centre of the room to obtain an additional air change in the shop. A test has been made by means of the Pitot tube and the total head available ascertained at the junction of the two main branches just before the Tee piece and at the fan outlet, thus we should have found that the total head at the fan was 4·89 inches water gauge and at the junction 3·83 inches water gauge gives us the friction head 4·89 — 3·83 = 1·05 water gauge between those two points. We can now design the third leg to set up a resistance of 3·83 inches water gauge. This duct may be straight, and let us assume we have estimated an approximate duct with areas the same as the others and by a similar process as outlined above have found that the resistance when passing a volume 50 per cent. of that already existing, viz. 1,667 cu. feet per minute (to give one more air change) is 3 inches water gauge only. We require that this should have the same resistance as the other two legs, namely, 3·83 inches water gauge, then by means of the formula

$$P_2 = \left(\frac{A_1}{A_2}\right)^2 P_1$$ we find that the areas of the duct must be :

$\sqrt{\dfrac{3}{3·83}}$ of the areas we have estimated = ·885 of the estimated sizes.

Now the main duct and the fan will have to pass 3,333 + 1,667 = 5,000 cu. feet per minute. By deduction we found above that this part of the system was responsible for 1·03 inches water gauge when passing 3,333 cu. feet per minute, hence the new pressure required for this portion to

pass 5,000 cu. feet per minute will be $\left(\dfrac{5,000}{3,333}\right)^2 \times 1·05 = 2·37$ water gauge,

and the fan will now have to pass 5,000 cu. feet per minute against a resistance head 2·37 + 3·83 = 6·2 inches total water gauge and will require 8·1 H.P. to drive it.

We may have another case when a third duct is added in a similar manner to above but still to pass the same volume. Each leg will of course then only be required to pass two-thirds of the volume it had previously to deal with. The resistance up to the Tee piece will be as originally viz. 1·05 inch, and the resistance of any branch will be :

$$\left(\frac{2}{3}\right)^2 \times 3·83 = 1·7 \text{ inches.}$$

The fan duty would then be 3,333 cu. feet per minute at 2·75 inches water gauge, requiring 2·4 H.P. approximately.

For convenience the same typical example has been used to show various methods of modifying the system to suit new requirements, but the same reasoning can be applied to any scheme, however large or complicated the duct system may be. The process is also applicable to exhaust as well as blowing systems, except that it must be borne in mind that when a test is made to ascertain the existing conditions at the fan, the total head of the fan is given by the facing-gauge reading on the inlet side, plus the total or facing-gauge reading on the discharge side, which when discharging direct to atmosphere will equal the velocity head pressure.

While on the subject of exhaust systems it should be mentioned that since in the majority of cases the fan discharges direct to atmosphere it is good practice to fit an efficient diffuser and so regain some of the pressure which would otherwise be lost. With a well-shaped discharge piece in accordance with the particulars given in the table mentioned earlier 75 per cent. of the loss at outlet can be reclaimed.

Diffusers are frequently fitted with an included angle of 7° to 14° opening out to 130 per cent. of the fan outlet size and the saving in pressure loss is given by :

Loss with fan outlet only at velocity $V = \dfrac{V^2}{4,000^2}$ inches water gauge.

With diffuser, loss at diffuser outlet

(A) $= \left(\dfrac{V}{1\cdot3}\right)^2 \dfrac{1}{4,000^2}$ inches water gauge, and 75 per cent. of the difference between this and the above is regained.

(B) Therefore loss in diffuser $= \cdot25\left(\dfrac{V^2\left(1 - \dfrac{1}{1\cdot3^2}\right)}{4,000^2}\right)$ inches water gauge.

Total loss $= A + B$.

With a fan outlet velocity of 2,000 feet per minute this would be $\cdot17$ inch water gauge with diffuser, as compared with $\cdot25$ inch water gauge without diffuser.

EXHAUST SYSTEMS

So far we have considered only schemes for forcing air into, or re-circulating air in a space, assuming that the air change is accomplished by means of leakage out of or into the space. Office buildings, theatres, public halls, and the like are, however, usually of more expensive construction, and such leakage may not be assumed. In such cases the air-blowing systems are supplemented by an exhaust system, the latter extracting an air quantity equal to that put in, or in some cases, to ensure a slight outward movement of air, the exhaust is arranged of sufficient capacity to extract 75 per cent. only of the air supply by the blowing fan. The design of such systems must be carefully considered to obtain a draughtless distribution of the air by arranging the inlet and exhaust grilles or openings in suitable positions.

This chapter is intended only to give some idea of the basic principles employed, the design of the more elaborate schemes adopted in modern large buildings being a subject best left to specialists in that branch of engineering, but some reference should be made to the apparatus employed so that they may be recognised and their function appreciated.

AIR CONDITIONING

Modern ventilation demands that particular attention is paid to the purity and condition of the air supplied. For eliminating much of the solid matter found in the air in large cities and factory towns, many different types of filter are used ; these may be in the form of a particular kind of cloth stretched across a suitable frame, or a series of baffle plates through which the air is drawn, the solid particles impinging on layers of felt ; such filters are made up in units of suitable dimensions so that they can be taken out easily for the dust to be shaken out of them periodically. Similar units are made with baffles formed of sheet metal, expanded metal, ferrules, or lathe turnings which are dipped in a viscous fluid before they are erected so that the air when passing through them leaves most of the solid particles adhering to the fluid ; these units also are taken out periodically and cleaned by immersion in a strong soda-water solution or other solvent and then redipped in the viscous fluid before being replaced.

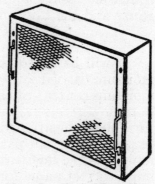

Fig. 558D.—Typical Filter Unit.
Size 18 × 18″ or 21 × 21″

FILTERS

Filters of this type are also obtainable which clean themselves automatically, either by the units being arranged to travel through a bath of viscous fluid, or the filtering surface being stationary the fluid is continually pumped over it.

Another type of air filter is more correctly an air washer ; this takes up considerably more space than the other types of filter but is very effective in eliminating the solid matter from the air and has the advantage that the resistance to air flow remains constant and does not build up as is the case with viscous fluid filters when they get dirty, as they must if they are doing their work properly.

AIR WASHERS

The Air Washer, a diagrammatic sketch of which is given in Fig. 558E, consists of a casing about 7 to 10 feet long, at the outlet end of which baffle plates are fitted, these are called " Eliminator Plates," and it is on these plates that the heavy dust particles impinge. In the remainder of the casing space nozzles are arranged to eject water either with or against the air flow, the nozzle being so designed that when water is forced through it is split up into very small particles. These nozzles are called "Atomising Sprays." The water, usually at a pressure of 25 to 30 lb. per sq. inch, leaves the sprays in a cone-shaped jet which diffuses into a very fine mist, this envelopes the dust particles and on reaching

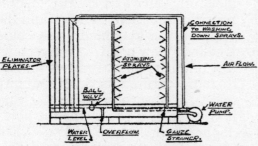

Fig. 558E.—Diagrammatic arrangement of Air Washer and Humidifier.

the eliminator plates adheres to and travels down them into a tank which is kept full of water to a depth of about 12 inches, by means of an overflow pipe, any moisture carried away by the air being made up by means of a ball-valve connection from the main water supply. A small centrifugal pump is employed to force the water through the pipe lines to the sprays, the pump drawing water from the tank; thus the same water is recirculated indefinitely.

Since all the dust and dirt from the air is deposited in the tank it is of course necessary to strain the water through filters made of fine mesh gauze and the tank must be cleaned out periodically.

HUMIDIFIER

It will be noted that reference was made in the above description of moisture carried away by the air, and this brings us to consideration of moisture content of the air for comfort conditions, which is an important item now receiving much more attention in modern ventilation schemes. The above-mentioned Air Washer in ventilation schemes does indeed play an important part in providing a means whereby dry air may pick up moisture, the finely atomised spray being admirable for that purpose. A more correct name for the plant being an Air Washer and Humidifier.

It has been ascertained that human beings, generally speaking, feel comfortable in a temperature of 60° to 65° F., with the air 40 per cent. saturated. A brief explanation is necessary for this statement to be understood.

Air at most times contains a certain amount of moisture, or water vapour, and at a certain temperature is capable of retaining a certain maximum amount of moisture, when the air is said to be " saturated."

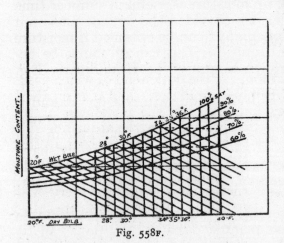

Fig. 558F.

The higher the temperature the more moisture will it hold; if, therefore, we have a quantity of air which is just saturated and its temperature is reduced by some means it will in time deposit some of the moisture, since at a lower temperature it cannot hold so much and the temperature at which this occurs is called "dew point"; conversely, if a quantity of saturated air has its temperature raised without any means of absorbing more moisture it will reach a state when it holds less than its maximum capacity at the higher temperature and will then be only partly saturated and this condition is expressed as a percentage.

The function of an Air Humidifier may be understood to some degree by a consideration of the following.

Air in winter time may have a temperature of 40° F., and we will assume is 60 per cent. saturated with moisture. In passing through a Humidifier of good design of the type described, it will pick up moisture until it is 90 per cent. saturated, but in doing so it will have reduced in temperature slightly, because to change water into water vapour requires a certain amount of heat, and this heat, if not supplied by other means, will be taken from the air, so reducing its temperature. When air absorbs moisture in this manner, if it could saturate itself, it would fall to a temperature called the " Wet Bulb " temperature, which in this case would be 35° F. Since, however, it will only be 90 per cent. saturated it will fall only to a temperature of 36° F., and its " dew point " would be about 34° F. These conditions can be shown graphically, as in Fig. 558F. If then the air is heated again to 40° F., it will be approximately 80 per cent. saturated.

To obtain the conditions originally stated, viz. 60° F., 40 per cent. saturated, it will therefore be necessary to add more heat to the air, but this must be done partly before or in the Humidifier and partly after, and must be so arranged that the air on leaving the Humidifier has a " dew point " the same as for air at 60° 40 per cent. saturated, which is about 30° F., and if 90 per cent. saturated, will have a temperature 37·5° F. The air enters with a " dew point " 34° F.; it therefore has to be heated up to 37·5° F. before passing through the sprays, further heat has to be added with the spray water to vaporise it, as it is absorbed by the air in order to maintain the temperature at 37·5° F., then on leaving the Humidifier it is further heated up to 60° F., when the moisture content will be 40 per cent.

The capacity that air has to pick up moisture is useful in summer time to obtain a cooling effect in buildings, as, provided the outside air is not already too moist, a greater feeling of comfort can be obtained if moisture is added to it and its temperature dropped. This can of course be accomplished by passing the air through a spray-type Humidifier. E.g. Suppose we have an outside temperature of 85° F., and 30 per cent. saturated, this is equivalent to a Wet Bulb temperature of 60° F. and if saturated to 90 per cent. would have a temperature of 62° F. It would also probably rise a further 5° F. in passing through the duct system and would finally diffuse into the rooms at about 70° F., when it would have a humidity of approximately 72 per cent., which is a more comfortable condition for most people in this country. This is known as " Evaporative Cooling."

It has been seen that specified conditions can be obtained by suitable arrangements of heaters, in a similar manner definite conditions can be obtained by assisting the natural cooling by employing refrigerated water in the sprays and so reducing the air below its " dew point," causing moisture to be deposited.

Air humidification is too great a subject to be gone into further, but it is hoped that the above brief description will serve to give some idea of what happens in this important piece of apparatus.

Air heaters used with or without a Humidifier are usually in the form of a number of vertical or horizontal steel or copper tubes fitted into headers at either end, and pipe connections are made to these headers.

The tubes may be plain or grilled, i.e. fitted with fins, to obtain greater heating surface. The heating medium may be steam or hot water. There are also many types of electric heaters.

MISCELLANEOUS

Where heaters are installed it is advisable to have some form of filter preceding them, as otherwise they soon become clogged with dust and lose a large percentage of their heating capacity ; they are also difficult to clean.

Duct-work is usually manufactured from black or galvanised iron sheets, occasionally of copper, and main ducts in large buildings are frequently formed in brickwork or concrete by the builders ; the latter should be carefully pointed and rendered smooth to reduce the friction as much as possible.

In designing schemes for large buildings such as theatres and public halls many things have to be taken into consideration in addition to the heat losses in winter or heat gains in summer ; these include :

Heat given off by people (a good average figure from this source being 400 B.Th.U. per person per hour).

Heat given off by lighting units.

Heat given off by apparatus.

In fact where large numbers of people are present, the problem of ventilation is chiefly a question of cooling even in winter.

Mention has already been made of the types of fans used in ventilation plants. The propeller types are most commonly used for exhausting purposes and are fixed in a wall or window frame, or they can be arranged equally well with their spindles vertical. The simplest and most effective method of mounting them is on a stout hard-wood board held in a wood frame, which can either be built into the wall or supported on roof timbers, and where absence of noise and vibration is desirable, pads or rings of piano felt may be inserted between the metal frame of the fan and the woodwork, felt washers also being inserted under the bolt heads.

The centrifugal fan is used for both exhausting and blowing where any appreciable resistance has to be overcome.

For reasonably quiet working the top speed of the blades must be limited ; this, however, varies with the design of the fan and the outlet velocity should not exceed 2,000 feet per minute. Further to quieten these fans they are frequently mounted on cork, felt, or special anti-vibration beds to damp down any vibration in the fan casing or the driving motor. It is also an advantage to drive the fan through a belt or rope drive in order to prevent engine or motor noise travelling along the shaft of the fan and so into the duct system.

Noise emanating from the fan can often be reduced by lining the ducts, or at least part of them, with felt or other special sound-absorbing material.

Many of the more elaborate installations embodying Humidifiers, Heaters, and Coolers are controlled automatically, so that with variation of outside or inside conditions instruments are operated which close or open dampers or valves; these may be operated electrically or by compressed air or oil lines.

The arrangement of such automatic control is a matter for specialists in the design of such schemes, as they have to be carefully considered in conjunction with the design of the particular ventilation scheme and the conditions required to be maintained. The chief components employed in automatic control systems are " Thermostats," which are affected by temperature, " Hygrostats," which are affected by air humidity, " Relay Valves " or " Electric Relay Contactors," " Diaphragm Valves," for compressed air or oil systems, " Magnetic Valves," for electric systems, and specially balanced dampers.

CHAPTER XII

GAS FITTING

THE " THERM "—TOOLS—BRITISH STANDARD PIPE FITTINGS—SERVICE PIPES—
METERS—Meter Sizes—Fixing Meters—Carcassing—FIXING APPLIANCES—Gas Cookers—
Gas Water Heaters—Storage Heaters—GEYSERS—Multi-point or Distributing Geysers—
Pressure Geysers with Automatic Pressure-operated Valves—Geysers having Broken Feeds and
Pressure-operated Valves—Geysers with Broken Feed and Non-pressure-operated Valves—
Geysers with Broken Feed and Interlocking Caps only—Charging with Water—Danger of
Attaching Hose to Certain Geysers—Stop Cocks—FLUE EQUIPMENT—Position of Baffler—
Terminals—GAS FIRES—" Inset " Gas Fire—Self-contained Gas Fire—Flues for Gas Fires—
Estimating Correct Size of Gas Fire—Adjustment of Gas Fires—Connecting up the Gas Fire—
Built-in Gas Fires—Flueless Heaters—PORTABLE HEATERS—MISCELLANEOUS DOMESTIC
APPLIANCES—GAS-LIGHTING FITTINGS—REMOTE CONTROL OF LIGHTING BURNERS.

GAS is steadily taking the place of coal in all types of buildings—in the artisan's home as well as in the large mansion, the commercial house, the restaurant, the factory, and public institution. No book of this nature would be complete, therefore, without a chapter dealing with one of the most important branches of the work of the plumber.

Before coming to the practical side of gas-fitting work it will be well to explain briefly the system of charge for gas which is now almost universally adopted throughout the country.

THE " THERM " AS THE BASIS OF CHARGE

The " therm " system of charge was adopted by Parliament (in the Gas Regulation Act, 1920) on the initiative of the Board of Trade, acting on the recommendations of the Fuel Research Board. Its purpose was to provide in the interests of the consumers a basis of charge suited to the modern conditions of gas consumption.

The utility of gas to-day, whether used for lighting, for heating, or for power purposes, depends directly upon its heating (or calorific) value ; not, as in former years, upon its " candle power." The value of a cubic foot of gas to the consumer therefore depends directly upon the number of heat units that quantity will develop when consumed. Each undertaking is required to declare what number of heat units per cubic foot the gas supplied by it contains. This is called the " declared calorific value of the gas."

The " heat unit " in this country is known as the British thermal unit (= 1 B.Th.U.). This is the quantity of heat required to increase by 1 degree Fahrenheit the temperature of 1 lb. of water. A " therm " is 100,000 British thermal units. Assuming the calorific value declared by a gas undertaking to be 500 B.Th.U.s, this means that each cubic foot of the gas supplied by that undertaking will develop not less than 500 British thermal units when burned. A " thousand cubic feet," the old basis of charge, would therefore represent at least (1,000 × 500 =) 500,000 B.Th.U.s, or 5 therms.

To ascertain the number of therms used, the number of cubic feet registered by the meter should be multiplied by the declared calorific value and divided by 100,000. For example :

8,000 cu. feet × 500 = 4,000,000, which divided by 100,000 = 40 therms.

To convert " therms " into cubic feet, the number of therms should be multiplied by 100,000 and divided by the declared calorific value of the gas. For example :

40 therms × 100,000 = 4,000,000, which divided by 500 = 8,000 cu. feet.

TOOLS

One of the first essentials in the carrying out of gas-fitting work is the provision of a suitable tool kit. This kit must not be too unwieldy or heavy, in view of the fact that it has to be carried about ; on the other hand, it must be sufficiently complete to enable all work on pipes up to, say, 1 inch diameter to be done satisfactorily and quickly.

One of the London gas undertakings has spent many months studying this matter in all its details, and as a result the following is a list of the tools with which its fitters are now usually provided :

Bag, tool.
Basket, tool.
Bit, brace, Jennings's, twist, size $\frac{3}{8}$ inch.
 ,,   ,,   ,,   ,,   ,, $\frac{5}{8}$ inch.
 ,,   ,,   ,,   ,,   ,, $\frac{7}{8}$ inch.
 ,,   ,,   ,,   ,,   ,, $1\frac{1}{8}$ inch.
 ,,   ,,   ,,   spoon, ,, $\frac{1}{4}$ inch.
 ,,   ,,   ,,   screwdriver, size $\frac{3}{8}$ inch.
 ,,   ,,   ,,   rose, size $\frac{1}{2}$ inch.
Box white lead and grease, size $3\frac{1}{4}$ inches × 2 inches × 1 inch.
Bags, cement and plaster, 2.
Bottle, oil, round, size $\frac{1}{2}$ pint.
 ,,   ,,   ,,   ,, 1   ,,
Brace, carpenter's ratchet, with ball-bearing head, size A, 8-inch sweep.
Bradawl, No. 11, size $\frac{1}{8}$ inch.
Broach, No. 1, gauge 34 P.G.
 ,,   ,, 2   ,, 48   ,,
 ,,   ,, 3   ,, 50   ,,
 ,,   ,, 4   ,, 60   ,,
Brush, paint, sash tool, size No. 3.
 ,,   ,, flat enamel, size $1\frac{1}{2}$ inch wide.

Can, oil feeder, conical, capacity $\frac{1}{2}$ pint, with screw needle cap.
Can, paint, capacity 2 pint, with lid with hole for brush and handle.
Case for candles, tapers, and solder.
    ,,   ,, broaches and broach holder, brass, with screw top.
Chisel, Rawlplug 8, 10, & 12.
    ,,   ,,   ejector.
    ,,   ,,   holder, No. 14.
Chisel, steel, flat, $\frac{3}{4}$ inch, octagonal, length 8 inches.
    ,,   ,,   ,, $\frac{3}{4}$ inch,   ,,   ,, 18 inches.
    ,,   ,, crosscut, $\frac{1}{2}$ inch octagonal, length 7 inches.
    ,,   ,, plugging, flat, $\frac{1}{2}$ inch octagonal, length 7 inches.
    ,, wood, flat, octagonal steel handle, size $\frac{7}{8}$ inch, length 10 inches.
    ,, wood,   ,,   ,,   ,,   ,, size $\frac{1}{2}$ inch, length 10 inches.
    ,, wood, gouge, octagonal steel handle, size $\frac{3}{4}$ inch, length 10 inches.
    ,, combination floorboard and tack-lifter, length 12 inches.
Combination tool, fold-up 5-tool pattern.
Cutters, 3-wheel rigid, No. 1 Barnes, size $\frac{1}{8}$ inch to 1 inch.
Drill, twist, with square, tapered, or round shank to fit hand braces, size $\frac{5}{32}$ inch.
Ditto   ditto   size $\frac{7}{32}$ inch.
Ditto   ditto   ,, $\frac{9}{32}$ inch.
Ditto   ditto   ,, $\frac{11}{32}$ inch.
Driver, pipe hook, length 6 inches, with $\frac{5}{8}$ inch $\times$ $\frac{3}{16}$ inch blunt face.
File, rasp, $\frac{1}{2}$-round cabinet, size 10 inches, with 5-inch handle.
    ,, half-round, bastard cut, size 10 inches, with 5-inch handle.
    ,, flat, Dreadnought, smooth cut, size 14 inches, with $5\frac{1}{2}$-inch handle.
File, cloth, piece on batten, size 4 inches $\times$ $1\frac{1}{2}$ inch.
Gauge, pressure, in case, size $2\frac{1}{2}$ inches $\times$ $9\frac{1}{2}$ inches $\times$ $1\frac{3}{8}$ inch.
Gimlet, size $\frac{3}{16}$ inch.
    ,,   ,, $\frac{7}{32}$ inch.
    ,, bellhanger's, length 2 feet, size $\frac{5}{16}$ inch.
Grips, domino type, size 6 inches.
    ,,   ,,   ,,   ,, 9 inches.
    ,,   ,,   ,,   ,, 12 inches.
Hammer, crosspane, $1\frac{1}{2}$ lb., with handle.
Handle, keyhole saw.
Holdall for drills, taps, etc.
Holder, broach.
Knife, clasp.
Lamp, electric, pocket.
    ,, spirit, with mouth blowpipe, and 2 feet rubber tube.
Pliers, 2-hole, size 6 inches.
    ,, bent nose.
Punch, nail, Starrett, length 5 inches, point $\frac{3}{16}$ inch.
    ,, centre, Starrett, length 4 inches, point $\frac{1}{8}$ inch.
Reamer, burr remover, size $\frac{3}{4}$ inch to 2 inches, Hall's No. 2.

Rule, 2 feet, steel, folding two-section, with sunk figures.

Saw, hand, carpenter's, 12-inch blade.

,, keyhole, narrow, length 9 inches, teeth 10 to inch.

2 spikes, $\frac{3}{8}$-inch round steel, 3-sq. tapering point, length 9 inches.

Screwdriver, length 6 inches, blade $\frac{1}{4}$ inch.

,, ,, 14 inches, ,, $\frac{3}{8}$-inch.

Snips, straight pattern, size 12 inches.

Sling (ratline), for meters, etc., 2 yards.

Stocks and dies, iron, solid Walworth, size $\frac{1}{8}$-inch to 1 inch.

,, ,, ,, brass die, with $\frac{1}{2}$-inch brass gauge thread to fit No. 0 Walworth stock.

Stocks and dies, frame for No. 1 Walworth stock to hold $\frac{1}{2}$-inch brass die.

Tap, taper, Whitworth thread, size $\frac{3}{16}$ inch.

,, ,, ,, ,, ,, $\frac{1}{4}$ inch.

,, ,, ,, ,, ,, $\frac{5}{16}$ inch.

,, plug, ,, ,, ,, $\frac{3}{16}$ inch.

,, ,, ,, ,, ,, $\frac{1}{4}$ inch.

,, ,, ,, ,, ,, $\frac{5}{16}$ inch.

Tongs, Stillson, size 14 inches ($\frac{1}{4}$ inch to $1\frac{3}{4}$ inch), with steel handle.

,, ,, ,, 18 inches ($\frac{1}{4}$ inch to $2\frac{1}{2}$ inches), with steel handle.

,, pipe-bending (Clark's or pipe and socket).

Trowel, size 5 inches.

Tubing, rubber, size 1 inch, 3-feet length.

Turnpin, diameter 2 inches, length 3 inches, straight taper to nil.

Vice, Samson, size up to 1 inch.

Wrench for taps, adjustable, to take up to $\frac{3}{8}$-inch.

Work on particularly large installations would, of course, involve the provision of additional tools, and probably a bench and a forge ; but for all ordinary purposes the kit described above will be found satisfactory, provided always that the tools are kept in good condition.

BRITISH STANDARD PIPE FITTINGS

Plate X shows the wrought-iron and British Standard Malleabilised cast-iron pipe fittings used in gas-fitting work and the correct terms by which they should be described. All tubes and fittings must be screwed with the British Standard Pipe taper thread and hemp must on no account be used when making screwed joints.

All fittings should bear the stamp of the British Standards Institution, which is a guarantee that they are made to quality and to gauge.

SERVICE PIPES

The " service " pipe is generally the pipe which is taken from the gas main in the roadway to the inlet side of the meter. In some large buildings with numerous meters on various floors—such as blocks of flats, offices, and the like—the " service " pipe is that which is taken from the main to inside the building line.   The pipe which is taken from the outlet end of the " service " pipe up to the various floors is called the " rising main," and branches from this to the inlets of the various meters are usually termed " extensions."

With these few elementary definitions, some practical points on the laying of services may be considered.

Size of Service Pipe.—The first point which has to be decided when laying a service to a building is its size, and in this connection two aspects must be considered.

(1) The service should be of sufficient size to supply satisfactorily not only just the gas apparatus which will be installed in the building at the outset, but the apparatus which may be required in the future by the occupants.   It is always advisable to err (if one errs at all) on the large side, rather than to discover at a later date that the road has to be taken up in order to provide a larger service.

(2) The length of the service pipe.   This is important, for it must be remembered that the amount of gas which pipes will discharge at the desired pressure decreases for every foot run above a maximum advisable length.   These lengths are as follows :

Maximum length for a 1-inch service,   40 feet.
         ,,   ,,   ,, $1\frac{1}{4}$,,   ,,   60 ,,
         ,,   ,,   ,, $1\frac{1}{2}$,,   ,,   80 ,,
         ,,   ,,   ,, 2 ,,   ,,   100 ,,
         ,,   ,,   ,, 3 ,,   ,,   150 ,,

That is to say, no 1-inch service should be longer than 40 feet.   If a longer service is necessary, a pipe of larger diameter must be used. Similarly with $1\frac{1}{4}$-inch barrel, the maximum length for a service pipe should not exceed 60 feet, and so on.   This rule need not always be applied quite so strictly to runs of internal piping,[1] but for service pipes, on which the whole supply to the building depends, the rule should never be broken.

For even small houses the service pipe should never be less than 1 inch.   Larger services are, of course, necessary for many houses, and the point made above regarding the maximum permissible length of service pipe of any given size should always be borne in mind.

When the distance from the main to the meter and the total maximum hourly consumption of all appliances which are to be installed and may later be installed in the building are known, the size of the service pipe may be calculated from Tables LXXXVIII and LXXXIX and the explanations which accompany them, given on pages 195 and 196.

Steam weight wrought iron or mild steel tubing coated with bitumen is recommended for use on service work, as it minimises the possibilities

_____
[1] See note at foot of table on page 195.

PLATE X

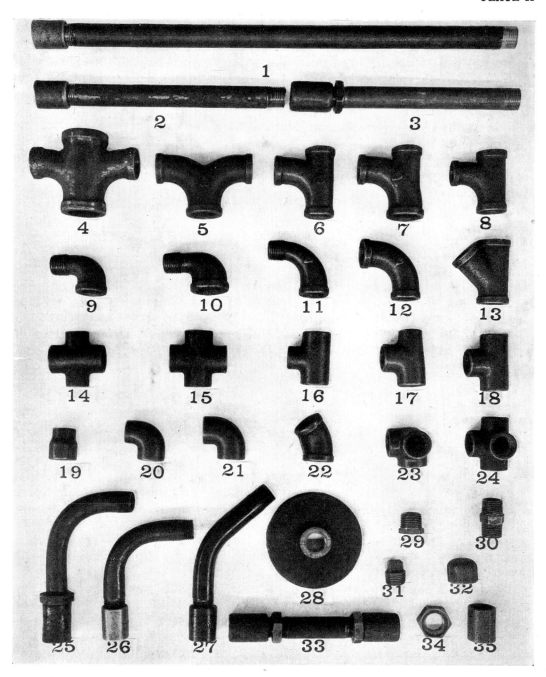

Some of the most commonly used gas-barrel fittings. 1. Wrought-iron Tubing from 2 ft. and upwards ; 2. Wrought-iron Tubing pieces 12 ins. to 23½ ins. long ; 3. Connector ; 4. Reducing Pitcher Cross ; 5. Reducing Twin Elbow ; 6. Pitcher Tee ; 7. Reducing Pitcher Tee : Run and Outlet ; 8. Reducing Pitcher Tee : Outlet only ; 9. Male and Female (Street) Elbow ; 10. Male and Female (Street) Elbow : Reducing ; 11. Bend : Male and Female ; 12. Bend ; 13. Lateral Y Tee ; 14. Equal Reducing Cross ; 15. Cross ; 16. Reducing Tee ; 17. Reducing Tee : On run ; 18. Tee ; 19. Reducing Socket ; 20. Reducing Elbow ; 21. Elbow ; 22. 45° Elbow ; 23. Side Outlet Elbow ; 24. Side Outlet Cross ; 25. Connector Bend ; 26. Bend ; 27. Spring Bend ; 28. Flange ; 29. Hexagon Bush ; 30. Hexagon Nipple ; 31. Plug ; 32. Cap ; 33. Double Connector ; 34. Back Nut ; 35. Socket.

GAS-BARREL FITTINGS.

of corrosion. The joints should be made with thread paint only. Hemp must never be used on British Standard Taper threads. With a view to reducing the number of joints, long pieces of barrel should be used. Elbows should never be fitted, bends being the proper fittings whenever required. Before the piping is screwed up, every length, bend, and connection should be examined to see not only that it is sound, but that it is clear of obstructions.

A service pipe must, whenever possible, have a fall towards the *main*. When this is not possible, small services must have a tee fitted opposite the point at which the pipe enters the building, and a connector must be extended from the tee outlet to a trap made up of bends. A length of pipe must then be brought up from the trap, and should be plugged at a point where a pump can conveniently be attached (see Fig. 538). When the service is of 3 inches diameter or above, a siphon should be fixed at the lowest part of the service *outside* the premises.

The part of the service or rising main which is inside the premises, as well as any extensions from the rising main, should be left exposed or easily accessible throughout their entire length, whenever possible.

When there is a side entrance to the house, the usual plan is to run the service along the path leading to it. It should be run at the side of the forecourt in the case of houses without a side entrance ; it should not be taken under the paved walk leading up to the house. The pipe should also be run as far as possible from the electric cable, if one is being installed.

TABLE LXXXVIII

Flows in Cu. Feet per Hour Corresponding with $\frac{1}{10}$ Inch Loss of Pressure between the Ends of Various Lengths of Straight Pipe of Nominal Diameter ranging from $\frac{1}{8}$ Inch to 3 Inches.

(Sp. gr. of gas, 0·50. Actual diameters are given in " Flow of Gas in Pipes," *Inst. Proc. Gas Eng.*, 1923.)

Length of Pipe. (Feet.)	Nominal Diameter of Pipe. (Inches.)									
	$\frac{1}{8}$	$\frac{1}{4}$	$\frac{3}{8}$	$\frac{1}{2}$	$\frac{3}{4}$	1	$1\frac{1}{4}$	$1\frac{1}{2}$	2	3
10	3	14	33	72	130	240	—	—	—	—
20	—	7	18	49	88	165	340	530	—	—
30	—	—	12	38	70	130	270	420	890	—
40	—	—	—	29	60	110	235	360	770	2240
50	—	—	—	23	52	98	210	320	680	1980
60	—	—	—	—	47	89	190	290	620	1800
70	—	—	—	—	40	81	170	260	560	1630
80	—	—	—	—	—	75	160	240	520	1510
90	—	—	—	—	—	71	150	230	490	1420
100	—	—	—	—	—	—	140	215	460	1340
150	—	—	—	—	—	—	110	170	370	1070
200	—	—	—	—	—	—	96	150	310	900
250	—	—	—	—	—	—	—	130	280	795
300	—	—	—	—	—	—	—	115	250	710

Bends and tees can be allowed for by adding to the over-all net length of pipe the lengths given in the table below. The gross length thus obtained is the length given in the table above.

When the service has been laid and before it is connected to the main, it should be very carefully tested before the trench is filled in. Should the main not be ready for connection, the service should be left capped near the main. The method of testing is to pump air into the service and attach a pressure gauge. If the pressure falls the service is unsound.

TABLE LXXXIX

Nominal Diameter of Pipe. (Inches.)	Addition to be made to Over-all Length of a Pipe (in Feet) for Increased Resistance introduced by Fittings.		
	Elbows.	Tees.	90° Bends.
$\frac{1}{8}$ to 1 . . .	2	2	1
$1\frac{1}{4}$ to $1\frac{1}{2}$ . . .	3	3	$1\frac{1}{2}$
2	5	5	2
3	8	8	3

The following considerations explain why it has been found convenient to relate all the figures in the table to a standard pressure loss of one-tenth. As a general rule the maximum pressure difference between a main and any gas-consuming appliance supplied from it should not exceed (say) five-tenths, which may be allocated thus : one-tenth to the service, two-tenths to the meter, and two-tenths to the piping between the meter and the gas-consuming appliance.

In ordinary house supplies the difference in altitude between the main and the gas appliance farthest from it will increase by one or two-tenths the pressure available for producing flow in the pipes. Thus, in general, there will be three or four-tenths available for overcoming the frictional resistances of the pipes from the meter ; and as the pipe between the meter and the farthest gas-consuming appliance is usually divided into three or four sections of different diameters, it will be seen that one-tenth loss can be allowed in each section at the maximum rate of flow in that section.

In practice the length of a particular section of pipe is generally known ; and it is required to find the diameter corresponding to a maximum rate of flow, which depends upon the appliance or appliances supplied through it. Where, as explained above, a loss of pressure of one-tenth is appropriate, the table can be used directly for finding the diameter, or, alternatively, if the diameter is known, for finding the corresponding rate of flow.

In some circumstances, however, a greater loss of pressure than one-tenth may be allowable (e.g. in a pipe from the outlet of a meter supplying a geyser only). The necessary correction can then be made in one of the two following ways :

(1) Divide the gross length of the pipe (i.e. the net length plus additions for bends, etc.) by the allowable loss of pressure in tenths, and thus obtain the gross length corresponding to the standard loss of one-tenth. This length can then be used in the table.

For example : Required to find the rate of flow in a 1-inch pipe 40 feet in length (gross) with a pressure loss of four-tenths.

$$\frac{40}{4} = 10$$

Flow in table corresponding to 1-inch pipe 10 feet long = 240 cu. feet per hour.

(2) Alternatively, the gross length can be applied direct to the table, and the following corrections made to the rates of flow found from the table.

For a loss of pressure of two-tenths, add 50 per cent. to flows in table.
" " " " three-tenths, add 80 per cent. to flows in table.
" " " " four-tenths, add 120 per cent. to flows in table.

The results obtained will be only approximately correct, but near enough for practical purposes.

Note.—The figures in heavy type in Table LXXXVIII are the maximum advisable lengths of pipe of the size indicated which should be run *beyond* the meter. The maximum advisable lengths for *service* pipes are given on page 194.

METERS

The service having been laid, the main cock should be fitted in a readily accessible position, so that the householder can manipulate it, when necessary. One of the next points to be considered is the position

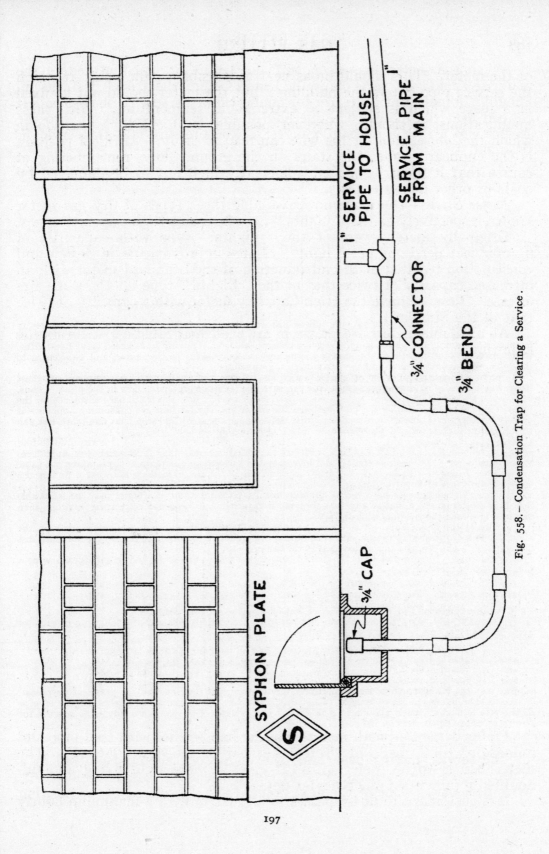

SYPHON PLATE

S

¾" CAP

1" SERVICE PIPE TO HOUSE

SERVICE PIPE FROM MAIN

1"

¾" CONNECTOR

¾" BEND

Fig. 558.— Condensation Trap for Clearing a Service.

of the meter. This should be as near as possible to the point at which the service pipe enters the building ; but the meter should not be fixed in a place which is subject to extremes in temperature. With these qualifications, it should, wherever possible, be fixed in a position in which the householder or his wife can read it easily. An ideal position is the cupboard under the stairs on the ground floor, remembering of course that it must be placed sufficiently high not to be damaged by coals or other heavy objects.

Meter Sizes.—There are now available three types of dry gas meter known respectively as the " Lights," Standard and High Capacity types.

Originally meters were of the " Lights " type with capacities of 6 cubic feet per hour per " light." Later improvements in design and construction resulted in the introduction of the Standard meter with an increased capacity of twice that of the " Lights " type for the same size of case. Now we have the High Capacity meter with a capacity of twice that of the Standard.

All available meters are shown in order of their rated capacities in the following tables :

TABLE XC SHOWING THE PRINCIPAL SIZES OF DRY METERS, IN ORDER OF CAPACITIES WITH UNION CONNECTIONS

Maximum Capacity per Hour. Cubic Feet.	Size of Case.	Classification.	Size of Caps, Linings or Bosses.	Bore of Linings and size of lead.	Height to top of Unions.	Width Outside Caps.	Depth Back to Front.
				Inches	Inches	Inches	Inches
25	3-lt.	3 Light	3-lt.	⅝	15½	11¼	8½
40	3-lt.	No. 2 Standard	3-lt.	⅝	15½	11¼	8½
45	5-lt.	5 Light	5-lt.	¾	17	13	9⅜
60	5-lt.	No. 3 Standard	5-lt.	¾	17	13	9⅜
80	3-lt.	80 cubic feet p.h. H.C.	5-lt.	¾	15½	11¼	8½
80	10-lt.	10 Light	10-lt.	1	19⅝	14⅝	11¼
120	10-lt.	No. 4 Standard	10-lt.	1	19⅜	14⅝	11¼
120	5-lt.	120 cubic feet p.h. H.C.	10-lt.	1	17⅜	13¼	9
150	20-lt.	20 Light	20-lt.	1¼	24	18½	14⅜
210	30-lt.	30 Light	30-lt.	1½	27½	21¼	16⅜
210	20-lt.	No. 5 Standard	20-lt.	1¼	24	18½	14⅜
210	30-lt.	No. 5 Standard	20-lt.	1¼	27⅜	21¼	16⅜
240	10-lt.	240 cubic feet p.h. H.C.	20-lt.	1¼	20¼	15½	10¾
300	50-lt.	50 Light	50-lt.	1½	33	25½	20¾
360	60-lt.	60 Light	60-lt.	1½	34	27½	21⅜
375	50-lt.	No. 5a Standard	50-lt.	1½	33	25½	20¾
420	60-lt.	No. 6 Standard	50-lt.	1½	34	27¼	20½
420	20-lt.	420 cubic feet p.h. H.C.	50-lt.	1½	24	19	13½
480	80-lt.	80 Light	80-lt.	2	39½	31⅜	24¾
600	100-lt.	100 Light	100-lt.	2	42¼	32¾	26
700	30-lt.	700 cubic feet p.h. H.C.	100-lt.	2	28	22¼	15

Fixing Meters.—Small meters may be fixed either with lead pipe and unions or with a malleable iron meter bar as shown in Plate XI. The meter bar is to be preferred, as it gives a more rigid fixing and undoubtedly presents a much neater appearance.

It is customary to fit by-passes to all meters with a maximum hourly

PLATE XI

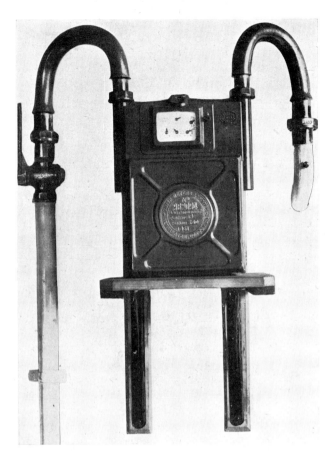

METHOD OF FITTING METER WITH LEAD CONNECTIONS.

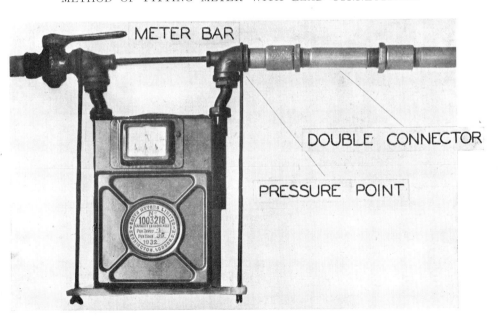

METER BAR

DOUBLE CONNECTOR

PRESSURE POINT

METER FITTED WITH METER BAR.

TABLE XCI SHOWING THE PRINCIPAL SIZES OF DRY METERS, IN ORDER OF CAPACITIES WITH FLANGED CONNECTIONS

Maximum Capacity per Hour. Cubic Feet.	Size of Case.	Classification.	Size of Loose Flanges.	Bore of Flanges.	Height over-all.	Width over Flanges.	Depth Back to Front.
			Inches up	Inches	Inches	Inches	Inches
900	150-lt.	150 Light	F. 2	F. 3	$51\frac{5}{8}$	$39\frac{1}{4}$	28
1200	200-lt.	200 Light	F. 2	F. 3	$56\frac{3}{8}$	45	33
1200	60-lt.	1200 cubic feet p.h. H.C.	F. 2	F. 3	29	$30\frac{1}{2}$	$18\frac{3}{8}$
1500	250-lt.	250 Light	F. 3	F. 3	$58\frac{1}{4}$	45	33
1800	300-lt.	300 Light	F. 3	F. 3	63	$48\frac{1}{2}$	$38\frac{1}{4}$
1800	80-lt.	1800 cubic feet p.h. H.C.	F. 3	F. 3	$36\frac{1}{2}$	35	$22\frac{1}{2}$
2400	400-lt.	400 Light	F. 3	F. 4	$71\frac{1}{2}$	56	41
3000	150-lt.	3000 cubic feet p.h. H.C.	F. 3	F. 4	$43\frac{1}{2}$	$39\frac{1}{4}$	$25\frac{1}{2}$
3000	500-lt.	500 Light	F. 4	F. 6	$79\frac{1}{2}$	58	46
6000	250-lt.	6000 cubic feet p.h. H.C.	F. 4	F. 6	54	48	$30\frac{1}{4}$

capacity of 600 cubic feet or more. In addition it is advisable, and sometimes necessary, to fit by-passes to meters, irrespective of their size, which are installed on premises where it is imperative that the supply of gas shall never be allowed to fail. This applies to hospitals, nursing homes, railway signal boxes and signals, incubators and many industrial operations.

Where the meter to be by-passed is fitted with brass unions for lead pipe, the usual method of fitting the by-pass is to connect the inlet and outlet pipes together in iron barrel. Two additional main cocks are required, one on the by-pass and the other on the outlet of the meter. All meters with by-passes should be fitted with these three valves or main cocks known as the inlet, outlet and by-pass controls.

Normally the inlet and outlet valves are open and the by-pass valve is closed and sealed. Should the meter fail for any reason and cease to pass gas, the by-pass valve may be opened and the gas supply restored. Also, should the meter at any time require to be changed, this can be done without interfering with the supply of gas, by first opening the by-pass control and then closing the inlet and outlet controls to the meter. Having thus shut off the gas on either side of the meter, it is possible to change it or carry out any repairs without causing annoyance to the consumer.

In order to prevent undue advantage of these facilities being taken by unscrupulous or unauthorised persons it is necessary to seal the by-pass control.

The actual position of the by-pass is determined by the position of the meter and the run of the inlet and outlet connections. With a meter fixed on the floor it is usual to carry the by-pass above it, although where vertical distance is limited it may be carried round the meter horizontally. Where the meter is fixed on a wall it is often convenient to run the by-pass underneath, but whatever method is adopted it is important to bear in mind the following points:

(1) The by-pass and connections are invariably of considerable weight,

and on no account must this weight be permitted to act directly on the connections of the meter.

(2) Provision must be made for the meter to be exchanged easily should the occasion arise ; and in this connection it must be borne in mind that the new meter may be of different dimensions from the old one.

Fig. 559 shows the method of fitting a large meter with a by-pass.

All meters, both main meters and check meters, should be provided

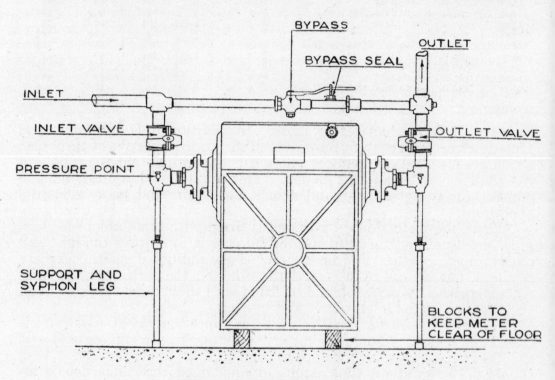

Fig. 559.—By-pass for large meter.

on the outlet connection with a small pressure nipple for the purpose of taking pressures and testing the meter.

Carcassing.—Those pipes and fittings extending from the outlet of the meter to the point or points of attachment to the gas-consuming appliances are termed the carcass. All new premises should be carcassed in such a manner that pipes are laid not only to every point where it is known that gas applicances will be fixed immediately, but to every point at which it is probable that gas appliances may be required in the future.

All such carcasses should be composed of either wrought iron or malleabilised cast iron to the British Standards Institution's Specification No. 154. Where brass tubing is used for the conveyance of gas from the carcass pipe to the gas appliance it should be to the following gauges for the respective diameters :

$\frac{3}{8}$ inch nominal diameter to be $\frac{12}{32}$ inch in actual outside diameter and 18 S.W.G.

$\frac{1}{2}$ inch nominal diameter to be $\frac{33}{64}$ inch in actual outside diameter and 17 S.W.G.

$\frac{5}{8}$ inch nominal diameter to be $\frac{21}{32}$ inch in actual outside diameter and 17 S.W.G.

This is to enable the brass tubing to be screwed to the British Standard Pipe thread instead of the now obsolete " brass " thread of 26 threads per inch. All tubes, couplers and fittings, both male and female, whether of wrought iron, malleabilised cast iron, brass or copper should be screwed to the British Standard Taper Pipe thread as laid down in the British Standards Institution's Specification No. 21. Couplers must in every case be reversed and all male threads painted with a good pipe-jointing compound. Female threads must not be painted, and the use of hemp or other superfluous packing material is strongly to be deprecated, except where used as a grummet between the coupler and back nut of a connector. All tubes and fittings should be examined as they are fitted to see that they are free from obstruction and defects. Only clear and sound tubes and fittings should be used, while burrs in pipe ends must always be removed.

On industrial installations and the like, where compressed air, oxygen or any other mixture under pressure is to be used, an improved type of back-pressure valve must be inserted in the pipe line between the meter and the point at which the air or other fluid will enter. Where a gas engine, compressor, fan, pump or booster is to be installed an anti-suction device should be fitted on the run of pipe between the meter and the appliance. In addition, where any of these appliances are to be installed an approved anti-fluctuating device must be fitted on the supply pipe from the meter. Should the plumber be called upon to carry out an installation of this nature he would be obliged to consult the local gas undertaking, who would afford him every assistance.

In premises such as apartment houses, blocks of flats, offices, or any building supplying more than one consumer, that part of each consumer's service between the tee from the riser pipe and the point where the service enters the party wall of each suite of apartments should be provided with a double connector—and if it be in concrete or other similar material the double connector fitting should be rendered accessible by the fixing of a suitable floor trap above it. This enables the supply to be disconnected if necessary, it being, of course, quite impossible to disconnect by means of the ordinary type of connector when the tube on either side is held rigidly.

All tubes must, where possible, be graded to the meter, at which point a suitable receiver should be fitted. Where the trapping of the tube is unavoidable a tee piece and cap should be fitted at the lowest point to facilitate removal of liquor or rust. All tubes should be laid at least 12 inches distant from any electrical conduit, fuse box, cut-off, meter or appliance. Wherever possible bends should be used in preference to elbows, as they offer less resistance to the flow of gas and are less liable to collect rust, etc., which would eventually cause an obstruction. At suitable points it is preferable to use tees instead of elbows in order to provide for any possible subsequent extension of the carcass. In addition to this it is desirable also to leave double connector fittings to obviate difficulty should subsequent extensions be necessary. Pipes taken vertically through concrete or composition floors should be encased in a sleeve, while pipes embedded in composition flooring must be protected in a suitable manner.

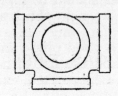

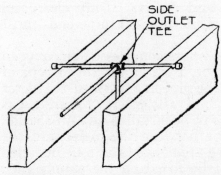

SIDE OUTLET TEE

Fig. 560.—Method of dropping pendant point between joists. Above—detail of side outlet tie.

Points for lighting brackets should be terminated in an elbow at a height of 6 feet 6 inches from the floor line. The face of the elbow should be flush with the face of the finished plaster or panelling of the wall. Drops for pendant points must be taken from a tee and the supply continued across the adjacent joist and capped as shown in Fig. 560. Pendant points should never be dropped from an elbow. Points for gas fires should be taken to the back of the centre of the hearth and terminate in an elbow looking up just flush of the finished surface of the hearth. A union cock with threaded lining and back nut should be fitted in a trap with hinged floor plate either centrally in front of the hearth or at the side about 3 inches from the outside of the trimmer, or whatever defines the hearth, and 4 inches from the wall. This concealed method of fitting gas fires should be adopted wherever possible, as it produces a marked psychological effect upon consumers. The majority of the public imagine that gas appliances must necessarily be accompanied by a visible length of pipe. To uninitiated people the word " gas " immediately brings to mind the word " pipe," in the same way as the word " wireless " in its infancy brought to mind visions of numerous poles and a network of wires. Details of this method of fitting is shown in Fig. 561. When the time comes for the fire to be fitted in position it is a simple matter to extend a short from the elbow up behind the fire and drill the back casting of the fire so that the supply is brought through it and connected up underneath the fender. When completed the carcass should be tested by means of an internal air pressure of at least 6-inch water column in the following manner. At any suitable point a tee piece carrying a cock on one outlet and a U-tube pressure gauge on the other is attached, while all other points are securely capped. Air is then pumped into the carcass through the cock until the U-tube gauge indicates the requisite test pressure. The cock is then shut and if the pressure in the carcass—after due allowance for cooling has been made—remains unchanged for 15 minutes, the carcass may be considered gas-tight. Should the pressure fall, steps must be taken immediately to make the carcass sound before it is charged with gas.

If the leak is a very small one and it is not possible to connect up the gas in order to locate the trouble, the pipes should be charged with acetylene gas by connecting them to a specially designed acetylene gas generator. It should then be quite easy to find the defect by the smell arising from

CONCEALED CONNECTION FOR GAS FIRE.

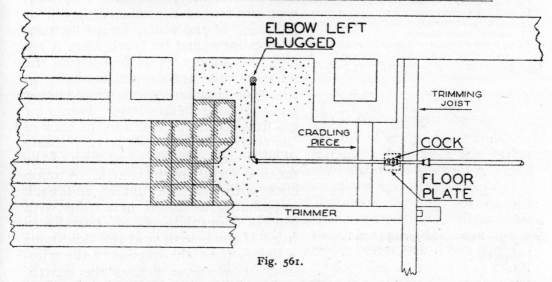

Fig. 561.

the escaping acetylene gas. It need hardly be pointed out that no light should ever be used when this test is being carried out, in view of the high inflammability of acetylene gas.

A further test of the piping should be carried out after the meter is connected and all applicances have been installed. The main tap should be turned on and the gauge attached as described above. The main cock should now be turned off and the gauge observed.

This latter test should be adopted whenever a further extension of piping is provided in a house and whenever a new appliance is fixed.

Should an escape be noticed outside the premises, the local gas undertaking should be immediately notified of the fact.

The following Table XCII has been compiled with the idea of assisting plumbers in determining the correct size of carcass pipes in domestic premises.

TABLE XCII
SIZES OF CARCASS PIPES TO BE RUN TO GAS APPLIANCES

Nature of Pipe Run.	Effective Length of Pipe.				
	up to 10 ft.	from 10 ft. to 20 ft.	from 20 ft. to 30 ft.	from 30 ft. to 40 ft	from 40 ft. to 60 ft.
	Inch	Inch	Inch	Inch	Inch
A. Rising pipe from meter in houses of 6 or less rooms	1	1	1		
B. Rising pipe from meter in houses of from 7 to 10 rooms	$1\frac{1}{4}$	$1\frac{1}{4}$	$1\frac{1}{4}$		
C. Principal pipe from meter in bungalows or flats of 6 or less rooms	1	1	1		
D. Principle pipe from meter in bungalows or flats of from 7 to 10 rooms	$1\frac{1}{4}$	$1\frac{1}{4}$	$1\frac{1}{4}$		
From pipe A, B, C or D, to each gas fire having up to 7 radiants or each gas poker point	$\frac{3}{8}$	$\frac{1}{2}$	$\frac{1}{2}$	$\frac{1}{2}$	$\frac{1}{2}$
To each gas fire having from 8 to 10 radiants or each gas-ignited fire	$\frac{1}{2}$	$\frac{1}{2}$	$\frac{1}{2}$	$\frac{1}{2}$	$\frac{1}{2}$
To each gas fire having from 11 to 15 radiants	$\frac{1}{2}$	$\frac{1}{2}$	$\frac{1}{2}$	$\frac{1}{2}$	$\frac{1}{2}$
To each gas cooker in dwellings having up to 6 rooms	$\frac{1}{2}$	$\frac{1}{2}$	$\frac{1}{2}$	$\frac{1}{2}$	$\frac{1}{2}$
To each gas cooker in dwellings having from 7 to 10 rooms	$\frac{1}{2}$	$\frac{3}{4}$	$\frac{3}{4}$	$\frac{3}{4}$	$\frac{3}{4}$
To each high-consumption storage water heater or each circulating storage water heater	$\frac{1}{2}$	$\frac{1}{2}$	$\frac{3}{4}$	$\frac{3}{4}$	$\frac{3}{4}$
To each low-consumption storage water heater or each gas iron or each refrigerator or each airing-cupboard heater	$\frac{1}{4}$	$\frac{1}{4}$	$\frac{3}{8}$		
To each plug for portable heater or each flueless heater or each drying cabinet	$\frac{1}{4}$	$\frac{3}{8}$	$\frac{1}{2}$		

FIXING APPLIANCES

The carcass pipes having been provided in the house and thoroughly tested, the next work to be undertaken is the fixing of the various appliances, regarding which the following information should be of assistance.

Gas Cookers.—Gas cookers are now fixed in almost every house. In some cases they are installed in the scullery, in others in the kitchen. Frequently now they are placed in the recess previously occupied by the coal range. The range is removed, the recess is tiled or rendered out with cement, and in the recess are fixed, in some cases, a gas cooker and a coke boiler; in others a gas cooker, gas water heater, gas fire, and perhaps a gas refuse destructor. Similar recesses especially designed for the gas appliances enumerated above have of course been installed in many new houses. The main points to be borne in mind when fixing the gas cooker in the kitchen or scullery are as follows :

Care should be taken in choosing the position for the cooker. It should not be in a direct line of draught, and it should be so placed that there is a good light on it—preferably facing a window.

A flue pipe should never be run from the oven through the wall into the open air. This is a dangerous practice, as a down-draught may easily blow out the oven lights when they are turned low. If the room is so small that ventilation of the oven is essential, a hood should be fixed over the cooker and a flue should be taken from the hood, preferably into a chimney. If this is not possible, the flue may be taken from the hood through the wall, but when this is done, steps must be taken to prevent down-draught. A flue from the outlet of the oven to a point inside the hood will then be all that is necessary. The flue should be open at the base—i.e. where it connects to the oven—in order to prevent a direct " pull " on it. In many cases the provision only of the hood with flue will meet all requirements.

If the cooker is not provided with a stand, it should be placed on a concrete base stone. This is absolutely essential when the floor is a wooden one.

Particular care should be taken not to place any strain on the feed bar or feed pipe of the cooker. Should a gas cooker have to be placed in close proximity to a wooden wall, suitable steps should be taken to protect the wall from the possibility of fire.

When fixing cookers with two or three ovens, they should be connected to the gas supply at both ends of the feed bar. This ensures a better distribution of pressure at all points.

When a gas cooker is fixed in a recess under a chimney, a flue pipe from the cooker to the chimney is seldom required, but it is desirable to fix at the top of the recess a register plate with a suitable opening, preferably a tapered hood, discharging into the chimney. This is a point which on some occasions has been overlooked by architects, who wrongly thought that, provided flues were taken into the chimney from the cooker, fire and water heater, the top of the recess could be completely filled in with a flat plate. The result has been, of course, that the odours and heat escaping from the food cooking on the hot plate have come into the kitchen instead of passing up the chimney.

When an opening is being constructed for the combined gas appliances described, sufficient head room should be provided to allow of the fixing of a back-plate and plate rack for the gas cooker. The height of the recess should never be less than 5 feet.

All modern cookers are provided with thermostats by means of which the user can adjust her oven to any one of a number of given cooking temperatures. Once a meal is placed in a thermostatically controlled oven it may be left without attention and taken out properly cooked at the end of a stated period of time. As a labour-saving device the cooker thermostat has proved to be of immense value to the modern housewife.

Gas Water Heaters.—A huge variety of gas water heaters is now available and types exist which are suitable for meeting every possible contingency. Broadly, they may be classified into three main groups—self-contained storage water heaters, instantaneous water heaters (geysers) and water-heating units for attachment to existing circulating systems.

All water heaters other than geysers are now also provided with thermostats which, when the water is sufficiently hot—normally about 140° F.—shut the gas supply down to a low rate just sufficient to maintain the water at this temperature. With a properly insulated system the maintenance gas rate will be between 1 and 2 cubic feet per hour.

In addition, many water heaters, including geysers, are provided with a thermally operated cut-off, especially when fitted on slot-meter supplies. The by-pass or pilot flame impinges on a bimetallic strip which is thus heated. Should the flame be extinguished the strip cools and by an ingenious arrangement shuts off all the gas to the appliance. The gas supply cannot be restored until the appliance is put into action again by the consumer.

Storage Heaters.—A large demand is arising for the new thermal

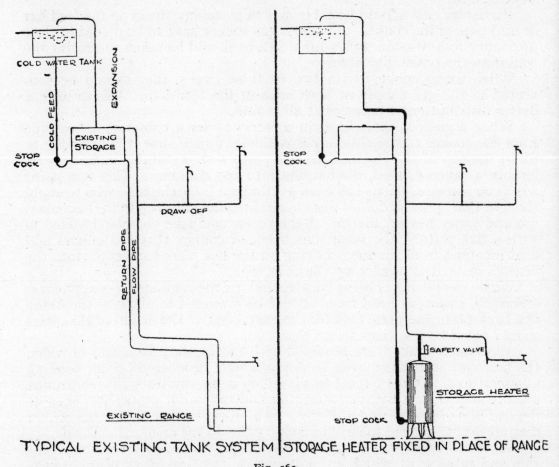

TYPICAL EXISTING TANK SYSTEM | STORAGE HEATER FIXED IN PLACE OF RANGE

Fig. 562.

storage gas water heaters. These are so remarkably economical in running costs that they are being installed in many households where hitherto gaseous water heating was considered too expensive a luxury. Two types are available, the low-consumption storage heater, and the high-consumption storage heater, each type being made in a number of sizes. The thermal storage heater shown in Fig. 563 is made in four sizes, having hot water storage capacities of 12, 20, 30 and 40 gallons respectively. The maximum consumption in every case is only 10 cubic feet of gas per

PLATE XII

Fig. 564.

THERMAL STORAGE HEATERS.

Fig. 563.

hour. The heater therefore can be connected up to any existing gas-supply pipe, and there is no necessity to provide a flue for the heater. All gas water heating appliances should be periodically overhauled so that they may continue operating at their original high efficiency. With this object in view, the water heater should be so fixed that it can be quickly dismantled for overhaul. The following are a few simple and practical suggestions to be followed when arranging the installation of

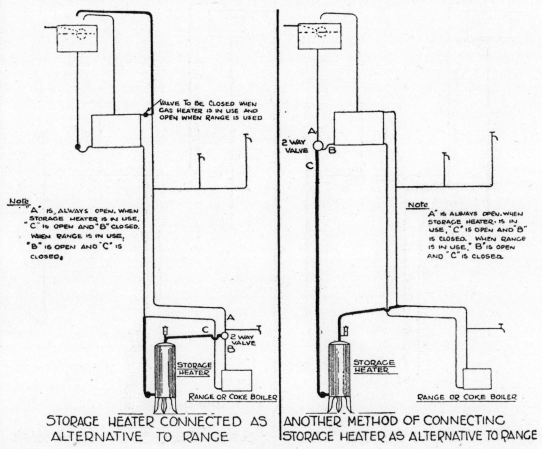

STORAGE HEATER CONNECTED AS ALTERNATIVE TO RANGE | ANOTHER METHOD OF CONNECTING STORAGE HEATER AS ALTERNATIVE TO RANGE

Fig. 565.

water heaters of the types shown in this chapter. The heater should be fixed in a position where it is easily accessible. The cold-water supply pipe must be one size larger than the largest hot-water delivery pipe, and a control tap must be provided. An emptying tap of sufficient size to empty down the cylinder rapidly is also necessary. This is generally supplied with the apparatus, but it must be fitted in such a position that the whole of the water in the cylinder can be drawn off. It is advisable to lag at least the first five feet of expansion (or delivery) pipe ; but for best results all delivery pipes should be lagged. Particularly is this necessary when the demand for hot water throughout the day is frequent. The cost of lagging is so comparatively small (under 1s. a foot run) that in many cases the small initial expense involved will be saved in lower gas consumption in the first month or two.

High-consumption thermal storage water heaters are made in a number of sizes, from 13 gallons storage capacity up to 38 gallons storage capacity, and with maximum gas rates from 36 to 95 cubic feet of gas per

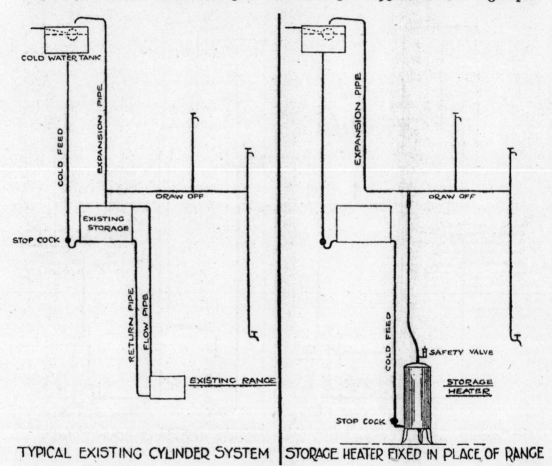

TYPICAL EXISTING CYLINDER SYSTEM | STORAGE HEATER FIXED IN PLACE OF RANGE

Fig. 566.

hour. They have a rapid " make-up," that is to say, they heat up cold water very quickly to replace any hot water withdrawn and are thus somewhat of a compromise between the low-consumption storage water heater and the well-known geyser. Owing to the higher gas rates, storage water heaters of this type must of course be fitted with flue-pipe equipment. This type of heater—all of which is shown in Fig. 564—is suitable for the large house in which there are heavy and frequent demands for hot water. In large houses where very long runs of delivery pipe would be necessary if all hot water were drawn from one heater only, it is sometimes advisable to install two water heaters. The first (fixed as near as possible to the kitchen sink) can be adjusted to provide water at 160° F. for kitchen purposes—washing up, scrubbing and the like. The second (fixed as near as possible in a central position in relation to hot-water taps to baths and lavatory basins) can be set to give hot water at say 130° F. As the water heaters are thermostatically controlled, the gas consumption is

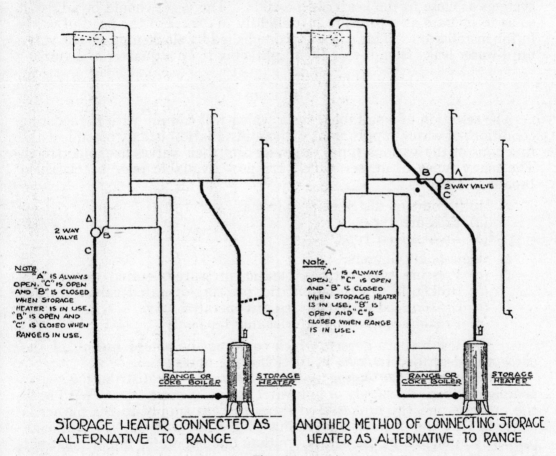

Fig. 567.

always kept proportionate to the demand for hot water. Economy results, too, from the provision of heaters which are (1) so adjusted that hot water for the purposes indicated is delivered at the most suitable temperatures, and (2) so placed as to ensure the shortest possible run of hot-water delivery pipe. In this latter case the economy is a double one, namely, in installation and running costs.

Figs. 562 and 565 to 567 will serve as a ready guide to the installation of gas storage water heaters either in place of, or to work in conjunction with, existing systems.

Both high- and low-consumption water-heating units are available for attachment to existing circulating pipes and storage cylinders or tanks. It is imperative to lag not only the storage tank but all exposed hot-water pipes. If this be done effectively the efficiency of such an installation should approximate closely to that of a self-contained thermal storage water heater.

A low-pressure safety valve must be fitted on all gas water heating systems as close to the heater as possible. The valve should be adjusted so as to operate at a pressure just slightly in excess of the head of water in the installation. This can be accomplished by slackening off the valve until water leaks from it and then tightening it up a quarter of a turn.

Geysers

The selection of a suitable geyser which will comply with the existing conditions of water supply in any given installation is only possible if the functions of the various types of geyser and their valves are understood. The many types of geyser which are now available may be classified broadly as follows :

1. Multi-point or distributing geysers.
   (*a*) Pressure types.
   (*b*) Broken-feed type.
2. Single-point Geysers.
   (*a*) Pressure type with automatic, pressure-operated valve.
   (*b*) Broken feed with automatic, pressure-operated valve.
   (*c*) Broken feed with non-pressure-operated valve.
   (*d*) Broken feed having interlocking taps only.

There are few modern geysers which could not be placed in any of the categories described *seriatim* in the following notes :

Multi-point or Distributing Geysers.—*General.*—The distributing geyser is designed to give a supply of hot water to one or more taps. With both the pressure and the broken-feed types the gas supply to the burner is controlled by the opening and closing of the hot-water taps. Although primarily intended for use with more than one hot-water tap, it must not be forgotten that they are sometimes particularly suitable, in the smaller sizes, for fixing to do duty as single-point heaters in places where strangers may frequently require to use them. This is because they are operated by the mere act of turning the hot-water tap and so do not call for any conscious effort on the part of the user. The neatness of the modern gas-distributing geyser is typified in the illustration—Plate XIII.

A distributing geyser installed as such—i.e. to supply more than one hot-water point—should not be fixed in a bathroom if it supplies taps situated outside the bathroom.

Distributing geysers are suitable for use as alternatives to coke boilers or coal ranges, but they should not be fitted in series with them.

PLATE XIII

MODERN GAS-DISTRIBUTING GEYSER.

Distributing Geysers.—Pressure types.—In the pressure type of distributing geyser the water is under pressure, and consequently the heater may be fitted at any level in the system.

All models are fitted with an automatic valve, by means of which the main gas supply to the burner is actuated by the differential water pressure set up when a hot-water tap is opened.

As a direct water connection exists between the inlet connection to the geyser and the hot-water taps it is not permissible, in most districts, to connect it to a main water pipe, and so the supply must be taken from a feed tank via a ball valve.

Some confusion exists with regard to feed tanks. If it is imperative to fit a pressure-type multi-point geyser where no tank is available, it will be necessary to run a main water supply to and fit a small tank at a point above the highest draw-off, sufficiently high to give a head of water in excess of that required to operate the valve. If this tank is to supply only the hot-water taps via the distributing geyser, the size of it is immaterial, for, provided there is sufficient pressure of water from the main and an adequate size of ball valve is fitted, water will flow into the tank as fast as it flows out. With every geyser there is a maximum rate of water flow through it, above which the rise in temperature is insufficient and, from the water-heating point of view, the appliance is useless. A consumer will naturally check the flow at the tap or taps to obtain water at the desired temperature, and it would be a poor main supply which could not maintain that rate of flow into the tank. There is no point in providing a large tank to act as a reserve, because, should the main water supply fail, the gas will be automatically shut off when there ceases to be a differential head to keep the valve open.

These remarks do not apply, of course, to existing feed tanks, which sometimes supply many taps, flushing devices, etc., apart from the supply to the geyser. Such installations are encountered—fortunately infrequently—where the rate of draw-off from the tank is occasionally greater than the rate of water flow into it and, in consequence, a sustained heavy outflow results in a lowering of the level of the water. If, in such an instance, the head of water at the highest draw-off from a distributing geyser closely approaches the minimum required to operate the valve, trouble is likely to be experienced.

The position of the geyser (i.e. the valve of the geyser) is immaterial. It can be fitted at the lowest part of the house or immediately below the cold feed tank, since it is the differential pressure which operates the valve, and the minimum differential pressure is determined by the vertical distance between the level of the water in the cold feed tank and the highest draw-off tap.

It must be repeated that the position of a distributing geyser has nothing to do with the successful operation of the automatic valve which is controlled by the head of water at the draw-off taps. There are, unfortunately, many houses where the highest draw-off taps are only a few feet below the cold feed tank, in some cases the vertical distance between them being only 2 or 3 feet. There is no pressure-type distributing geyser available which will operate successfully with a lower effective head than 5 feet, so that the fitting of such an appliance is useless unless it is permissible either to connect to the main water supply, to raise the existing tank or to fit a separate tank for the geyser at a suitable height. If none of these be possible, it must be clearly recognised that the fitting of a pressure-operated distributing geyser is quite out of the question, and recourse must be made to a more suitable type of water heater, many of which are available.

*Distributing Geysers.—Broken-feed type.—*While possessing the advantages that they can be connected to any water supply either from the tank or the main, and that their valves operate independently of water pressure, these geysers are handicapped by the fact that they must be fitted at a higher level than the highest draw-off.

A ball valve is incorporated as an integral part of the geyser, and when water is drawn off, the lowering of the water level causes the valve to open and water to enter from the main supply. The incoming water is made to actuate the gas valve.

While it is imperative to fit a distributing geyser of this type in such a position that the outlet from it is above the highest draw-off, it is desirable to fit it as high as possible, because the rate of flow of water at any tap will depend on the head of water between the tap and the level of the water in the geyser.

*Pressure Geysers with Automatic, Pressure-operated Valves.—*Being, in principle, similar to the pressure-operated distributing geysers, single-point geysers of this type can, as a rule, be connected direct to the main. The water supply, therefore, must be taken from a storage tank. As the valve is at approximately the same level as the point of discharge, the effective pressure to operate the valve is the head of water determined by the vertical distance between the valve and the level of the water in the feed tank.

It is important to ascertain the head of water necessary to operate the valve of a geyser of this type and to ensure that the requisite head is available before estimating to fit it.

*Geysers having Broken Feeds and Pressure-operated Valves.—*Geysers of this type, having a broken feed, may be connected direct to the main, where there is certain to be sufficient pressure to operate the valve successfully.

Provided sufficient head is available, they may, if desired, be supplied from a tank. If a geyser of this type is to be fitted and sufficient head of water exists in the tank supply, the deciding factor would be the distance between the proposed geyser position and the nearest suitable water pipe.

*Geysers with Broken Feed and Non-pressure-operated Valves.—*Geysers of this type may be regarded as general purpose heaters, as they can be fitted to either the tank or the main water supply—whichever is the more convenient and economical to employ. Being independent of water pressure, the distance below the tank at which a geyser of this type is fitted is immaterial, provided it is sufficient to give the requisite rate of water flow.

Geysers with Broken Feed and Interlocking Taps only.—Although from the point of view of successful operation it is immaterial whether geysers coming in this category are fitted direct to the main water supply or the supply from a tank, there is one serious objection to the former source of supply. In the event of main supply being shut off temporarily while the geyser is alight, the geyser would be damaged, because, not being provided with any form of automatic valve, the gas would remain full on while the cold water would cease to flow in. The small quantity of water in the heater would, of course, rapidly be evaporated.

To avoid this happening it is advisable always to connect geysers which have interlocking taps only to a supply from a tank of a size large enough to provide an adequate supply should there be a failure of the main water supply.

Charging with Water.—With all water heaters it is imperative to make certain that they are completely charged with water before lighting the gas. This is ensured when water issues from the spout or taps. Geysers, in particular, are very quickly damaged if this precaution is neglected.

Danger of Attaching Hose to Certain Geysers.—It may sometimes be necessary to warn the consumer not to attach—as is frequently seen—a length of hose to the spout of the geyser to take the outflowing hot water below the level of the water in the bath. With some types of geyser it is possible for the attachment of this length of hose to form a siphon which has the effect, when the water is turned off, of either lowering the level of the water or even draining the geyser completely.

Stop Cocks.—The water supply to all water heaters should incorporate a stop cock to facilitate maintenance and to avoid the annoyance which would be caused by shutting off all the water.

With a geyser having a broken feed and no water-throttling device the provision of a stop cock in addition to that normally supplied with the geyser will enable the rate of water flow to be checked and so prevent the accidental flooding of the geyser.

FLUE EQUIPMENT

The following remarks apply to the practical consideration of flue equipment, not only to water heaters, but to all other appliances which it may be considered desirable to ventilate by means of flue pipe.

It must first be clearly understood that no flue pipe must be taken from a gas appliance either direct to the outside air or to an existing chimney without some form of suitable down-draught diverter (baffler) being introduced in the flue pipe.

The functions of the baffler are two-fold.

(1) It prevents interference with the combustion of the gas in the appliance due to unfavourable pressure conditions outside the building and from which no natural-draught flue can possibly be immune.

(2) It " breaks " the flue and so prevents a direct " pull " on the

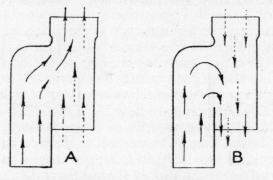

NORMAL CONDITIONS   ADVERSE CONDITIONS

BENTEE

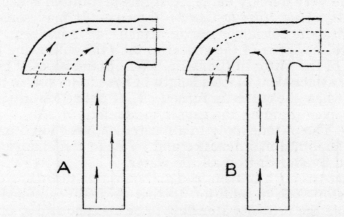

NORMAL CONDITIONS   ADVERSE CONDITIONS

TEE BAFFLER

Fig. 568.—Two types of baffler for fitting to flue equipment of gas appliances.

appliance. Appliances are designed to give their highest efficiency without flue pipe, the addition of which causes the efficiency to be lowered.

Several types of baffler are available—two of which, the Bentee and Tee Baffler, are shown in Fig. 568. At A in both cases, the effects of normal up-draught are shown. The products of combustion are denoted by thick arrows, while air is shown as dotted arrows. At B, the bafflers are shown working under adverse conditions. The majority of water heaters—particularly geysers—being cylindrical in form and having flue connections at the top, lend themselves to the fitting of a cylindrical type of baffler which will be concentric with the appliance. Two forms of such baffler are shown in Fig. 569.

At *a* and *c* the bafflers are shown with normal conditions of up-

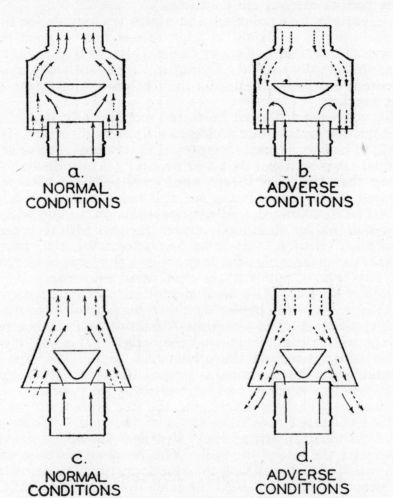

a.
NORMAL
CONDITIONS

b.
ADVERSE
CONDITIONS

c.
NORMAL
CONDITIONS

d.
ADVERSE
CONDITIONS

Fig. 569.—Two types of cylindrical baffler for fitting to flues of gas appliances.

draught. The path of the products of combustion is depicted by solid arrows, and air is shown by dotted arrows. It will be seen that the products of combustion from the appliance ascend until they meet the curved dish where the " pull " existing in the flue pipe above the baffler entrain them to the terminal. The bases of the bafflers are open and, consequently, air from the apartment is also entrained and carried up the flue.

At *b* and *d* the effects of down-draught or down-blow are shown.

The downward stream of air due either to a definite wind blowing in at the terminal (down-blow) or the existence of a greater air pressure outside the apartment (down-draught) is unable to enter the flue pipe below the baffler and takes the easy path offered by the annular openings into the room.

At the same time, the products of combustion are entrained into the room but perfect combustion continues.

It is important that plumbers and others responsible for the installation of flue equipment should be able to recognise a good baffler. So many types of so-called bafflers or draught diverters, although elaborate in design, are actually useless. Cylindrical types without a clear opening at the botton, but having instead a number of slots, are generally not to be recommended.

In this connection it must be stated emphatically that the ordinary open-end flue tee is also quite useless as a draught diverter. It functions quite well, of course, as an interrupter of up-draught, but since the limbs are of equal cross-sectional area and no device is introduced to make one path easier than the other it fails when conditions are adverse. It is to be regretted that open-end tees are still being fitted : it is a practice which must be discouraged. All contingencies can be met with the available types of baffler described—either the cylindrical types, the tee baffler or the " Bentee." It must be appreciated, too, that all these bafflers are interchangeable—i.e. they achieve the same object and may be fitted to any type of appliance as circumstances demand.

Position of Baffler.—With modern appliances of good design—geysers, storage heaters, etc.—the baffler should be fitted as close to the appliance as possible, although it is sometimes desirable to fit about one foot of flue pipe between the appliance and the baffler. This length of flue pipe below the baffler is termed the primary flue pipe. The pipe above the baffler extending to the terminal is termed the secondary flue pipe. The secondary flue pipe must be as long, vertically, as possible.

Terminals.—Wherever practicable the flue pipes from gas appliances should be terminated above the eaves of the roof. Where this is not possible a terminal known as the " Ventile " should be fitted with the back flush with the face of the wall. This terminal has been scientifically designed with a view to utilising the kinetic energy of the wind to evacuate the products of combustion. At the same time it presents an extraordinarily neat appearance. No matter how good the terminal, however, it is still imperative to fit a baffler as part of the flue equipment of the appliance.

GAS FIRES

The fixing of gas fires will undoubtedly prove to be the major part of the gas-fitting work of the plumber, for gas fires are being demanded in ever-increasing numbers each autumn.

The fires themselves have now been brought up to an exceptionally high standard of perfection from the point of view of external design, high heatng efficiency and hygiene. Many installations can still be found, however, where the fixing of the fires leaves much to be desired.

Gas fires are of three types, namely :

(*a*) The " inset " gas fire—for fixing inside an existing coal grate.

(*b*) The self-contained gas fire—the complete gas fire with burner, firebrick back, flue and metal exterior, which is generally fixed in front of the coal grate or in a chimney recess.

(*c*) The " built-in " gas fire—a fire designed specially for fixing *instead* of a coal grate, and commonly discharging its products of combustion into a special " economy " flue, which can often be built in the thickness of the wall.

The " Inset " Gas Fire.—The inset gas fire (see Fig. 570) as a rule consists of little more than a burner and a firebrick back, with a casting to combine the two ; it sometimes has special radiants or imitation " coke " fuel, and is made in shapes and sizes to fit right into coal grates. In fixing this type of fire, the bars of the coal grate (if there are any bars) should be removed, and the inset fire should then be set sufficiently far back in the opening to ensure the complete removal of the products of combustion when the fire is alight. As a general rule, no part of the radiants should project farther into the room than the canopy (if any) of the coal grate

The Self-contained Gas Fire.—When fixing a self-contained gas fire in front of a coal grate, the fire should, wherever possible, be set back tight against the moulding of the grate. The sizes and designs of gas fires are now so numerous that little difficulty will be experienced in getting a fire which will match and appear to be a part of an existing grate. Square-topped fires should generally be used to fit in the square mouldings and frames of modern slow-combustion gas grates, the canopy of the grate being, of course, removed. If any uncovered gap remains at the top of the gas fire when it is in position, the gap can be filled with asbestone, or sheet metal or iron, brass or copper. Another design of fire has a special top somewhat of the shape of a Cupid's bow. This is suitable for fixing in front of an old hob grate when it is desired to leave uncovered its ornamental moulding. In dealing with hob grates, the gap which shows behind the gas fire, between the top of the hobs and the moulding of the grate, can be filled in by a sheet of asbestone (or metal) which can be painted to match the grate. The round-top gas fire is suitable for fixing in front of old-fashioned register grates. In some cases it will be necessary to remove the fire-bars of the coal grate in order to allow the fire to be fixed tightly back.

If the gas fire cannot be fitted right back to the coal grate, or if it is desired to cover up unsightly ornamental ironwork or tiles, the recess should be covered in either with asbestone or with an art-metal surround of suitable finish, so made that it can be adjusted to cover any size of opening. When fixing these surrounds, a wooden framework is made (of battens) of the size of the opening, and this frame is fastened securely in position by means of wedges. To this framework the asbestone is screwed. When art-metal surrounds are used, it is generally advisable to provide the wooden frame and also the asbestone surround, and then to fasten the metal surround to both frame and asbestone by round-headed screws—this to prevent the buckling of the somewhat thin metal sheets.

Flues for Gas Fires.—To the flue outlet or spigot of the self-contained gas fire a flue elbow or lengthening piece should always be fixed. The flue should be sufficiently long to take the products of combustion above the arch bar or brick arch of the grate opening right into the chimney itself. If the flue enters the chimney at an angle, a space of at least 2 inches must be left between its outlet end and the face of the brickwork. It must never be taken close up to the brickwork, or the products of combustion will not escape freely. The elbow or lengthening piece should be securely fastened with a ¼-inch B.S. Whit. screw to the spigot of the fire. The spigots or flue outlets of most gas fires are now drilled and tapped for the reception of these set screws.

Estimating Correct Size of Gas Fire.—As with hot water, so with gas fires—it is *always* better to have an ample margin of reserve. Gas fires are so easily controlled by means of the Duplex tap, and greater economy results when there is sufficient margin in hand to enable this to be done.

One of the greatest advantages which is claimed in favour of the use of gas fires is their suitability for dining-rooms, bedrooms, etc., which are used intermittently. In such rooms a gas fire can be lighted half an hour or so before the room is to be occupied, so that it is comfortably warm by the time it is required. If, however, the room is larger than normal, it is obvious that a larger fire will be required if the room temperature is to be raised sufficiently in a short time.

An accurate determination of the correct size of gas fires may be made in the following manner, where the heat required to offset the losses brought about by the several factors is stated in terms of the number of radiants required.

1. Calculate the volume of the room—i.e. the length by the breadth by the height—in cubic feet.

For every 300 cubic feet provide one radiant.

2. For every 60 square feet of exposed wall add one radiant.

3. For every 20 square feet of window glass add one radiant.

Example.—A room measures 11 feet × 18 feet × 9 feet high. Two walls are exposed—one of them 18 feet long and the other 11 feet long. There are french windows at one end of the room measuring 8 feet × 5 feet. What size of gas fire is necessary?

$$(1) \text{ Volume of room} = 11 \times 18 \times 9$$
$$= 1,782 \text{ cubic feet.}$$

Therefore
$$\frac{1,782}{300}$$

or approximately 6 radiants will be required.

PLATE XIV

Fig. 570.

Fig. 571.

Fig. 572.

Fig. 573.

GAS FIRES.

(2) The area of the exposed walls is 261 square feet less, 40 square feet (the area of the glass), which is ;

221 square feet

so $\dfrac{221}{60}$

or approximately 4 more radiants will be required.

(3) The area of the windows is 40 square feet, which means the addition of $\dfrac{40}{20}$

or 2 radiants.

So, in order to give really satisfactory results in this room, it will be necessary to install a gas fire having 12 radiants, i.e. a 17-inch fire.

Supposing the calculation indicated a number of radiants which do not coincide with a standard size of fire, the next largest size should be selected.

Adjustment of Gas Fires.—The burners of gas fires of normal pattern should be adjusted with a well aerated flame, the inner cone of which should be 1 inch to $1\frac{1}{4}$ inches long. The correct gas rate should be 2,250 B.Th.U.'s per radiant per hour.

Connecting up the Gas Fire.—When the flue has been properly made up and the fire is ready to be fixed, the top of the fire should be sloped backwards towards the grate and the flue guided up the chimney. The bottom portion of the fire can then be pushed towards the grate, and the whole thing will then be in position for fixing.

Where possible the supply pipe to the fire should be concealed as explained on pp. 202 and 203, but if this cannot be done, the connection between the " floor " or " skirting " point and the fire should consist of brass tubing and fittings. The appearance of this work is greatly enhanced, however, if the brass pipe and fittings are specially " finished " to match the fire. Great care should be taken to bend or set the brass tubing nicely round the mantel jamb when this is necessary. Many cases can be found where an otherwise perfect piece of fitting work has been entirely discounted by the careless setting of the brass tubing. The connection should (in the case of small or medium-sized fires) consist of a $\frac{1}{2}$-inch brass elbow tapped $\frac{1}{4}$-inch B.S.P., for connection to the gas-fire point just outside the trimmer, a control cock, and the necessary length of brass tubing to reach the point at which it is connected to the fire. Whatever type of control cock or valve is used, it should be a substantially made one of good quality. This cock should always be provided, despite the fact that the fire itself has a tap. It is useful for ensuring a correct supply of gas to the fire when the fire tap is turned fully on. It also facilitates the disconnection of the fire should this at any time be necessary.

Built-in Gas Fires.—Built-in gas fires have been specially designed for fixing straight away in new houses. They generally consist of a cast-iron combination of gas fire, mantelshelf, jambs and raised hearth. Built-in combination sets are being fixed by the thousand in housing schemes throughout the country ; they can sometimes, of course, be fixed in old property which is being modernised. Built-in fires without the mantel register are also obtainable. These are, as a rule, let into the brickwork, and the surround, hearth, etc., are then made to the architect's design (see Figs. 572 and 573).

Built-in fires are usually fitted to what are termed " economy " flues, which are frequently built in the thickness of the wall ; for with gas fires flues of areas materially smaller than those required for coal fires can be utilised. The considerable saving in building costs which has resulted from the use of " economy " flues has in some instances led to the provision of flues of insufficient capacity to take away the products of combustion. The following table shows the minimum sizes of flue which should be provided for different sizes of gas fire.

TABLE XCIII

No. of Radiants.	Size of Fire Front.	Minimum Flue Area Recommended.	Size of Flue Suggested.	
			Brickwork.	Concrete Blocks.
	Inches	Sq. In.	Inches	Inches
5	8	20	$4\frac{1}{2} \times 4\frac{1}{2}$	$2\frac{1}{2} \times 9$
6	9	20	$4\frac{1}{2} \times 4\frac{1}{2}$	$2\frac{1}{2} \times 9$
7	10	24	$4\frac{1}{2} \times 9$	$2\frac{1}{2} \times 12$
8	11	24	$4\frac{1}{2} \times 9$	$2\frac{1}{2} \times 12$
9	$12\frac{1}{2}$	30	$4\frac{1}{2} \times 9$	$2\frac{1}{2} \times 12$
10	14	36	$4\frac{1}{2} \times 9$	$2\frac{1}{2} \times 15$

Each gas fire should have a flue to itself, from the flue elbow of the fire right up to its highest point above the ridge of the roof. The flue should end with a suitable terminal, and should never be made to discharge under the eaves of a building. The flue can be constructed in brickwork or by means of special concrete blocks. Parging is not necessary, but the inside of the flue should, of course, be carefully trowelled.

The built-in fire should be made to discharge into an opening slightly wider than the fire outlet, and this opening can with advantage be gradually reduced until, at the point where it joins up with the flue, it has attained the same dimensions as the flue. This arrangement provides a kind of expansion box into which the products of combustion from the fire can easily discharge and afterwards find their way up the flue. This plan cannot always be adopted, but it is the best one wherever it is possible.

Flueless Heaters.—Many excellent types of flueless heaters, both portable and fixed, are to be had. The rate of gas consumption of such appliances is very low and they may be fitted in any well-ventilated room with complete confidence. Batteries of flueless heaters in halls, churches, cinemas, etc., should be provided with an air thermostat. This is fitted in a convenient position on the wall, etc., of the building and when the air of the room reaches the predetermined temperature at which the thermostat is set to operate, the closing of the small valve in the device is relayed to a main gas valve fitted on the supply of the heaters. The gas supply is shut down to a small maintenance rate and will only be restored to full rate when the temperature of the air in the room falls.

An excellent type of flueless heater is illustrated in Fig. 571. It fits flat on the wall or may be fitted into a recess so as to be flush with the face of the wall. A fresh-air duct from the outside admits air to the bottom of the panel; there it is heated and passed to the top, where it is discharged through louvres to the room. No air for combustion is taken from the room, but fresh warmed air is supplied from *outside*. Besides the circulation of warmed air, a slight low temperature radiation is obtained from the panel. An adjustable damper in the panel enables the flow of warmed air to be reduced at will. When the flow of warmed air is reduced, the temperature of the panel and consequently the radiation component is increased.

PORTABLE HEATERS

Recent scientific research has resulted in the production of really safe and efficient portable gas heaters. Two types are available : portable air heaters and portable radiant heaters. The latter may be of the simple copper or plated bowl fire type or mounted in an attractive art metal screen.

A particular point of interest in connection with flueless heaters is the plug-in connector. This novel and inexpensive fitting enables gas appliances to be plugged-in at any convenient point, while the gas cannot be turned on until the plug is firmly seated and locked in its socket. The flexible tubing now used for portable appliances is known as " Corflex." It is made of special gas-resistant rubber having an inner core so constructed that it is almost impossible to extinguish the gas either by kinking the tube or treading on it. One end of the Corflex is attached to the portable appliance by a firm screwed joint and the other has screwed to it the plug of the plug-in connector. The socket of the plug-in connector may be fitted on the floor or wall (as shown in Fig. 574) or may be had in a flush-fitting type for fixing behind the skirting-board.

MISCELLANEOUS DOMESTIC APPLIANCES

No modern kitchen is now considered complete without a gas-operated refrigerator and a gas clothes-drying and airing cabinet.

The larger models of gas refrigerator are water-cooled, while the smallest model is air-cooled. The great demand for these appliances is calling for considerable work on the part of plumbers. Every housewife now realises the value of refrigeration—in fact, she is rapidly becoming refrigerator-minded.

Gas-operated refrigerators are all thermostatically controlled. Only a small rate of gas consumption is required to cool the cabinet and, when it reaches the desired temperature, the thermostat comes into operation and cuts the gas down even further, so that a negligible amount is required to maintain the cabinet at the required degree of coldness.

Gas clothes-drying and airing cabinets are popular. They will dry and air the whole family washing in a few hours. Here again, a thermostat is employed and the gas rate cut down when the desired temperature is reached. The thermostat is adjustable to various settings according to the material being dried and aired.

Space does not permit of detailed descriptions of the many other domestic gas appliances now available. Special mention must be made of the gas fire-lighter. It consists of a simple poker blade with an insulated handle attached to a flexible tube. The blade is drilled or slotted and the flames issuing from the holes will ignite a coal or coke fire in a few minutes without wood or paper. Six fires can be lighted in this manner for the cost of a bundle of wood, and with considerably less trouble. Coal or coke grates and coke boilers should be provided with a plug-in connector near them so that the poker-lighter may be applied when it is necessary to light them.

Gas-Lighting Fittings

While the fixing of gas-lighting fittings involves but little work on which special advice is required, a few points regarding the design of burners may be dealt with.

The upright burner is now quite out of date. Wherever possible, inverted burners—of good quality—with super-heaters should be installed. The super-heater consists of a small chamber situated above the burner or burners. This chamber becomes very hot, due to its close proximity to the mantels. The gas and air mixture passes through this chamber immediately prior to combustion, and in consequence also becomes heated. The heating of the mixture results in increased flame temperature, and this in turn causes a marked increase in the amount of light given out by the incandescent mantle. The light given out by a super-heated burner compared with that given out by an inverted burner without super-heater is approximately 50 per cent. greater for an identical consumption of gas.

Burners constructed of aluminium are strongly to be recommended, though other finishes are obtainable where it is desired to provide fittings to harmonise with surroundings. Clusters of small mantles on super-heated burners are better than a small number of larger mantles. The small mantles are better " filled " by the gas flame, and they have, in addition, a longer life.

PLATE XV

Fig. 574.—Plug-in connector for flueless heaters.

Fig. 575.—An attractive modern gas-lighting fitting.

All gas-lighting fittings fixed in house property should be suitably shaded, but care should be taken to recommend shades which do not absorb too much of the light. Silica-ware globes and shades are becoming popular on account of the " softness " of the light which results from their use ; also their long life, due to the fact that they successfully withstand the heat from the mantles. Owing to this latter property, they can be fitted very close to the mantles, and in consequence can be used in smaller sizes than glass-ware globes, an advantage from the point of view of appearance, and also of efficiency, as the temperature of the mantles (and therefore their incandescence) is increased by the heat radiated back from the globes.

Gas lighting has advanced with the times, and panel brackets and pendant fittings are available to tone with all modern schemes of decoration. An attractive modern fitting is shown in Fig. 575.

REMOTE CONTROL OF LIGHTING BURNERS

Gas-lighting burners may be switched on and off from a distance by three methods. The first is a simple cable device somewhat resembling the Bowden cable. It is very positive in action and may be adapted for two- or three-way switching for halls, landings, etc. The latest catalytic type dispenses with the use of a by-pass. The second method is the well known pneumatic distance lighter. For the lighting-up of lamps in series in large shops, churches and the like, there is another very reliable type of distance control which actuates the main valve above the burner head when the full pressure of gas is allowed to pass to it, this taking place when the control cock (situated in any convenient position) is turned on. Clock control for gas-lighting fittings is also obtainable, and shop windows can therefore be left lighted after the shops are closed, with the assurance that at any predetermined time the lights will be automatically turned off. Full particulars for the fixing and adjusting of these systems of distant control are generally provided by the makers.

CHAPTER XIII

GLAZIERS' WORK

APPLIANCES. MATERIALS: Glass — Putties — Lead Glazing — Solder — Brads, etc **WORKMANSHIP. PATENT GLAZING. WRITING AND EMBOSSING. WASTE GLASS MEASURING.**

THE equipment needed in ordinary glazing is very simple, few appliances being required and few of them complicated.

Most important are the cutting implements. The greater part of cutting is done with diamonds, cut to a proper point and mounted in brass holders with wood or horn handles. The head of the holder is at a slight angle to the handle. When in operation the handle is held between the first and second fingers, the thumb pressing against the flat part underneath. The diamond must be held at about the angle indicated by the slant of the head. If held too upright, the diamond will " score " and its point will soon be worn down ; if too low, the cut will not be deep enough. Slight pressure is needed, the diamond being drawn along in a firm, continuous stroke. The cut must never be gone over again. If the cut is well done, the glass should snap off evenly and smoothly. Usually the diamond head or handle is provided with a rack of steel, two or more grooves of different gauges, in which fragments of glass are held to snap off from the panes.

Rough-surfaced glass is usually cut with a hardened steel wheel or disc, mounted in much the same way as a diamond. Some of the holders are fitted with a receptacle for holding extra wheels, and also have racks attached.

The next implement is the beam compass, used for cutting circles and sections from large sheets of glass and is provided with a diamond set in steel block. With this writing diamond, circles from 2 inches to 30 inches in circumference can be cut. Like the writing diamond, the beam is held in an adjustable chuck which slides on a graduated rod, passing through a slotted standard with thumb-screw.

The glazier's square should be of boxwood, the long arm 24, 30, 36, 42, or 48 inches long, and marked on both edges to $\frac{1}{16}$ or $\frac{1}{32}$ inch.

For cleaning out old putty, a hacking knife is required. This has a short broad blade, thickened at the back and with square, sharpened end. A hammer is applied to the back or the end of the wood handle, to hack away. A fairly good hacking knife can be made out of an old triangular file, with one angle ground to a cutting edge.

The putty knife should be of good steel, rather stiff, short, the blade broadening towards the end and terminating in a spear-shaped or a clipped point.

A light hammer with square pane is needed, and a small pair of pincers for removing old brads.

For lead glazing a brazier's outfit is necessary. Also a wooden mallet and hardwood tools for bending down the cames leaves.

The table or bench on which glass is cut must have a hard, perfectly even, smooth surface, otherwise much glass will be broken. It is useful if the table is marked off in square feet, with inches indicated, as this saves much loss of time in measuring.

Special cradles or frames are needed for carrying heavy leaded lights and lifting them into position and holding them there until fixed.

For drilling holes, hard-tempered steel drills are used ; or if the holes are to be not less than $\frac{1}{2}$ inch in diameter, a broken triangular file, ground to a point at the broken end and fitted into a woodworker's brace, will do. The main things are to keep the work well moistened with turpentine and not to drive the drill too fast.

MATERIALS

Glass.—The glass most commonly used by glaziers is sheet, plate, crown, and armoured, but there are many others.

Sheet glass is made up in large batches and then sorted into firsts, seconds, thirds, and fourths, according to their freedom from faults. Fourths are generally reserved for factory glazing and other positions where appearance is not of much importance. It is obtainable colourless (known as " white " ; it should be free from greenish or yellowish tinge), white opal (milky), ruby, signal green, bright blue, orange, and red. It is made in six weights per super foot, 15 oz., 21 oz., 26 oz., 32 oz., 36 oz., and 42 oz. The first three are usually employed in glazing, and are respectively $\frac{1}{13}$, $\frac{1}{10}$, and $\frac{1}{8}$ inch thick. While sheet glass is made in sheets up to 60 inches × 40 inches, as a rule 15-oz. glass is obtained in sheets of 24 inches × 24 inches ; 21-oz. glass, 30 inches × 30 inches ; 26-oz. glass, 35 inches × 35 inches ; and 32-oz. glass, 40 inches × 40 inches. These sheets are cut up into stock panes or cut squares.

Amongst the special types of sheet glass the following should be mentioned :

Rolled sheet glass, which is semi-transparent and used chiefly for glazing partitions in offices and workshops, in factories, and for horticultural purposes.

Fluted sheet, made both in narrow and wide corrugations. While it obstructs vision, it causes very little loss of light.

Muffled glass has a rippled or dappled surface, but is smooth and polished, and is procurable " white " and coloured.

Frosted sheet, produced by mechanical or chemical means, is obtainable with one or both sides treated.

Sanded sheet has a roughened surface produced by scattering sand over the flattening table when the soft glass is spread out. It partly obstructs vision.

Cathedral sheet is unbleached, roughly made glass, and has irregular surface. Much used in leaded windows and metal casements with small panes.

Speckly or specky sheet is much like cathedral sheet, but with the bubbles and specks artificially increased.

Antique sheet is prepared in the same way as prevailed in medieval days, and is an exact replica of the old glass. Chiefly used by glass stainers.

Ambeth glass, made in Sunderland, is made in colourless and tinted sheets. It is chiefly used by glass stainers, as it fires and takes stains well.

Flashed glass is " white " glass which, while in a soft condition, has a thin or thick film of coloured glass laid over.

Plate glass is made in various types, that used for high-class glazing usually being polished. It is rolled and polished on both sides and is made in sheets up to 200 feet $\times$ 16 feet 8 inches, in thicknesses of $\frac{1}{8}$, $\frac{3}{16}$, $\frac{1}{4}$, $\frac{5}{16}$, $\frac{1}{2}$, $\frac{5}{8}$, $\frac{3}{4}$, $\frac{7}{8}$, 1, $1\frac{1}{8}$, $1\frac{1}{4}$, and $1\frac{1}{2}$ inches. The $\frac{1}{4}$ inch is mostly used for ordinary glazing. If uniform thickness is required, extra price is charged.

Rolled glass is bright on one side and dull on the other, and therefore does not give a very clear vision. It is made in thicknesses of $\frac{1}{8}$, $\frac{3}{16}$, $\frac{1}{4}$, and $\frac{3}{8}$ inch, and is largely used for factories, warehouses, and skylights.

Cathedral rolled plate is usually about $\frac{1}{8}$ inch thick, and is made in a great variety of colours for use in leaded lights.

Double rolled is polished on both sides, and, like hammered and stippled (which have interesting surfaces), is fairly bright.

Hammered and stippled plate come under the category of figured rolled, which are given various finished surfaces. They usually obstruct light, but some (such as " maximum ") add brilliancy by deflection. Flemish rolled plate has an irregularly figured surface, not a regular pattern.

Corrugated rolled plate is much the same as fluted sheet, but made to the gauge of corrugated galvanised sheets, being chiefly used as roof tiling.

Prismatic plate has horizontal prisms on one side, and is used chiefly for lighting dark passages, as, though it obstructs vision, it increases illumination by refraction.

Rough-cast plate is made in thicknesses ranging from $\frac{1}{2}$ inch to $1\frac{1}{2}$ inch, for pavement lights.

Crown glass is made in large discs from the blowpipe and has a crown or blob in the centres and becomes thinner towards the edges. It is cut into " roundels " (under 12 inches in diameter) and quarries, most of them with " bullion " or " crown " in the centre. Chiefly used for glazing windows with small panes. It is procurable both " white " and coloured.

Slab glass is also a product of the blowpipe or glassmaker's iron, the molten glass being blown into a square-sided case-bottle mould. The sides and base are cut to form small panes, up to 7 inches × 12 inches. It is procurable " white " and coloured and has a remarkable brilliancy. It is an expensive glass.

Safety glass includes the armoured or wired rolled glass and " Triplex." The first consists of glass in which wire mesh has been imbedded when in a semi-molten condition. It is practically unbreakable and provides great resistance to fire, so is largely used in factories, for skylights and other exposed positions. It is cut in the usual way with the diamond ; brought to the edge of the bench, bent downwards, then upwards, and it will break off. " Triplex " is composed of two sheets of glass with a sheet of transparent xylonite between, the three being cemented together. It is practically unbreakable. It is indistinguishable from ordinary good-class glass. While principally used in motor-car and aeroplane work, it is also employed where particular precautions have to be taken against accidents from concussion or attacks by burglars.

Glass should be stored upright, on edge, and lifted out vertically. If laid flat, there is great risk of breaking when lifting.

Putties.—For wood glazing, putty is made by kneading sifted powdered whiting in raw linseed oil. It should be perfectly smooth, free from grittiness, soft but not sticky. A slight addition of red lead or litharge will hasten hardening, and the putty can be coloured by adding umber, sienna, or ochre.

For iron, steel, or bronze glazing, metallic putty is used, which is the same as the above, with the addition of white lead, red lead, litharge, or manganese.

In metal glazing, and in wood glazing exposed to much vibration or concussion, strips of rubber or wash leather are used for bedding. This bedding should be thin and soft.

For temporary work, putty may be made plastic by adding tallow or fish oil.

Thinned metallic putty is used to brush on in leaded lights.

For glazing in stone, mastic is used, and is a mixing of gypsum, litharge, and boiled linseed oil. Portland cement is a good substitute.

Lead Glazing.—For lead glazing, cames are used, which are long strips of lead of H section, the cross bar being known as the heart (which should be thickest) and the four wings as the " leaves." The leaf is slightly turned back and finished with flat (square), round, or beaded edge. The cames are made in a number of weights, the thickness of the leaf ranging from $\frac{1}{8}$ inch to $1\frac{1}{2}$ inch. When a leaded light is of a considerable size, it is apt to sag, and as a protection against this saddle bars are placed horizontally against the window outside, which are fastened to the cames by means of wires and solder. Saddle bars are of iron, steel, or copper ; but a modern substitute for these is steel-cored lead strips.

Solder.—The solder for lead glazing should contain 50 per cent. of tin.

Brads, etc.—For wood glazing, glazier's brads will be required, though small acute-angled triangles of sheet zinc are preferable.

WORKMANSHIP

In wood glazing, new work, and old soft wood, the rebates should receive a coat of priming, to prevent absorption of oil from the putty, which if deprived of its oil would be apt to perish and crumble away.

In old work the putty must be carefully cut away and all brads removed.

Before cutting, dust the table, examine the sheets, and if slightly hollow, place hollow side upwards. Give clean, sharp cuts, completing cut where a length is slipped, but do not go over the cut twice. Bring to edge of table and snap off by bending; or lift and place rule just under cut and snap off. In circular and oval working, after cutting of circle, make straight cuts from edge to circle at frequent intervals and snap off strip by strip.

The panes must be cut $\frac{1}{8}$ inch less on all sides than the actual opening. With a tight fit glass may shiver while being put in, or afterwards as the result of vibration, or the unequal expansion of the glass and its framing. A bed of putty is laid in the rebate with the putty knife, and the pane gently pressed well home. In most sliding sashes the top part of the bottom sash has a groove. This has to be partly filled with putty and the pane gently pushed up into the groove. In all but very small panes the glass must be secured by driving into the wood small brads, close to the glass. The small triangles of sheet zinc are preferable, as they can be pressed into the wood and against the glass quickly and safely. More putty is then applied and finished off with a smooth surface, at an angle from the edge of the rebate to the glass. Excess putty on the back of the glass is then removed.

In high-class work, where heavy glass is used, especially in places subjected to vibration or shock—for instance, doors—instead of bedding putty, thin strips of rubber or wash leather are used.

In high-class work the glass is often placed in the rebate of frames without putty, covered with beadings and fastened down by means of screws. But for external work the beading must be bedded in red lead.

In metal glazing the same processes are observed, but metallic putty is used, and in place of the brads or zinc triangles, lead plugs are passed through holes in the framework and pressed against the glass. It is even more essential in the case of metal than that of wood that the glass should not come into actual contact with the framework. Wash-leather and rubber beddings are largely used, though in up-to-date steel sashes putty grooves are the rule.

Lead lights are built up on the bench, the panes or quarries of coloured glass being fitted into the cames, brushed with cement, and the leaves pressed down against the glass on one side and then on the other. The cames are cut according to plan and soldered together where necessary. The outer cames, framing the lights, are generally much heavier. In plain geometrical work, the building-up is not a difficult matter. Greater care is required with pictorial work, where the contours vary greatly. When complete, the light is treated as a sheet of glass, and fixed in in the usual way, though generally with the reinforcement of saddle bars or their equivalent.

In the matter of artistic stained glass (or illuminated glass as it is also called) the artist provides a complete coloured drawing, indicating leading and all details. He may even paint the " white " or tinted glass with vitrifiable enamels and cause them to be fused on the glass in the kiln. Or this painting may be left to skilled craftsmen. The glazier has to carry out the design, putting together a kind of jig-saw puzzle. The pieces of glass are all put together on a flat table, and then one by one taken up and fixed on the cames, the cutting and soldering of these going on slowly in accordance with the design.

In more simple geometric or floral designs, the glazier may have to employ greater discretion in selecting quarries of good colour.

PATENT GLAZING

There are a number of patent systems of glazing, particularly for roofs, skylights, pavement lights, and horticultural work. These are almost invariably carried out by specialist firms or licensees, and when such glazing is demanded it is usually a matter of sub-contracting. The operatives are trained in the work, which is outside of the scope of this book.

Some patent glazing, however, can be applied by any competent glazier, following the manufacturer's instructions.

Patent glazing certainly gives the most satisfactory results on flat roofs or those of very low pitch, where drainage is a difficulty, and especially where condensation may be heavy on the interior of buildings, such as laundries, factories, and so on.

WRITING AND EMBOSSING

Writing on glass is usually carried out with the writing diamond described on page 224, and may be left in outline or etched over.

Embossing is also used for writing as well as decoration, and is a process of etching by means of acids, which produce a frosted appearance. This is done by preparing a drawing of the design, the outline being pricked. This drawing is then placed flat against the pane of glass to be used, and the outline painted over with gummed ink or other substance which will adhere to glass. The drawing is removed and that part of the glass not to be etched is painted over with Brunswick black. As soon as this is dry, a wall of mixture of tallow and Burgundy pitch is built round the sheet. Then hydrofluoric acid or white (French) acid is poured on ; it at once commences to eat its way into the glass, and when the etching has penetrated deep enough, the acid is poured back into its gutta-percha bottle, the glass rinsed with pure water, and the Brunswick scraped off after softening with turpentine. As the action of the two acids differ, it is possible to obtain varied effects by using one after the other and narrowing the field of action of the second acid by painting over the partly etched surface with the black paint. Sometimes the two acids are mixed together. This kind of embossing is frequently employed on flashed glass, the coloured film being eaten away to leave the design in white.

WASTE GLASS

Far too much "waste" glass finds itself into the unremunerative cullet heap. It is wise to collect all waste glass and go over it in slack times. From the smaller pieces panes measuring 3 × 4 inches or 4 × 6 inches are cut ; these come in handy for skylights. Next in size are the 8 × 10 inch and the 7 × 9 inch, utilised for cellar windows and sashes of old-fashioned houses. The most common sizes are 9 × 12 inches, 9 × 13 inches, and 10 × 14 inches ; these are in great demand for ordinary sash.

In some cases even larger panes are cut—$12\frac{1}{2}$ × 24 inches, or $12\frac{1}{2}$ × 26 inches, where the original size was large. The encrusted putty on the edges is scraped off, the glass washed, and then it is stored away in boxes, with the size noted in a label pasted on each box.

Coloured-glass fragments will be most useful to those who go in for lead glazing.

MEASURING

When cut, add 25 per cent. on cost of sheet glass to cover risk of breakage, waste, etc.

Measure and charge glass per foot super, counting fractions of an inch as a full inch.

Measure dimensions between rebates for square frames. Irregular shapes to be charged as squares, measured over extreme points. Circular cutting and risk to be charged extra per foot run.

Description and quality of glass to be stated, and method of glazing, whether bradded, sprigged, or bedded in leather or rubber.

Lead quarry lights to be kept separate ; also all leaded glazing.

Bent glass to be charged extra per foot super.

Writing, embossing, and gilding to be charged extra per inch.

Scaffolding, where necessary, to be charged, or percentage to be added to price of glazing.

Repairing leaded lights to be charged time and material.

CHAPTER XIV

BELL HANGING AND FITTING

Tools and Appliances—Bell-pull and Crank Wiring—Electric Bells—Wires—Wiring—Connections.

BELL hanging in the great majority of cases, both in private and business premises, is a matter of the installation of electric bells. In some old houses, however, and in a few exceptional cases of new wiring, the old bell pull and cranked wires are still in use. This method is quite simple. Nevertheless, whichever system is adopted, the bell hanger must be a handy man, with a working knowledge of masonry and carpentry, while for electric-bell installation skill in soldering and ability to handle insulating materials and manage primary and secondary batteries will be needed in addition.

The bell hanger will, as a rule, have to pierce brick or composite walls, and lath and plaster partitions ; to drill through wood floorings and joists, in order to run the wires or conduits through, and he must be able to do this without causing undue damage. Care is particularly necessary in drilling joists or any form of wood support, which must not be weakened, and in the case of electric installations well protected from direct contact with the wires.

Tools and Appliances.—The tools and appliances required are : Brick drill, for drilling through walls (with this a racket brace is needed), gimlets of different sizes and length of shaft, bradawl, screwdriver, keyhole or compass saw, tenon saw, hammers, file, pincers, taped nose-cutting pliers. For electric-bell work will be required a knife for stripping off insulation ; soldering bit and galvonemeter for testing wires when connected up with battery.

Bell-pull and Crank Wiring.—For this system all that will be required in most cases are wire, cranks, nails, and screws, with bells mounted on broad spiral springs.

Plain or fancy linked chains are sometimes used for gate or entrance-door bells. The pull is terminated by a loop or other form of handle, and just above this should be threaded through an eyeleted staple, driven into the wall or door post, to keep the pull taut. The upper part of the chain on entering the wall usually passes over an ordinary grooved disc pulley and is then fastened to one arm of a crank, the other arm of which is fastened to the spring on the bell, or to a rocker arm on the bell. In the latter case the base of the rocker is pierced with a hole through which a metal pin passes, resting in brackets fastened to the walls, the bell thus swinging free in response to the pull.

Wires of different gauges are supplied. Wires should always be galvanised, and it is advisable that they should not be too heavy. Gauge, however, will depend upon the length of the runs and the weight of the bells. Almost invariably wires are exposed. Sometimes they are stretched as far as possible between floor and ceiling, but while this hides them, it has the disadvantage that if any wire becomes slack or breaks, the flooring has to be taken up to get at it. More rarely the wire is concealed behind the wood skirting at the base of the walls, or by a hollow beading nailed or screwed to the top of the skirting, or to the top member of a moulding to a dado. In ordinary cases the wires are carried close below the ceiling cornice, or if the frieze be broad enough close to a projecting moulding which will partly conceal it. Wires should be stretched in as straight lines as possible, using cranks at any bendings as well as at the pulls, and the bells. Cranks are pieces of metal in the form of an open bow, pierced at the base for nailing or screwing to a small block in the wall, and having the two arms eyeleted for fastening the wires. The pull is wired to one arm of the crank, and the wire fastened to the other ; at the bell end the wire is fastened to an arm and the other fastened to the pin attached to inner spiral of the spring. Thus when the pull is tugged, one arm of the crank is depressed and the other elevated, pulling the wire and so influencing the spiral spring. By this it will be seen that the wire must not be too taut, nor must it have any slack. By the skilful placing of cranks it is possible to carry the lines round corners or at right angles. Where it is necessary to give two lengths of wire, the ends should be bent in the form of hooks, one within the other, and the ends, about 1 inch or $1\frac{1}{2}$ inch long, wound round on the wires. Such joints must not be made near cranks or any position where the wire passes through a wall or partition.

Galvanised wire and cranks can, with a very little trouble, be painted with oil or water colours, so as to harmonise with the decorations and thus be less conspicuous.

Lever pulls, usually with ornamental wall plates and levers, are on the same principle as the crank, but the mechanism is concealed. The wire is brought down, or up, concealed in a small groove in the wall behind the wall-paper, or covered by an ornamental beading.

Electric Bells.—As we are here solely concerned with installation, and mainly with wiring it is not necessary to describe the different types of bells, or even dwell upon the sources of energy. As to this last it will suffice to point out that electricity may be obtained from a primary battery (the usual course), a secondary battery (accumulator), or, if the supply system is alternating current, direct from the lighting circuit passed through a double wound transformer. The last is only used in big establishments. A secondary battery has to be periodically recharged (at uncertain intervals, regulated by the strain on the battery), which is a lengthy process. Primary batteries may be wet or dry. The wet batteries are charged with ammonium chloride solution when the plates are put in, and require to be filled up with water. Dry batteries contain sal-ammoniac in gelatinous form and will work without attention until exhausted. Batteries may be placed at any distance from bell or switch, but in a dry, cool place.

It is absolutely necessary that there should be a complete circuit through the bell spring and switch to battery.

Wires.—Copper wires are supplied ready insulated, wrapped round with insulating tape, usually in the form of twin wires, the two within one wrapping, but are also obtainable as single wires. The latter are not advisable, except in very extensive premises where economy may be effected by using the system of gas or water lead piping for the return circuit to the battery. In such a case a wire is connected from the switch to the nearest gas bracket or water top (close contact by wiring and soldering being assured), and the battery with the nearest point of the piping.

Wiring.—Wiring is either on surface or in conduits, tubes, concealed behind the plaster, wall-paper, wainscoting, wood beading, or other convenient method. In surface wiring the wires' are suspended by means of staples. The bent form of staple is the ' insulating saddle." If ordinary staples are used, the wire passing under them must be protected by an extra wrapping of black adhesive tape, and the staple must not press down too hard on the wire. In the conduit system, the tubes are either first fixed and the wire then drawn through, or the wire is threaded on the tubes, which are then fastened in place. Tubes may be fastened by merely plastering in grooves, or by means of staples, or by covering with partly hollowed wood beading. Wires must not be unduly stretched, allowed to kink, or otherwise damaged. If two wires are fastened under one staple or cross each other, they should be separated by wrapping round with extra adhesive tape.

Connections.—When the bell is reached, one of the line wires must be cut, stripped for an inch or two of its insulation and cleaned with emery cloth. This uncovered part should then be wound tightly round a pencil, so as to form a spiral spring. The clean end is passed under the loosened nut of the binding screw and the screw turned tight. The main end is fastened under the other binding. On reaching the switch (whether of tumbler or push-button type), the wires must be stripped, cleaned with emery cloth, and connected with the switch. The same proceeding is necessary when connecting up with the positive and negative plates of the battery.

When joints have to be made in wires, they must be stripped, cleaned with emery paper, the end of each bent into a loop to hook one within the other, and the ends wound tightly round the wire. The joint must then be soldered, using resin without any acid. After wiping the joint, it should be wound round with insulating tape, and if necessary made secure with rubber solution.

The three principal points in wiring for electric bells are to see that the wires are not damaged either by undue bending or removal of insulation, that the wires are properly and thoroughly connected with switch, bells, and battery, and that all joints are carefully soldered without the use of acid and then thoroughly insulated.

CHAPTER XV

NOTES ON SPECIFICATIONS

PLUMBING : Exterior—Roofing—Soil and Waste Pipes—Ventilation. INTERIOR : Water Supply—Tanks and Cisterns—Waste Pipes—Closets—Baths—Sinks—Ventilation. HEATING. ILLUMINATION. VENTILATION. GLAZING.

SPECIFICATIONS are the written directions by an architect or a building owner laying down particulars as to the work required and the materials to be used in the course of such work. They are, therefore, of great importance, as they place the contractor who accepts them under definite obligations, but also safeguard him when he keeps strictly within the regulations laid down. In view of these facts, specifications as a whole need to be carefully perused, each clause being considered separately and then in relation to its bearings on others. Without this study the full meaning of the document cannot be realised.

Some specifications are very brief ; others long and detailed. Both are open to criticism. If the work is of small importance, a short specification with few details will not matter ; but in extensive operations, involving much labour and the supply of large and varied quantities of materials, too vague directions may give rise to misunderstandings and even serious disputes. On the other hand, too lengthy and binding clauses may, in the course of a long job, prove very onerous, especially if the architect is one who sets his face against variations " on principle." In any case, positive deviations from a specification should only take place after the approval, and in serious deviations the written consent, of the architect.

Another point in connection with specifications is that they must conform to the regulations and by-laws issued by the Local Sanitary Authority and the Water Supply Authority. The contractors must be familiar with such by-laws ; the architect, who may come from quite a different district, may not be so, with the result that his specification may require correction. No doubt in such a case the contractor is bound by the by-laws ; but if there is a conflict between these and the specification, there may arise disputes with the clerk of works and delays in obtaining certificates.

Such are some of the main points to be taken into account. It should always be remembered that it is wise to take forethought in order to minimise the chances of dispute.

The following specifications are not intended to be definite models, but are given merely as examples of current practice, with clauses which suggest comment.   Alternative clauses are occasionally given and blanks left for obvious variations in filling in, especially in connection with materials.

Specimen Specifications
Plumbing

1. The Contractor shall supply all jointing material, copper nails, oak and lead wedges, wall hooks, tacks, lead collars, and other accessories necessary to ensure the work shall be perfect and complete.

2. All interior plumbing and drainage work to be done to the satisfaction of and in accordance with the regulations of the Local Authority and the Water Company [Authority], and in the event of these varying from any clause in this Specification, immediate notice shall be given to the Architect.

3. Notices shall be given to the Local Authority and the Water Authority, and charges shall be paid for making connection to main, and provision made for watching and lighting enclosure while such connection is being made, and the road and footway disturbed in so doing shall be made good to the satisfaction of the Authority.

4. The whole of the work is to be tested at the Contractor's expense, at such time and in such manner as the Architect shall direct, and to his satisfaction [within .... days of completion and by the .... method].

Note.—A clause is sometimes inserted here relating to scaffolding, which in new work is provided by the builder, but in much repair work by the Plumbing Contractor.

Exterior Work

5. All sheet lead shall be best English milled [cast, *for cheap work*], uniform in thickness and texture, and free from cracks and other defects and neatly dressed without injury to the surface and not to be laid in sheets larger than 11 feet × 2 feet 6 inches. [These dimensions should vary according to the nature of the work and the weight of the materials ; on slopes " creeping " has to be guarded against.] Due allowance shall be made for expansion and contraction without injury. No solder shall be used in laying gutters, flats, and other work to roofs, except where unavoidable.   All nailing shall be done with copper nails. The flats and gutters shall be laid to a minimum fall of $1\frac{1}{2}$ inch in 10 feet towards the drips and outlets, and shall be well and neatly dressed into rebated drips and over rolls, with bossed ends to rolls and bossed intersections.   Lapped joints to flashings shall be used and must not be less than 3 inches, and for valleys, ridges, and hips not less than 4 inches.   All edges where necessary shall be welted.

6. All gutters indicated upon drawings shall be formed with 7-lb. lead, the sole to be 12 inches wide at the narrowest part, with drips not less than 2 inches deep [in exceptional cases $1\frac{1}{2}$ inch is allowed] and not more than 10 feet apart.   The undercloak shall be closely dressed into

the rebate in the drip and securely nailed, the overcloak tightly dressed over the drip and down the vertical face of the drip to within $\frac{1}{4}$ inch of the gutter bottom, the wings to be turned up 9 inches under slates [tiles etc.] and dressed over tilting fillets and 6 inches against walls or other vertical faces, and shall be of sufficient length to give 5 inches [6 inches] horizontal lap at the wings, and shall be cut and dressed to meet the requirements of the drips. All lead where turned up against vertical faces shall be covered by a flashing of 5-lb. lead 6 inches in height, the upper edge being dressed to a right angle and inserted $1\frac{1}{2}$ inch into joint of brickwork [groove in masonry] immediately above the edge of the turned-up part of the gutter, the remainder of the flashing being dressed against the turned-up part of the gutter, the cover flashing being secured to the wall with lead wedges and the joint pointed in cement. [In the case of masonry, flashings and other lead, are burnt in.] All gutters behind small stacks of chimneys shall be 6 inches wide at the narrowest part and shall slope both ways from centre, and shall be of 6-lb. lead, dressed over tilting fillet under slates [tiles] at one side and turned up 6 inches against vertical work of stack and dressed 4 inches round returns of chimneys, covered with 5-lb. lead cover flashing as laid down for gutters. All aprons to fronts of chimney stacks shall be 5-lb. lead 12 inches in width, the upper edge dressed to right angle and secured into joint in brickwork [groove in masonry] as prescribed for flashings, and shall be turned down faces of stacks and neatly dressed on top of slates [tiles] for a distance of 6 inches, except where marked (exposed positions), where the distance shall be 9 inches, and be dressed 4 inches round returns of chimney. All horizontal abutments of roofs against vertical faces shall be provided with similar aprons. All sloping abutments of roofs against vertical faces (such as parapet walls, chimney stacks, etc.) shall be provided with soakers and cover flashings of 5-lb. lead dressed down 4 inches over soakers stepped down in brick [stone] courses and secured into joints of brickwork [grooves of masonry] as prescribed for flashings. No flashing or apron shall be in longer lengths than 8 feet and shall lap at least 4 inches at their junctions.

7. All wood flats shown in drawing shall be covered with 7-lb. lead and carefully dressed over the wood rolls, which shall be cut of timber 2 inches $\times$ $2\frac{1}{2}$ inches [$2\frac{1}{2}$ inches $\times$ 3 inches] and well undercut. The undercloak of lead shall be made to cover two-thirds of the wood roll, the overcloak being dressed right round the roll and with 1 inch of lap on the horizontal surface of the flat, the lead to stand up 6 inches against all walls and be covered with 5-lb. lead flashings 6 inches wide and secured to brickwork [masonry] as prescribed. The drips shall be 2 inches deep and as described for gutters. Where the flat terminates at a gutter, the lead shall be dressed down into the gutter for a distance of 3 inches [4 inches] and terminate immediately above the surface of gutter. Where the flat terminates to a raking roof sloping away from the flat, a lead apron shall be provided of sufficient width to cover the vertical edge

of the flat and to allow for dressing over the slates [tiles] for a distance of 6 inches [9 inches] down the slates [tiles], the lead of the flat being dressed down 4 inches over apron, but shall not reach the lower edge of the vertical surface. The edge of the flat shall be finished with a roll, the apron passing up behind the roll, and the lead of the flat dressed round the roll and down the vertical edge of the flat for 1 inch. Where the flat terminates against a raking roof sloping upwards from the flat, the lead shall be dressed up under the slating [tiling] for a distance of 9 inches and be dressed over a tilting fillet as prescribed for gutters.

8. All gutters between two roofs [or in valleys] shall be formed as shown on plan. They shall be covered with 7-lb. lead, dressed up vertical sides, to the tilting fillet, with proper drips. An apron of 5-lb. lead shall be dressed over tilting fillet, taken in 6 inches under slates [tiles] and turned down 4 inches into gutter [shallow gutters where marked to have the lead turned down within 1 inch of surface of gutter].

9. All cover flashings shall be secured with lead tacks 2½ inches wide out of 6-lb. lead and shall be of sufficient length to admit of being secured to the brickwork [masonry] under the flashing, and to pass down behind the flashing and turn up 1 inch upon the exterior face of the flashing, to which it shall be closely dressed, the tacks being placed at intervals of not more than 2 feet 6 inches in the length of the flashing. A lack shall be placed at all laps. All ridges and hips shall be secured by lead tacks 2½ inches wide out of 7-lb. lead, fixed under the roll and of sufficient length to be secured under the lead covering to ridges and hips and to pass down under the wings of the above lead coverings and turn up 1 inch upon its exterior face, to which it is to be tightly dressed, the tacks being placed on both sides of ridges and hips and placed at intervals of not more than 2 feet 6 inches.

10. All soakers are to be of 4-lb. lead, one to each slate [tile], and to be 1 inch longer than the gauge of the slate [tile], to lie 5 inches under the slates [tiles] and turn up 4 inches against wall, with stepped cover flashings fixed over.

11. Place slates of 7-lb. lead where ends of iron pipes or stays pass through roof, properly bossed and dressed round pipes, and with full lap of slating.

12. A cesspool of 7-lb. lead to be formed in gutters where marked on plan, not less than 12 inches square and 6 inches deep, the lead bossed to shape [all junctions to be made in angles and finished with broad wiped solder joints], dished and rebated to receive tufted end of 4-inch drawn lead pipe of 7-lb. lead, bent to necessary curve to connect cesspool with head of rainwater pipe. All cesspools to be covered with copper wire dome. All lead pipes passing through walls to be covered with tarred felt. Lead of gutters to be dressed down the sides of cesspools 3 inches. All cesspools to be supplied with overflow pipes.

13. Flanks of all dormers abutting against roof shall have gutter flashings formed of 5-lb. lead dressed over tilting fillets and 8 inches

under slates [tiles] and turned up 4 inches against side of dormer [slates, or tiles, to finish at least 3 inches from side of dormer].   The dormer cheeks shall be covered with 6-lb. lead turned over and close copper nailed along the upper edge and have secret tacks [or copper ties] where necessary for supporting the lead.   Such covering shall overhang the flashing of gutter 4 inches and be cut to take the rake of the roof and turned round front with wide ear and dressed over oak [pitch pine] sill and copper nailed in its water groove.   [Or, when roof abuts against side of dormer, lead soakers shall be used, as prescribed above the lead covering of dormer cheeks being dressed down over them.]

14.   Shaped and rounded rolls of ridges shall be covered with 6-lb. lead [in lengths not exceeding 8 feet], dressed well into the angles under the roll, and lapped 7 inches over the slates [tiles] on each side with 6-inch lapped horizontal joints, the lead under the lap being copper nailed to roll, the whole secured with lead tacks, the exposed ends being neatly bossed.

15. Hips shall be covered with 6-lb. lead [in lengths not exceeding 8 feet] in the same manner, but each sheet copper nailed at the upper end and secured with lead tacks, the exposed ends being neatly bossed and fixed with solder.

16. Valleys of main roof shall be covered with 6-lb. lead, 18 inches wide, dressed to slope of boarding, turned over tilting fillet on either side, and dressed 6 inches under slates [tiles], and have lapped joints of not less than 4 inches, each sheet being copper nailed at the upper end, the lower end of valleys being neatly dressed into eaves or other gutters and upper end dressed under ridges or other covering to which it joins.

17. Sills and [brick, masonry, wood] strings and cornices shall be covered with 6-lb. lead, dressed over top member of moulding, and upper edge turned up 5 inches and inserted $1\frac{1}{2}$ inch into brick joint [groove in masonry], the lead being secured with soldered dots and screws [oak, or lead, plugs in brick, or lead dowels in masonry].

18. Stone cornices shall be covered with 6-lb. lead dressed over top member of moulding, the lead fastened to weathered top of cornice with lead dowels and dots, and turned up against face of wall with a 5-lb. lead cover-flashing.

19. Soil pipes shall be equal to 8-lb. lead and have lead tacks soldered on to them, three pairs to every 10-foot length of pipe, with not less than two screws [or nails, or spikes, or wall hooks] to each tack [and to be carried down in a vertical line from top to bottom] and continued to the highest part of roof full bore, for ventilation ; any part of the pipe exposed to damage shall be protected by wood [or iron] casings.

Note.—It is usual to specify that these ventilating pipes shall be at least 20 feet from any window and capped by a galvanised wire dome.

20. All pipes shall be of cast iron with socket and spigot end, with bead on spigot end, and the spigot large enough to receive molten lead, and ears cast on [not less then 56 lbs. per 6-foot length].   They shall be

securely fixed to walls by long, strong iron pipe nails, shredded through 1-inch lengths of ½-inch wrought-iron pipe forming distance pieces to keep the pipe from the wall. [Earless pipes shall be secured to walls by strong wrought-iron pipe clips [or brackets in two sections bolted together, one section having fung, or lewised, end for building into walls].] All pipes shall be coated outside and in with Dr. Angus Smith's composition [lined with glass and painted outside]. All bends, branches, swan necks, and other parts shall correspond in every particular to the pipe. All joints shall be made with molten lead and well caulked. The whole pipes shall be carried down in as vertical a line as possible.

21. The lead soil pipe at its juncture with drain shall have a brass ferrule wiped on [fixed by an approved method], to be connected to socket of stoneware drain with neat cement joint. [The soil pipe to be connected to iron drain shall be fitted with a ferrule to be inserted into socket of iron pipe and secured by a packing of kemp and molten lead run in and well caulked] [or The iron soil pipes shall be connected to stoneware drain with a cement joint [to iron drain with molten joint well caulked].]

22. Soil pipes above highest branch shall be continued upwards of the full diameter and jointed [or secured to the wall] to a height of .... feet above eaves [roof] and be covered with copper wire [galvanised wire] dome [or the exterior soil pipe shall be continued in lead piping above highest connection of full bore, and taken through wall immediately below cornice and carried up along underside of rafters and taken through roof near ridge with lead slate, and finished with wire cap.

Note.—This is an alternative clause to the last paragraph of clause 19, to which clause, and Note, the reader should refer, as well as to the following.

23. All traps to branch soil pipes shall be ventilated from a point not less than 3 inches or more than 12 inches from their highest part, and on the side nearest to soil pipe by lead [or iron] pipes not less than 2 inches interior diameter, connected by wiped [or approved] joint [or *when iron*, molten lead caulked] to a vertical pipe of the same size and weight, carried up next to the soil pipe and taken into it 4 feet above the topmost branch. The pipes shall be carried by tacks [pipe nails, or brackets].

24. All exterior waste pipes from sinks, baths, hop closets, on the upper floors shall be of lead of .... diameter .... lb. weight per lineal foot, and fixed as in the case of lead soil pipes, and carried up and finished in the same way. Expansion joints shall be inserted every 5 feet.

Note.—Many architects object to lead waste pipes and specify iron pipes of the same character, and fixed in the same way as iron soil pipes.

25. All rainwater pipes shall be of lead .... inches in diameter [rectangular .... inches by .... inches] and equal to .... lb. sheet lead, being fixed by tacks [nails, etc.] as for soil pipes, and have necessary bends, and be finished at top by plain rectangular [semi-circular] hopper

heads [or ornamental cast or embossed hopper heads as per drawings] and covered by galvanised [copper] wire dome.

Note.—The diameter of the pipes, and consequently their thickness, will depend upon the roof area to be drained and the number of pipes. See Table at end of this volume.

Interior Work

1. This clause usually refers to Notices and Testing, and the same observations relate to these points as for exterior work.

2. All lead pipes shall be hydraulic drawn [for high-class work] and of equal thickness throughout, all connections being made by a wiped joint [by approved method]. All joints shall be of the full bore throughout and if not less than .... lb. per lineal yard.

Note.—See Table on page 298 for light, medium, and heavy-weight lead pipes.

3. All overflow waste pipes from safes and air pipes shall be of light weight. All service pipes from cisterns and waste pipes shall be of medium [heavy] type.

Note.—The description of service pipes is usually prescribed by the Water Authority, but where there is no public service is calculated on the service demanded and the character of service ; whether by gravitation, pumping, etc.

4. The rising main shall be a .... inch lead pipe taken directly to cistern and fitted with gunmetal high-pressure ball-valve, with copper ball No.....

Note.—When the services are taken direct from the rising main, in place of the above, the dimensions of the pipes are given and separate stop valve to each service prescribed.

5. All horizontal supply pipes shall have a fall towards main and drainage cock and all service pipes towards the outlets.

6. The usual alternative clause when iron pipes are used is as follows : All wrought-iron pipes shall be lap welded, of uniform thickness, and capable of withstanding a hydraulic pressure of over .... lb. per sq. inch, and shall be galvanised and put together with all the necessary bends, tee-pieces, and connections. [Often elbows are prohibited, or, if used, the round type prescribed.] Ordinary bends to be made without heating pipes ; sharp bends to be made before galvanising. All pipes to be screwed, socketed, and put together with red lead [graphite compound]. Connections with iron cisterns shall be made with a long thread and back nuts. The sizes and weights of pipes shall be as follows :

7. Connections with (lead) pipes and (lead) cisterns shall be made with brass connections and unions.

8. All stopcocks shall be full-way screwdown, of approved pattern, with union to each end, and have engraved labels. They shall be fixed close to the junction with cistern and main service, and fixed to every

main service pipe from cistern ; to every branch service from down and rising main ; to every service pipe, water-waste-preventer cisterns and intermediate cisterns, and to bath and valve closets.

Note.—Many specifications demand that the price for stopcocks should cover the cost of any stamping required by a Water Authority.

9. The supply pipe shall be fitted with a strong stopcock fixed under an iron cover, and a further strong stopcock fixed in an accessible position where the pipe enters the premises [in a brick pit with a galvanised iron cover, immediately before the pipe enters the building]. A small drainage cock shall be fixed just above stopcocks.

10. All lead pipes shall be wrapped in tarred felt where passing through walls. The rising main and all main supply pipes in roof [and where likely to be exposed to frost] shall be carefully packed and covered with slag wood on canvas backing [*or*, other alternative method to be specified].

11. Bib cocks shall be full-way screwdown, of approved pattern [*for lead pipes* : and have a screw ferrule fixed with solder into the body of the pipe, the end of pipe being soldered solid].

12. All pipes fixed in chases shall be enclosed with wrought deal casings fixed with brass cups and screws, and all pipes liable to damage cased in. (This, of course, is joiner's work.)

13. All pipes shall be supported on bearers [*or*, shall be supported by lead tacks fixed with solder to the pipe, two pairs to every 10-foot length in pipes 2½ inches bore and over in diameter, and three pairs to every 12-foot length in pipes of 2 inches bore, with not less than two screws [nails, spikes, or wall hooks] to each tack.

14. Outside waste pipes from baths, sinks, and lavatories shall have sockets 5 inches deep for expanding joints, the entering pipe being inserted to within 1 inch of bottom of socket, with indiarubber ring spring on and with lead ring covering.

15. All pipes in chases to be fixed with soldered [*or* other approved] flanged joints, soldered around the pipe and fixed to deal block of sufficient strength to carry the pipe, the deal block to be well secured to the wall, the joints being not less than 5 feet apart.

16. Provide and fix a lead [galvanised, wrought-iron, riveted] cistern to contain .... gallons, with all necessary perforations for pipes and overflows.

Note.—Provision is often made for jacketing or casing cisterns. This is almost invariably done with lead cisterns.

17. Cistern, baths, valve w.c. apparatus, and slop sink shall have beneath them a safe of 5-lb. lead, turned up 4 inches against walls, the head to be laid on closely-jointed boarding with smooth surface and with fall to outlet at one corner and with lead waste pipe taken through wall, the outlet to discharge in the open, clear of any rainwater head, and 12 inches lower than the inlet ; the lead waste being 50 per cent. larger in diameter than the service pipe.

Note.—Safes are usually dispensed with in the case of tiled or tesselated flooring.

18. All main waste pipes shall be taken up the full bore to a height of .... feet above the eaves [roof] as ventilator and finished with a wire dome. (See Note to clause 19, Exterior Plumbing.) All waste pipes shall enter gully traps above the level of standing water, and shall be provided with a trap inserted in the pipe as near as possible to cistern, bath, valve w.c., or slop sink, etc., each trap with access for cleaning.

19. Provide and fix where shown on drawing closet.... (This clause will vary considerably according to the pattern of closet used, as well as in conformity to the Local Sanitary By-laws and Water Regulations. It is usually followed by a clause relating to waste preventers, something to this effect :)

20. Provide and fix, not less than 6 feet above floor, a .... gallon galvanised iron [*or* porcelain enamelled iron] valveless and noiseless siphon waste preventer, with galvanised cover, carried on brackets, with pull and chain, ... inch ball valve with copper ball No. ...., with $\frac{1}{2}$-inch union for service pipe, 1-inch ferrule and 1-inch lead overflow, $1\frac{1}{4}$-inch [$1\frac{1}{2}$-inch] union and $1\frac{1}{4}$-inch [$1\frac{1}{2}$-inch] lead flushing pipe fixed with brass clips to wall, and connected to flushing rim with indiarubber cone.

21. Provide and fix where shown on drawing, on proper bearers, a flushing rim slop sink (*or* other pattern prescribed), with lead trap complete ; and provide and fix a siphon flushing cistern over the slop sink, with service flushing pipes, wastes, complete. The wall above the sink shall be lined to a height of 3 feet with white glazed tiles.

22. Provide and fix a wash-up sink at side of slop sink.

23. Provide and fix where shown on drawings a 5 foot 6 inches .... bath (full description is given), and lay on from hot and cold water service 1-inch branches and connect with supply valves, and also connect overflow with waste-water pipe, the waste pipe ventilated as prescribed above. (The best practice prescribes that the overflow should discharge free from the waste pipe.)

24. Provide and fix where shown on drawings a .... lavatory basin. Connect same to hot- and cold-water service with $\frac{3}{4}$-inch branch supply pipes, and put in $1\frac{1}{2}$-inch .... trap to $1\frac{1}{2}$-inch branch waste connected to main waste, with $1\frac{1}{4}$-inch lead ventilating pipe from trap taken through exterior wall.

25. Housemaids', nursery, pantry, and scullery sinks may be specified. They are now mostly of enamelled fireclay or unlined teak, but porcelain enamelled iron, wood lined with lead, tinned copper, or white metal is also used. The closest attention is needed as regards overflows, wastes, and ventilation.

Zinc Worker

1. All zinc shall be of the best quality, of uniform colour, free from spots and speckles, tough and pliable.

2. The roll cap roofing of flat [slope] shall be of No. .... gauge zinc in sheets 3 feet wide.

3. All zinc for flushings to be of No. .... gauge.

4. All gutters to be of No. .... gauge.

5. Eaves of gutters to be moulded .... inches by .... inches, No. .... gauge.

6. All grids to down pipes shall be channel shaped, No. .... gauge, and ventilators No. .... gauge.

7. All zinc shall be laid on deal boarding and secured by zinc clips passing under wood rolls without soldering and shall not come into contact with iron or lime mortar ; all rolls, drips, and falls to be such as to permit of expansion and contraction of the sheets.

8. Wood rolls on flats to be fixed at 2 feet 10½ inches centre to centre in direction of slope, to be fitted with 2-inch wide holding-down clips, fixed every 3 feet of roll and turned over the bent-up edges of sheet against roll, with 2½-inch deep drips 7 feet 5 inches from centre to centre ; sheets, clips, and rolls shall be covered with caps of sheet zinc secured by fork connections ; ends of rolls being finished with solid folded saddle-piece and stop end.   On slope the zinc sheets shall be laid as above, substituting welted joints for drips, the edges of the two sheets being fastened with 2-inch wide zinc clips nailed to boarding, doubled in securely.   Ridge shall be covered with a zinc roll cap with edges bent round to form head, secured with holding-down fork.   The eaves shall have projecting sheet doubled back to form a head, and with strip of zinc No. 16 gauge nailed along edge of boarding under margin of sheet.

9. Flashings shall be tucked into wall 4 inches [6 inches] up and pointed with neat cement, turned down over sheet and finished and stiffened by being bent round to form a bead.

10. All gutters shall be laid to have a fall of not less than 2 inches in 10 feet, nor less than 9 inches wide, and go in 10 inches under slates [tiles, sheets] from the sole of the gutter, and turned up 6 inches against vertical surfaces, with 2-inch deep drips every 7 feet 6 inches apart ; all zinc being secured with holding-down clips.

11. Eaves gutters shall be fixed with stay tubes every 1 foot 6 inches apart and screwed to wood fascia.

12. Provide and fix in eaves gutters over each outlet into down pipes channel-shaped grids, with small perforations.

13. Zinc cisterns shall be lined with No. 16 gauge zinc, properly lapped and close nailed with zinc nails ; the outlets being formed with brass unions.

Coppersmith

1. All copper sheets and tiles for roof shall be No. 24 gauge, weighing 16 oz. per foot super.

2. Vanes shall be No. 21 gauge weighing 21 oz. per foot super.

3. Copper sheets shall be laid on boarding provided with wood rolls

fixed .... apart in direction of slope, with caps welted over turned-up sheets, the junctions of sheets across flow and saddles, and end stops all being securely welded.

4. Lay on boarding .... copper tiles, cut to shape and of embossed pattern, and with top edge bent over to hang on to wood batten.

5. All copper tubes for hot water shall be .... in diameter and weigh .... lb. per foot run, and shall be jointed with screwed couplings with bent angles and full bore of tube all round.

Glazing

1. All glass shall be free from defects or scratches.

2. All putty for wood frames shall be oil putty, for steel or iron frames metallic putty, for stone or terra-cotta oil mastic. All glass to be well bedded and back puttied and sprigged where necessary. All putty to be trimmed and cleaned off. Copper clips, nails, screws, to be provided as required.

3. Plate glass shall have the edges blacked. All fluted and patterned glass shall be cut and fixed with pattern vertically or horizontally as required and in uniform manner.

4. Windows of .... shall be glazed with 21-oz. sheet glass, seconds [thirds], in putty.

Windows of .... shall be glazed with polished plate [rolled, patent] glass, on putty [beads, mouldings].

5. The .... doors shall be glazed with plate glass [rolled, rough cast, figure rolled, corrugated rolled] bevelled on one side and fixed in beads [mouldings] with rubber [wash leather strip] bedding.

6. Provide .... feet super of .... patent pavement lights of p.c. valve of .... per foot super ; fix same in pavement where shown on drawings, according to manufacturers' directions.

7. All windows of toilet-rooms, bath-rooms, w.c.s, shafts, shall be glazed with figured rolled glass of approved pattern [ground glass].

8. Take out and renew all damaged glass and leave glazing in perfect condition.

Lead and Stained Glass

9. Lead lights shall be thoroughly cemented on both sides and guaranteed weathertight.

10. Provide and fix in wood frames [stone] .... feet super of leaded lights, glazed, of 21-oz. sheet, thirds, in panes 7 inches × 5 inches in heavy hand-turned $\frac{3}{8}$-inch leads, and fixed with $\frac{3}{8}$-inch saddle bars in mild rolled steel [iron or bronze].

11. Provide and fix leaded lights in plain squares 7 inches × 5 inches of patent plate in steel cored leads, solid without saddle bars.

12. Provide and fix .... panes of embossed plate glass, bevelled, of approved design, for entrance door [Triplex or wired rolled safety glass for doors in ....].

13. Provide and fix .... panes of stained and painted glass, in accordance with approved drawings.

14. Provide and fix galvanised wire guards to outside of .... feet super windows of approved mesh and gauge.

Heating Engineering—Low-pressure Hot Water

1. Provide and fix in position indicated a horizontal return flue [vertical independent] boiler, of .... type, made by .... of ...., tested by hydraulic pressure to .... per sq. inches and provided with a drain cock, safety valve loaded to .... lb. per sq. inch, and suitable flow and return nozzles and branches.

Note.—A written guarantee of tests should be obtained from the manufacturers or merchants.

2. The safety valve shall be fixed with direct and free connection with boiler shell.

3. Provide and fix automatic damper and gear, and suitable doors for easy and complete cleaning of flues.

4. Provide and fix an iron pipe from drain cock to drain gully.

5. Provide cast-iron [wrought-iron] main flow pipes .... bore, and connect them to boiler with socket joint made tight with cement [flange and bolts made tight with canvas, *or* tape and white lead, *or* wire in grooves], and connect the pipes with each other in the same way [with screwed unions and white lead, *in* the case of wrought-iron]. The pipes shall be of uniform quality, free from flaws. All exposed pipes in rooms and passages shall be connected with socket joints and rust cement [screwed unions and white lead]. All joints must leave the bore of pipe full and free. All bends shall be of largest possible radius ; no L bends allowed.

6. Provide as per schedule. Fix radiators at points marked on drawing and connect to main supply pipe with valves to regulate and shut off water. [*For ventilating radiators* : Connect direct to the main supply pipes with no intervening valve or cock ; and connect with air opening in wall.]

7. Provide and fix to each radiator and bend [*or*, to each bend where necessary] an air-escape valve, of type .... made by ....

8. Provide and fix to each radiator an automatically controlled valve of the type .... made by ....

9. At the point marked on drawing fix a cistern [dimensions specified] with ball cock, and connect it to house-supply main and to the main return by suitable-sized pipes, that to return being of wrought-iron. At the top level of main flow fix a wrought-iron pipe not less than 1 inch bore and lead it up and through wall to discharge in open, the end of pipe being turned outwards with a quarter bend, the top of the bend being 3 feet above water level in cistern.

10. Pipes shall be placed in chases in the walls and covered with a

cast-iron grating of approved design, and the pipes shall be reckoned as heating the room. [*Or*, and shall be covered with non-conducting cement of approved quality, painted two coats of approved colour, and shall not be reckoned as heating the room.] Flow and return pipes led up a wall or through a ceiling shall be covered with non-conducting cement [*or*, with slag wool bound round with wire. Where pipes enter floors they shall be cased with a wood fillet screwed to floor, leaving a space of ¼ inch clear round the pipe.

11. Fix over each radiator a hood, supported by solid wing corbel bracket, the whole to act as a baffle to deflect heated air.

12. Fix behind radiators placed in front of wainscoting a sheet-iron screen, of not less area than that of radiator, not lighter than No. 16 gauge, fixed ¾ inch from wood by screws and ferrules.

13. Main flow in basements shall be covered with non-conducting material. Pipes led across ceilings in corridors shall be covered with non-conducting material and cased in with wood or sheet-iron.

14. Fit to fuel door air inlets provided with slide or swivel regulator.

Hot-water Supply

1. Provide and fix in position indicated in drawings a cylindrical dome-top cast-iron [wrought-iron] boiler [saddle or return flue boiler of wrought-iron] with proper flow and return openings, and fitted with suitable safety valve, drain cock, and wash-out plugs ; the safety valve shall be fitted to the shell top direct [to the main flow pipe] as near to the boiler as possible.

2. Provide and fix all needed dampers and soot doors.

3. Provide and fix proper flow and return pipes to boiler branches, leaving a plugged Y-tee in each, to connect with gas boiler or circulator. Lead the main flow to the rooms to be heated and thence back to the boiler by the nearest way. All bends shall be of large radius, and such as to take up all expansion. Couplings and sockets shall be of standard size and interchangeable. All pipes to be supported by stands and brackets, with rollers.

4. All taps 3 feet or more from the main shall be connected by double pipes. The combined area of the two pipes shall be equal to that of one pipe (that is, two of ⅜ inch to one of ½ inch) ; they shall be connected to different levels of the main.

5. Fix an iron cistern with ball-cock supply above the boiler and connect it to main cold-water supply. Connect bottom of cistern to hot-water return pipe, and lead expansion pipe from top of main flow to pour into the cistern. From top of cistern lead to roof [*or* to down-running pipe, *or* to open air] an overflow pipe in size next larger to the cold-water supply.

6. Place a cylindrical reservoir cistern in convenient place [a point marked on plan].

7. The boiler and all exposed pipes shall be covered with non-conducting material.

In connection with low-pressure hot-water systems, clauses are generally inserted stating that the installation is to provide and maintain the following internal temperature when the outer air is at 32° F. (here follows an examination of rooms with their respective temperatures). It is further laid down that the range of temperature in sets of similar rooms should not be more than 3° F. and that halls and corridors may be 7° F. cooler than rooms.

Meaning of " Approved "

When perusing a specification, a note should be made wherever the words " approved method " or " approved pattern " occur, so that these may be considered and their meaning determined beforehand when possible, or at least before the processes are actually adopted or the goods ordered. Where it is a question of fittings, involving more or less heavy expenditure, a pattern should be deposited or fully described and the particulars initialled. This is particularly important in connection with work for all public bodies and institutions.

Inspection

When examining work, the points coming specially under observation are :

Roofing.—That lead is dressed close over the rolls ; tacks are well placed ; joints properly formed to resist creeping and yet allow for expansion and contraction ; edges are dropped well over the end of the boarding towards gutters.

Water Supply.—That there is no leakage ; pipes are properly fixed ; and that supply is carried to all points where required.

Sanitation.—That soil pipes are water- and gastight ; joints well made ; wastes lead into the open or away from soil pipes ; overflows lead into the open ; that pipes are well ventilated, with openings above or away from windows and protected.

Hot-water Heating.—That the boiler is well set ; the pipes rise 1 in 70 to 1 in 120 from boiler ; air pipes are inserted at the highest points of the runs and carried to convenient outlets ; cistern is in a convenient position for filling ; that joints are well made with indiarubber rings and cement, or kemp yarn and red or white lead ; that the capacity of expansion tubes is proportionate to the quantity of water in the apparatus ; and that dips are avoided.

Generally.—That the materials are sound and the workmanship skilled and neatly finished.

CHAPTER XVI

QUANTITIES

EXTERNALLY. INTERNALLY : Stopped Ends—Cisterns—Baths and Lavatories—Lead Soil and Vent Pipes—Zinc Work—Castings—Hot-water Work—Cylinders, Tanks, etc.—Gas Fitter—Bell Hanging—Central Heating—List of Quantities—Quantities for Central Heating.

BILLS of quantities are documents drawn up by quantity surveyors, and are based on the architect's specification (giving particulars of quantities and descriptions of materials) and his plans (giving dimensions). It is on these bills of quantities, and having due regard to methods of work laid down in the specifications, that estimates are based. The two documents should enable the estimator to arrive at the prime cost of the job. He then has to take into consideration, as we shall see in the next chapter, various factors, such as contingencies, overhead charges, insurances, profit, etc.

When dealing with plumber's quantities, as the work of the plumber so readily divides itself into two sections, " External " and " Internal," it is usual to bill these separately, the external work coming first. The greater part of the lead used at the present time is " milled," both on account of cheapness and also from the fact that the sheets run in more even thickness, whilst cast lead, even with the best work, varies considerably. The latter is, however, sometimes used in roofs of churches, public buildings, and similar cases, where a large surface is exposed, on account of the more agreeable colour.

The description in the quantities, both as regards material and labour, should distinctly state whether the work is in cast or milled lead, as in both labour and material the former is more costly.

Architects in their specifications frequently omit to give the dimensions of the widths of lead and also the widths of turn-ups, etc. The dimensions hereafter given are those usually considered correct, but are, of course, subject to variation should the architect specify otherwise. There is one point that the plumber, sanitary engineer, or surveyor must always bear in mind, and with only $\frac{1}{8}$-inch scale drawings before him, will in the majority of cases require his careful attention, and that is the width of the gutters. It will be frequently found that the widths shown on plan are insufficient, after allowing for the increasing width at the higher end, owing to the rise in the slope of the gutter and the drips, and the plumber or surveyor will find it necessary to set these out to a large scale in order to arrive at the correct average widths. As he is dealing with a somewhat expensive material, it behoves him to use care in doing this. This may appear a somewhat troublesome business, but with practice he will find that it will take little, if at all, longer to do this correctly than to do so in a slipshod manner, and in addition he will have the satisfaction of feeling, whatever arises, his dimensions will bear the closest investigation.

The writer has endeavoured throughout these chapters to impress upon the engineer or surveyor the absolute necessity, if he has any idea of becoming proficient in his work, of avoiding anything like a loose or slovenly way of doing it ; in no trade does this apply more than to the plumber. Moreover, in these days of hurry, the architect, however desirous of turning out a complete set of drawings, finds that he has to prepare these in as short a space of time as possible, and may occasionally overlook little points of detail. It is in these little matters that the engineer or surveyor, by conscientiously doing his work, can become the helpmeet of the architect by clearing up doubtful points in the early stages of the work rather than leaving them to be discovered at a later date, when they cause delay and trouble to all concerned, which could have been avoided had the discovery been made earlier.

Externally

Gutters, Flats, Flashings, etc., per cwt.—The lead for these is measured at per foot superficial and abstracted under the headings of the various weights : 5 lb., 6 lb., 7 lb., or otherwise, as the case may be, and afterwards weighted out and collected. If the drips and rolls are not shown, take the former at not more than 10 feet and the latter at not more than 2 feet 6 inches apart. The lead to flats and gutters next walls usually turns up 6 inches, and up slope of roofs 9 inches from sole of gutter. Allow beyond the net width of the lead 7 inches for 1½-inch and 9 inches for 2-inch rolls, and 6 inches for 1½-inch, and 8 inches for 2-inch drips. Measure horizontal cover flashings 6 inches wide and stepped ditto (over soakers, etc.) 8 inches wide, apron flashings 12 inches wide and stepped ditto 14 inches wide, valleys 21 inches wide. Keep lead in soakers and stepped flashings, also secret gutters, separate, or take an item for the latter of " extra labour " at per foot run. Coverings to hip and ridge rolls are kept separate and should be measured 18 inches wide. Work of somewhat unusual character, as to small turrets, etc., should also be kept separate. Allow beyond the net lengths of flashings, valleys, coverings to hip and ridge rolls, etc., 6 inches in every 10-foot run, and also the same at each angle. This allowance will cover the lead required for the " tacks " as well as for " passings." The ordinary labour to dressing over wood rolls is included with the item, but the bossings at mitres, intersections, ends, etc., should be numbered separately. Welted, rolls—i.e. without a wood core—should be measured as " labour " at per foot run, with the mitres, etc., numbered as last described.

The following items are also measured at per foot run. Dressings over mouldings (stating the girth), double welt, bedding edges of lead in white and red lead ; copper nailing (" open " and " close ").

The following items are billed as numbers : Extra labour and solder to cesspools (if extra large, state size) ; mitres, etc., to mouldings (stating the girth) ; dressing lead around ends of sills ; bossing and dressing lead around finials, crockets, etc. (giving full description and size ; a sketch being frequently required) ; solder dots and screws ; copper tacks, outlet pipes from cesspools (stating diameter, weight of lead, length, the number of bends, and including the solder joints and any other connections and bands or tacks if necessary) ; gratings over cesspools ; outlets of gutters and to tops of vent pipes (stating if galvanised iron or copper wire and the shape) ; lead rain-water heads (these are generally given at a p.c., but if not, a full description with the thickness of lead and the size ; in the latter case a sketch will generally be required).

Lead rain pipes, per foot run, as hereafter described, to soil and ventilation pipes.

INTERNALLY

In measuring internal plumber's work the plumber or surveyor has to exercise his discretion as to the run of the pipes, etc., taking the shortest convenient run from point to point, bearing in mind that while in the better parts of the premises they should be out of sight as much as possible, they also should be easily accessible in the case of failure.

Lead Linings to Cisterns, Sinks, etc., per cwt.—Measure the lead for these at per foot superficial, and afterwards weight out as described for gutters, etc. Measure at per foot run soldered angles, close copper nailing, and other similar items, and number bossed angles to safes, stating the height of the angles.

Lead Water Pipes per Foot Run.—Give internal diameter and the weights per yard or per foot run. It is a good plan in the heading to the internal plumber's bill to make an abstract of the weights of the pipes for the different sizes of " services," " wastes," and " overflow and ventilating pipes." It will then be merely necessary to mention in the item to what category they belong. Keep the pipes laid in trenches and those fixed on walls separate, again separating the latter where they are fixed to glazed facing or tiled wall lining, describing also whether fixed with wall hooks, lead tacks (in the latter case describe the tacks and the distance they are apart), or brass or copper bands. Include with all pipes up to $1\frac{1}{4}$-inch diameter the bends, but if over this size number these separately. Any pipes of 3 feet and under in length, such as over-flows to waste preventers or short lengths of wastes, including the bends (stating how many in the length) and the joints, should be numbered. Measure wrapping pipes with felt or other similar material at per foot run.

Solder Joints.—Number these, stating the size of the pipes. In the case of a smaller pipe being jointed to a larger one, the plumber is entitled to the average diameter of the two pipes, but in practice it is not usual to mention less than a $\frac{1}{4}$-inch in variation in size. Running joints in the lengths of the pipes (unless a variation in size) are included with the pipes. Where a lead pipe is jointed to a lead lining of a sink or cistern, describe the joint as tafted. The soldered joints to cocks, etc., are usually included with the brass work unless a fitting such as a bath or lavatory is supplied with the cocks complete In the latter case keep separate as " to brasswork, including tinning."

Stopped Ends.—Number these, stating the sizes of the pipes.

Joints to Earthenware.—Number these, giving the sizes of the pipes. Some require indiarubber cones and others sleeve pieces : in this case a solder joint and a caulked joint are all that is necessary, and may be measured with the ordinary soldered joints.

Brasswork Generally.—There is such an infinite variety in the brass fittings used by the plumber that the student would do well to study and thoroughly master the uses to which these various fittings are put to enable him to take the " right thing in the right place." These should, of course, be numbered. In addition to the great variety, there is also a very great difference in the quality and cost, and therefore a very full description should be given, and, if possible, a list number and the makers' name. This applies with particular force to cocks and valves. In any case, they should be described as " including stamping by the water company." The solder joints to brasswork are included with the items as previously noted.

Cisterns.—Number these, stating size or the number of gallons they are to contain. If the space is confined, examine a maker's list to see whether a " stock size " will fit. If not, describe as " purpose made." Describe the thickness of the plates, either B.W.G. or the thickness as " $\frac{1}{8}$ inch bare," " $\frac{1}{8}$ inch full," etc. If with angle around top or special frame or stay bars, etc., describe these also. Mention the height to which they are hoisted, and measure bearers, etc., separately. The holes in cisterns are usually included with the items of boiler screws and other brass connections with the cisterns.

Connections with Company's Main.—Number this, giving the size of the connection and including the screw ferrule and drilling, and tapping the main, and make the item cover any fees payable to the Water Company.

Baths and Lavatories.—These are generally put in at a p.c. or l.p. and maker's name. Note whether the price given includes taps and other fittings, and whether a trap will be required, or whether it is contained in the bath itself ; if no p.c. is given, give full description and the size. Lavatories, as noted for baths ; note whether the overflow required a piece of lead pipe as connection, also whether a top has to be taken. Water-closets, as noted for baths. The waste preventers are frequently included in the price complete. If a pedestal closet, see whether the price includes the seat ; also the brackets for seat and waste preventer. Describe whether fixed to wood floor or otherwise, and how brackets for seat and waste preventer are fixed; whether plugged to ordinary brickwork, glazed facing, or through tiled wall lining.

Lead Soil and Vent Pipes.—These are measured per foot run, giving internal diameter and the weight of the lead " per foot superficial " as " equal to 7 lb." (or " 8 lb.," or otherwise as the case may be). Describe the method of fixing, and the facing to which it is fixed, also the kind of tacks, bands, etc., used in fixing, and the distance apart. If of very elaborate description, number these separately. If fixed in a chase, keep this separate, and describe as such. Short lengths, as from the water-closets up to the main pipe, are generally numbered, including with the item the number of bends and the joints. Number also beaded and perforated ends at top.

Iron Soil and Vent Pipes.—These are measured per foot run, as described to drain pipes. Note that in the event of the branch from the water-closet being lead and the main pipe iron, a brass " sleeve-piece " or " collar " will be required, as also at the connection of a lead soil pipe with the drain.

It is a good plan to have a note in the heading of the bill that all work is to be done to the satisfaction of the Water Company, but the surveyor should at the outset get a copy of the Regulations of the Water Company in whose district the work is situated to enable him to take his work correctly, both as regards weights of pipes and also the description of the fittings. He will also find a copy of the Regulations of the Local Sanitary Authority of great assistance to him where, as is sometimes the case, he has to use his discretion in selecting the various fittings.

Zinc Work.—The various thicknesses of zinc are denominated by " numbers," such as " 12 gauge," " 14 gauge," etc., but the matter is somewhat complicated by the fact that there are two distinct systems of numbering, the " English " and the " Vieille Montagne Zinc Company's," zinc manufactured by the last-mentioned company being generally considered the material for good work. It follows, then, that besides the number of the gauge the particular system of numbering must also be stated. In the event of " No.   gauge Vieille Montagne Zinc " being described, it will follow that the gauge is that of the " V. M. Company." Another point to be mentioned—and this is the difference between the best and inferior work—is as to whether the work is to be executed " without solder." This allows for the expansion and contraction of the sheets, and thus prolongs the life of the work. Zinc being made in sheets about 2 feet 10 inches by 8 feet, the rolls are usually taken at about 2 feet 8 inches centres, and the drips 7 feet 6 inches apart, it being thus possible to get each bay out of one sheet without joints. The rule as to drips also follows in the gutters.

Flats, per foot superficial, stating the " gauge." It was formerly the practice to measure zinc work in the same manner as lead work, but owing doubtless to the fact that more attention has been given of later years to the laying of the former material, by which the work is of a much higher class than formerly, the following is the system usually adopted : Measure the full width of the flat, and after allowing for " turn-ups " next wall, add the extra for turn-ups next rolls ; the length being measured as for lead work but the allowances for drips being more numerous on account of their being a less distance apart. The cappings to rolls are measured at per foot run, stating the girth of the zinc and including the clips. The ends to rolls are numbered as " capped ends " and " saddle pieces," as are also mitres, stating if " solid," i.e. out of one piece of zinc without solder, or " soldered," as the case may be. Whereas in lead work it is usual to bill gutters, flats, and flashings together, in the zinc work each item is kept separate. Gutters per foot superficial, stating the gauge measure generally as described for lead.

Castings.—Flashings per foot run, stating the gauge and the width and if "stepped." The bottom edge of zinc flashings is frequently " beaded " for strength. If this is so, mention with the description of the item. Soakers : Number these, stating gauge and size. Zinc is frequently used instead of lead for these on account of the lesser thickness of the former material, thus working in between the slates and tiles without the awkward tilt caused by the greater thickness of the lead. Rain-pipes, per foot run, stating gauge and diameter and the description of joints—" beaded " or otherwise—and how fixed. Number shoes, knees over plinths, etc. Eaves gutters per foot run, stating gauge, shape, and size, and how fixed, whether screwed through to fascia or fixed with iron brackets ; in the latter case give description of brackets and the distance apart. Number ends, outlets, angles, etc., as described to iron gutters. Coverings to cornices, etc., per foot run, generally, stating the gauge and the girth of moulding, numbering the angles, etc. Labours, etc., per foot run—welt, double welt, zinc nailing, etc. Number extra labour to cesspools, also labour and materials to finials, rainwater heads, etc., giving sizes and full descriptions.

Copper Work.—The system of measuring zinc work applies also generally to copper work, with this exception, that whereas the thickness of zinc is distinguished by " gauges," that of copper is by the number of ounces per foot superficial, as " 14 oz.," " 16 oz.," etc.

Hot-water Work.—Tubes per foot run. State diameter, the full description of tubes, whether " wrought-iron welded," " steam," and if galvanised, and state that the item includes short pieces. Number bends, elbows, springs, tees, connectors, nipples, etc. Note that it is advisable to take " disconnecting pieces " and long screws in long lengths of pipes to enable the work to be disconnected for repairs in the case of stoppage, etc.

Cylinders, Tanks, etc.—Number these, stating whether copper or galvanised iron, with the thickness and also the capacity. They are frequently described as "tested up to   lb. per sq. inch." Number the connections between pipes and cylinders and tanks and boiler, including the holes and the back nuts.

Valves, etc.—Note that these must be screwed for iron; and if no p.c. or l.p. is given, give full description and state they are for " hot water." If baths or lavatories come fitted complete with valves, etc., take an item of connecting hot-water pipe to bath valves, etc., as the case may be. At the end of " Hot-Water Work," in bill, take an item of " testing hot-water system," frequently described " at   lb. pressure."

Gas Fitter.—The gas fitting is frequently put in as a " provisional sum," but as it has sometimes to be measured, a few notes as to the system employed will be useful.

Tubing, per foot run, stating diameter, and whether " composition " or " wrought iron." If the latter, it is usual to include all bends, elbows, tees, short pieces, etc., stating this in the item. Where it is proposed to put in only the pipes, take " plugs " at the different " points to stop off." The Gas Company usually lays on the gas up to the meter without charge. If the meter is supplied by the contractor, number this, describing the number of lights, and whether " wet " or " dry." If the meter is supplied by the Company at a rental, take an item of " fixing only meter," including with it the length of lead pipe connecting the meter with the main. If a small meter, take a wood bracket for same.

Fittings are usually given at a p.c. or l.p., and if given as a lump sum, take an item as number, of fixing " wall brackets " " one (two or three) light pendants," as the case may be. Number blocks for brackets. Take an item of " attendance " on gas-fitting to " No. points," including with this holes through floor and walls, and fixing floor boards with screws for removal. At the end of the gas-fitter's bill take an item of " allow for testing gas services with gas-bag."

Bell Hanging.—Bell-hanging is also frequently put in at a " provisional sum," but if to be billed in detail the following system may be adopted : In the case of swing bells, number these, stating the weight of each, and whether pendulums are included, and take the wires as numbers, also including brackets, etc., and describing the wire, i.e. material B.W.G., etc., and stating if in tubes, and the material, and if bedded in plaster. Bill these as " No. —— pull from —— to ring bell in ——," and so on. This, of course, necessitates reference to the drawings, but a glance at the drawings will give a bell-hanger a better idea of the extent of the work than any measurement. Number pulls (at p.c. or l.p.), also bell-boards (stating for No.   bells). In the case of electric bells, somewhat the same system can be adopted, but frequently one bell or gong answers for a number of points ; in this case an " indicator " is required. Number this, stating for how many bells, and also the description of bell or gong. Describe the wires by B.W.G., and the covering of same. Number pulls as described for swing bells. Take an item of attendance on " No.   bells."

Central Heating.—Fig. 575A illustrates the sectional elevation of a portion of a central-heating system, and to prepare the Quantities to cover the work, the first essential is to examine thoroughly the pipe runs involved from boiler to radiators with the returning pipes to the former, and to visualise them in a mental picture.

The example is only given as a guide, and no complications have been introduced so as to ensure that the method can be followed.

Having completely mastered the above-mentioned points, proceed to " take off " the materials as follows :

No. 1 *Boiler.*—Describe same from the Makers' Quotation for same, giving the makers' name, dimensions, etc., with the price delivered, etc., and ascertain that the figure includes for the stoking tools, gauges, safety valve, etc., etc., all of which should be mentioned.

No. 2.—8-column Radiators. *No.* 1.—6-column Radiators.

(Describe each of these items in similar manner to that for boiler from particulars obtained from quotation, and state dimensions.)

Note.—It may be that the particulars as mentioned above are given in the Specification covering the work ; if so, they should be reiterated in the enquiry to the manufacturers concerned, to obtain the price on which to base the estimate, or again, the Specification may deal with the matter by stating a " prime cost " figure.

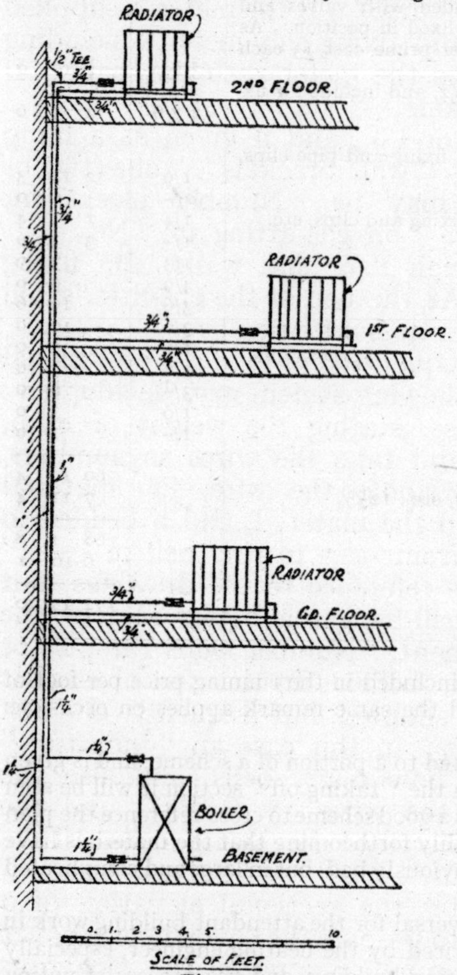

Fig. 575A.

" TAKING OFF "

Basement

2/7′ 0″ $1\frac{1}{4}$″ wrot-iron steam pipe.
2′ 0″ $1\frac{1}{4}$″ ditto ditto
11′ 0″ $1\frac{1}{4}$″ ditto ditto
6′ 0″ $1\frac{1}{4}$″ ditto ditto
No. 2. $1\frac{1}{4}$″ connectors and back nuts.
No. 2. $1\frac{1}{4}$″ bends.

First Floor

2/10′ 0″ $\frac{3}{4}$″ wrot-iron steam pipes.
9′ 0″ $\frac{3}{4}$″ ditto ditto
12′ 0″ $\frac{3}{4}$″ ditto ditto
No. 2. $\frac{3}{4}$″ bends.
No. 1. $1 \times \frac{3}{4} \times \frac{3}{4}$″ Tee.
No. 1. $\frac{3}{4}$″ connector and back nuts.

Ground Floor

2/11′ 0″ 1″ wrot-iron steam pipe.
6′ 0″ $\frac{3}{4}$″ ditto ditto
10′ 0″ $\frac{3}{4}$″ ditto ditto
No. 2. $1\frac{1}{4} \times 1 \times \frac{3}{4}$″ Tees.
No. 2. $\frac{3}{4}$″ bends.
No. 1. $\frac{3}{4}$″ connector and back nuts.

Second Floor

3′ 0″ $\frac{3}{4}$″ wrot-iron steam pipes.
6′ 0″ $\frac{3}{4}$″ ditto ditto
No. 1. $\frac{3}{4}$″ connector and back nuts.
No. 2. $\frac{3}{4}$″ bends.
No. 2. $\frac{3}{4}$″ equal Tees.
No. 1. $\frac{3}{4} \times \frac{3}{4} \times \frac{1}{2}$″ Tee.

From these " taking off " particulars they are brought into " abstract," that is, under similar headings as follows, to permit of the necessary additions to be made as shown :

No. 1. Boiler as described.
No. 2. 8-column Radiators as described.
No. 1. 6-column ditto ditto

$1\frac{1}{4}$″ W.I. Pipe.	1″ W.I Pipe.	$\frac{3}{4}$″ W.I. Pipe.	$1\frac{1}{4}$″ Connectors.
14′ 0″	22′ 0″	6′ 0″	No. 2
11′ 0″		10′ 0″	
6′ 0″		20′ 0″	
		9′ 0″	
31′ 0″		12′ 0″	
		6′ 0″	
2′ 0″ short length		63′ 0″	
		3′ 0″ short length	

$\frac{3}{4}$" Connectors.	$1\frac{1}{4}$" Bends.	$\frac{3}{4}$" Bends.	$\frac{3}{4}$" Tees.	$1\frac{1}{4} \times 1 \times \frac{3}{4}$" Tees.	$1 \times \frac{3}{4} \times \frac{3}{4}$" Tees.	$\frac{3}{4} \times \frac{1}{2}$" Tees.
No. 1	No. 2	No. 2	No. 2	No. 2	No. 2	No. 1
1		2				
1		2				
3		6				

It is now a comparatively simple matter to bring these facts into Bill form, and would result as under :

				£	s.	d.
		No. 1	Messrs. X boiler provided with stoking tools, safety valve, etc., etc., all as described in quotation dated . . . at £35, or alternatively as per description and prime cost given in Specification, £35, including handling into position and fixing complete.	£40	40	0	0
		No. 2	Messrs. X 8-col. Radiators provided with valves and clips complete and hoisted and fixed in position. As per quotation £3 each, or as per prime cost £3 each given in the Specification.	£3 15/–	7	10	0
		No. 1	Ditto ditto 6-col. at £2, and include for fixing, etc.	£2 7/6	2	7	6
yds.	feet						
	31	run	$1\frac{1}{4}$" wrot steam pipe, including all fixing and pipe clips, etc.	1/9	2	14	3
	3	run	$1\frac{1}{4}$" ditto in short lengths	2/–		6	0
	22	run	1" wrot steam pipe and including fixing and clips, etc.	1/4	1	9	4
	63	run	$\frac{3}{4}$" ditto ditto	1/–	3	3	0
	3	run	$\frac{3}{4}$" ditto in short lengths	1/3		3	9
		No. 2	$1\frac{1}{4}$" connectors and back nuts	4/9		9	6
		No. 3	$\frac{3}{4}$" ditto ditto	3/6		10	6
		No. 3	$1\frac{1}{4}$" bends	3/6		10	6
		No. 6	$\frac{3}{4}$" bends	1/6		9	0
		No. 2	$1\frac{1}{4}$" × 1" × $\frac{3}{4}$" Tees	3/6		7	0
		No. 2	1" × $\frac{3}{4}$" × $\frac{3}{4}$" do.	3/–		6	0
		No. 2	$\frac{3}{4}$" equal Tees	1/6		3	0
		No. 1	$\frac{3}{4}$" to $\frac{1}{2}$" Tee	1/–		1	0
					60	10	4
			Add Overhead charges, insurances, etc., $12\frac{1}{2}$%		7	11	4
					68	1	8
			Add for Profit, say 10%		6	16	2
					£74	17	10

Pipe clips and hangers as required are usually included in the running price per foot of piping, and therefore have not been detailed, and the same remark applies on occasions with connectors.

It will be noted that the considerations are limited to a portion of a scheme, and is given by way of an example of the method followed. In the " taking off " section it will be seen that the particulars are noted for each floor, and it is a good scheme to cross-reference the plan and these figures, as by so doing satisfaction is readily forthcoming that the materials have not been duplicated or omitted, both errors being obviously bad, but in large and complicated systems of heating easily made.

In the consideration of Quantities it is not universal for the attendant building work in cutting away for holes in floors and walls to be priced by the heating engineer, especially should the proposed heating scheme be in an existing building, and the process of noting the plan and " taking off " mentioned in the preceding paragraph will be found to be of great service, enabling one to appreciate the work involved ; the class of construction in floors or walls, etc., can be added to the information, and what is still more important, the making good and out to the various disturbances to existing materials and constructions.

There also occur very important factors in ascertaining such facts for pricing the Quantities for an estimate, namely, accessibility of the work and ordering the materials required in exact or most economical lengths. It will be seen that the piping is described as part in short lengths, which also includes, incidentally, all joints, cutting, screwing, pipe clips, hangers, etc. The risk of estimating is reduced to a minimum by tabulating, say, in the column of the Bill of Quantities the lengths required in detail, and order accordingly. Moreover, the inspection of the job with the plan will prove perhaps that a long run of pipe shown obviously in one length cannot be got into position in consequence of partitions being in the way, awkward position of doorways, windows, fittings, etc., and necessitates two or even three sections to fix same. By noting such conditions, the price can be adjusted to cover the extra work and the ordering of material more exact to requirements.

It must be clearly understood that the majority of these latter notes are directed to the work of the heating engineer in alteration work or work in an existing building, and not so much to new work where the building is in carcase form. Care should not be lacking in deciding the fixing of the pipe runs and also to get them approved. Such omission may lead to disputes at the finish of the job, the former remark to extra work to be included for, for instance, a pipe board or special clip fixing as against the stereotyped plug and pipe clips to wall. In estimating do not forget the covering up of existing work and protection of premises involved generally ; in many cases this has proved to be an expensive item. There is another item frequently overlooked, namely, the fact that the work cannot for some reason or other be pursued continuously or at certain hours of the day, causing additional expense to the heating engineer. It is a legitimate expense, and should be included in the estimates. A note of any special boiler, radiators, or other fittings, and whether in stock, should be ascertained from the suppliers, or whether delay would arise.

The prices of steam pipe can be obtained from suppliers, and is usually list price subject to several discounts.

Appended is a current NET price list, and it will be noted that the cost of pipes varies in the lengths ordered, emphasising the importance of keeping to the nearest possible lengths required.

TUBES, ETC. (GALVANISED STEAM)

	½″	¾″	1″	1¼″	
	s. d.	s. d.	s. d.	s. d.	
2–4 feet	— 5	— 6	— 8	— 11	per foot run.
4–6 feet	— 4½	— 5½	— 7½	— 10½	per foot run.
6–9 feet	— 4	— 5	— 7	— 9	per foot run.
Connectors	— 11	1 2	1 7	2 0	each.
Bends.	— 8	— 10	1 2	1 10	each.
Tees	1 1	1 4	1 7	2 1	each.
Elbows (round) . .	1 0	1 2	1 5	2 0	each.

TUBES FOR STEAM (RED)

Prices in this instance range about 1*d.* per foot run less than the above list, and fitting *pro rata.*

CHAPTER XVII

ESTIMATING, PRICING, AND RENDERING ACCOUNTS

PLUMBING : Detailed Estimate—Lump-sum Estimates. COPPERSMITH. CENTRAL HEATING : Hot-water—Steam—Hot Air. VENTILATION. GAS FITTING. RENDERING ACCOUNTS.

PLUMBING

ON most large buildings the quantities for the plumbing are taken out by the surveyor, and a Bill of Quantities is sent to the sanitary engineer and plumber for his price. The bill sets out all the items in detail, the milled lead for roofs, gutters, flashing, soakers, etc., being given in weight ; soil, anti-siphonage, waste, and service pipes are given at per foot run ; while the fittings are numbered and described and given at per each.

Detailed Estimate.—As these quantities are taken from plans, they are not given as exact, but form the basis price, and when the job is finished, it is measured up, and the variations, either additions or deductions, are added to or deducted accordingly.

In such cases, for estimating, take out the cost of the materials at the current price, and as the price of lead is subject to market fluctuations, care is necessary in estimating, to guard against loss from a rising market. The labour for lead-laying should be priced at per cwt., and for the iron and lead pipes at per foot run, the iron pipes to include for all blue lead joints. The joints to fittings being counted and allowed for with the fittings. All bends in lead pipe under $1\frac{1}{4}$ inch are included in the run of the pipe, but above $1\frac{1}{4}$ inch are paid for as extra labour to making bend in lead pipe. The various apparatus and fittings are usually specified to be of a particular manufacturer's make, and given as a P. C. item, and to these the estimator must add the cost of handling and fixing, also profit, where the item shows none.

Beyond the knowledge of the best market for the various materials and the time the work should take, the estimator is not worried by having to take the responsibility of accurate measurements, the surveyor being responsible for these, so that this class of estimating is really pricing bills of quantities, the labour being the crux of the estimator's ability.

Lump-sum Estimates.—In the majority of cases a lump-sum estimate is asked for, and here the onus of measurement besides prices of materials and labour, devolves on the estimator.

In roof work he has to measure before he can calculate the weight of the lead required for floats, flashings, gutters, ridges, etc., which is charged for by weight, instead of measurement, at so much per cwt. including all labour required in laying. In gutters, allowance must be made for turning up under slating 9 inches from bottom, and 6 inches against walls and for copper nailing, and for the flashing to make the weathering when turned up against the brickwork. For laps, rolls, and drips it is usual to allow 4 inches in length for each lap to flashing, and 8 inches for each drip when measured on the flat. Bossed and soldered ends to rolls, soldered dots, small cesspools, and outlet pipes to gutters, although included in a lump-sum estimate, are charged for separately and by numbers in a priced account, and not by weight, and lead dressings to mouldings are charged for at per foot run, with the number of mitres. The estimator takes all these items at cost price separately, and carries them to a summary which includes the whole of the materials and labour required for the job, and to the total cost is added country money (if any), fares, cartage, establishment charges, and profit.

In pricing accounts for plumbing work, all pipe work is priced at per foot run, according to diameter and weight, and includes fixing and holdfasts and running joints. Joints are charged extra and numbered and include solder and labour. The diameters and weights of service pipes have already been given. Soil pipes are usually out of 7- or 8-lb. lead, the latter being the weight generally specified; stopcocks and bibcocks should be accurately described and charged at per each, the price including joint whether to lead or iron pipe; also plugs and washers, wastes, traps, gratings and ferrules.

Water-closets, urinals, lavatory basins, and baths are charged according to the description of each, and price includes handling and all connections.

For the water-storage cisterns the size is calculated on an allowance per day of 25 gallons per person or 20 gallons per room, and the total number of gallons divided by 6·25 (1 cu. foot of water equals 6·25 gallons) gives the cubic capacity of the cistern required; and although the makers' lists give the required size of cistern for the number of gallons given, it is often necessary for the plumber to work to a special size to suit the surroundings. The cisterns are priced not only as regards their capacity, but according to the gauge of the metal used, this varying from 18 gauge to ⅜-inch plate or more according to size. The following is a guide for costs in sheet lead and pipe.

Milled lead in sheets, delivered in London per ton, current price. Country add £1 10s. per ton.

Lead pipe in coils, add about 5s. to current price of lead.
Soil pipe in 10-foot lengths, add about 5s. to current price of lead.
For lots under 5 cwt., extra per ton, add about £1 10s. to current price.
Cut to sizes, extra per ton, add about £2 to current price.

For estimating and measured prices, profit, etc., must be added; and a guide for the labour is as follows:

Milled lead laid :

 in flats, current price per cwt. plus profit and labour only, 10s. per cwt.

 in gutters and flashings, ditto, 17s. 6d. per cwt.

 in hips and ridges, ditto, 17s. 6d. per cwt.

 in stepped flashings, ditto, 19s. per cwt.

 in soakers, laid in, ditto, 5s. per cwt.

 in lining cisterns, cisterns, etc., ditto, 16s. 6d. per cwt.

Labour and Materials :

 Soldered seam, per foot run, 1s.

   „ angle, per foot run, 1s.

   „   „ short lengths, up to 6 inches, each 9d.

 Copper nailing, open, per foot run, 3½d.

   „   „ close, per foot run, 7d.

   „   „ very close, per foot run, 10d.

 Lea wedgings to flashings, per foot run, 4d.

 Labour welted edge, single, per foot run, 2d.

   „   „ double, per foot run, 4d.

 Soldered dots, including screws, each, 2s.

 Bossed ends to rolls, each, 1s.

 Extra labour and solder to cesspools, each, 10s.

 Plain cast lead clips and fixing, 1-inch, 1s. ; 1¼-inch, 1s. 3d. ; 1½-inch, 1s. 6d. ; 2-inch, 2s. each.

 Plain cast lead tacks and soldering, 2-inch pipe, 3s. 6d. ; 2½-inch, 4s. ; 3-inch, 4s. 9d. ; 3½-inch, 5s. 9d. ; 4-inch, 6s. 3d. each.

 Lead pipe, per foot run, prices to include for all bends, in 1¼-inch pipe and under, and also for all soldered joints in running lengths, wall hooks, and fixing.

TABLE XCVI

Service :

	Weight per foot.				per foot. s. d.				each. s. d.
½" pipe,	2 lb.,	current price ;	fixing,	0 7;	branch solder joints			2 6
¾" „	3 „	„	„	„	0 7	„	„	„	2 9
1" „	4 „	„	„	„	0 10	„	„	„	3 0
1¼" „	5⅓ „	„	„	„	1 2	„	„	„	3 6
1½" „	7 „	„	„	„	1 7	„	„	„	4 3
2" „	10 „	„	„	„	2 0	„	„	„	5 3

Waste :

1" „	2½ „	„	„	„	0 8	„	„	„	3 0
1¼" „	3½ „	„	„	„	0 11	„	„	„	3 6
1½" „	4⅔ „	„	„	„	1 2	„	„	„	4 3
2" „	6 „	„	„	„	1 9	„	„	„	5 3
2½" „	8½ „	„	„	„	2 3	„	„	„	6 3

Drawn lead soil and ventilating pipes, prices per foot run for material (take current price for pipe) and labour, but exclusive of all soldered joints (except running joints), tacks, labour to bends, all of which are to be numbered and charged extra.

TABLE XCVII

Per foot run.		s. d.							each. s. d.			each. s. d.
3½", current price ;	labour,	2 0 ;	cast lead tacks and soldering,						5 6 ;	soldered branch joints,		7 6
4" „	„	2 0	„	„	„	„	„		6 3	„	„ „	8 9
4½" „	„	2 6	„	„	„	„	„		7 0	„	„ „	10 0
5" „	„	2 9	„	„	„	„	„		8 0	„	„ „	11 3
5½" „	„	3 0	„	„	„	„	„		9 3	„	„ „	12 6
6" „	„	3 6	„	„	„	„	„		10 6	„	„ „	14 0

Cast-iron soil pipes from 2 inch, 2½ inch, 3 inch, 3½ inch, and 4 inch should be of London County Council weight and coated with Dr. Angus Smith's solution. These are in general use for outside wastes and soil pipes, fixed with holderbats cut and pinned into brickwork and with properly caulked lead joints. These are priced at per foot run to include joints and fixing, and the fittings are now made in such a variety of lengths and angles that almost any position for branches can be obtained, without the necessity of lead pipe for the connections, and the junctions are made with reducing arms or branches, to take the anti-siphonage direct, which makes a very neat job, and the labour costs about half that for lead pipes of the same diameter.

Drawn lead traps with brass cleaning screw from 1¼ inch to 4 inch are mostly in two shapes " P " and " S," and two weights, " Light " and " Strong," and are priced at per each, fixing and soldered joints extra. Domical wire guards, either copper or galvanised iron for surmounting soil and waste pipes, are charged at per each, and so are all fittings such as baths, lavatory basins, urinals, sinks, water-closets, which with water-waste-preventing cistern, seat, down-flush pipe, etc., are usually termed as " water-closet suite complete," valves, both stop and bib, boiler screws, plumbers' unions, and ferrules (with profit and labour added), joints being charged separately. Cisterns are charged separately from the ball valves and overflow pipes, and all holes are charged at per each according to size. For daywork, the charge for a plumber is usually about 2s. 6d. per hour, which charge includes establishment charges, insurance, use of plant, supervision, and profit, and for plumber's mate 1s. 9d. per hour, but of course the price fluctuates with the rise or fall of wages, though these have been fairly constant the last two or three years, and are never likely to fall to the old pre-war level. Railway fares, time in travelling, country money, charged extra.

COPPERSMITH

This work is measured in the same way as that of the plumber or zinc worker, but as the price of copper is subject to violent market fluctuations, it is usual to insert the clause " subject to market prices " in all contracts ; it is also usual to add 20s. per cwt for cutting sheet copper. Riveted copper furnace pans are priced at per lb., copper circulating cylinders at per each.

Zinc Worker.—This work is measured in the same way as that of the plumber or coppersmith. The estimator should tender for good quality zinc, which when well laid is a permanent and economical material for roofing purposes ; but if inferior zinc be used, trouble is sure to follow, for it contains other metals in admixture, and a voltaic action is set up which rapidly decomposes it. Care also should be taken to avoid iron nails, and all contact with iron or lime. In estimating, allow sufficient play for contraction and expansion, and arrange the drips and falls so as to avoid the necessity of any soldering, for flats nothing lighter than No. 16 should be used, and for gutters No. 15. Zinc half-round and O.G. gutters from 2 inches to 5 inches in 7-foot lengths, are usually priced at per dozen according to the gauge, and rain-water pipes in 8-foot lengths, 1¼ inch to 4 inches also, with heads, shoes, and bends. Daywork for the zinc worker is usually charged about 2s. 5d. per hour, and labourer 1s. 7½d. per hour, with the usual extra charges for country work and travelling time.

CENTRAL HEATING

Hot Water.—This is either to estimate, or daywork and materials. Usually an estimate is required, and the only particulars given to the heating engineer in most cases is the inside temperature required when it is freezing outside ; and if for a new building, he is given a set of plans, from which he has to take his particulars and set out his scheme. For this the cubical contents of all the rooms, corridors, staircases, etc., must first be ascertained, and the heat losses through walls, windows, floors, and ceilings in detail, that is for each room, passage, etc., and the radiating surface and piping required in each, the sum-total giving the number of radiators and sizes of piping required, feed tank, etc., also boiler and mains and all fittings. These are taken out on an estimate form, of which Table C is a type.

In daywork the various lengths and sizes of piping (steam barrel) are charged out at per foot run, including profit and waste. Fittings are numbered according to sizes and charged at per each ; radiators either at each or according to the number of feet of heating surface ; radiator valves and aircocks at per each, also radiator stays. The boiler should be described in detail and is usually priced at, or near, list price, smoke pipe is charged at per yard according to size, and smoke pipe fittings at per each. The number of gallons of feed tank and gauge should be stated. Hot-water fitters and mates time is generally charged as one item, the total number of hours being stated, and the combined rate is usually charged at from 4s. to 4s. 6d. per hour, to which must be added travelling time, fares, and country money (if any)

Steam.—The estimating for steam-heating work follows the same lines as hot-water heating, with the addition of steam traps and dirt pockets for each radiator, and automatic air-bents to radiators and vertical piping as mentioned in Chapter X. In daywork the items

TABLE XCVIII

By whom taken E. J. Smith *Date* 12/10/32

For Messrs. Brown & Robinson, Commercial Road, Peckham,

At New Building, City Road.

Class of Work Hot Water Heating.

Particulars of Materials, etc.

		Cost.			Selling.		
		£	s.	d.	£	s.	d.
1 2B7 Ideal Britannia Boiler, 24/10/–; insulated jacket, 3/10/– set of stoking tools, 20/–		29	0	0			
1 1" Safety-valve, 9/6; straight thermometer, 5/9; 1 draw-off tap with hose union, 6/3; 1 altitude gauge, 11/– . .		1	12	6			
1 30-gallon feed tank, 17/–; and ½" Croydon ball-valve, 2/9			19	9			
570 ft. Ideal Classic 4-col. Radiators, 36" high	1/8	47	10	0			
290 ft. " " 6-col. " 30" "	1/9	25	7	6			
18 ¾" Angle valves with union, 2/18/6; 18 ¾" G.M. unions, 27/–; 18 ⅛" air cocks, 9/–; 18 rod stays, 13/6		5	8	0			
80 ft. 2½" Steam barrel	1/5	5	13	4			
110 ft. 2" " "	–/11	5	0	10			
75 ft. 1½" " "	–/8	2	10	0			
75 ft. 1¼" " "	–/7	2	3	9			
80 ft. 1" " "	–/5	1	13	4			
310 ft. ¾" " "	–/3½	4	10	5			
2 2½" Cons. and nuts, 13/–; 4 2½" bends, 30/–; 2 2½" × 2" × 2" easy sweep Tees, 13/–		2	16	0			
2 2" Cons. and nuts, 9/–; 2 2" bend, 10/–; 2 2" to 1½" by ¾" cut cross, easy sweep, 8/–		1	7	0			
2 1½" Cons. and nuts, 6/–; 2 1½" × 1¼" × ¾" easy sweep crosses, 6/–			12	0			
2 1¼" Cons. and nuts, 4/6; 2 1¼ × 1 × ¾" easy sweep crosses, 4/–			8	6			
2 1" × ½" × ¾" out, easy sweep Tees, 4/–; 50 ft. ½" barrel as air pipe, 12/6			16	6			
4 2½" Barrel hangers, plates and ⅜" shorts, 6/–; 4 2" do. 5/– .			11	0			
2 1½" Distance clips, 1/6; 2 1¼" do., 1/–; 2 1" do., –/8 .			3	2			
6 ft. 8" Smoke pipe, 13/–; 1 wrought clip for do., 4/6; 2 8" smoke pipe elbows, S.D., 22/6		1	19	0			
Allow p.c. item £20 for contingencies					20	0	0
Fares, Sundries, Supervision		3	15	0			
Hot-water fitter and mate . . . . . 300 hours	3/–	45	0	0			
		188	17	7			
Add for working expenses, insurance, and profit, 30% .		56	13	5			
					245	11	0
Total					265	11	0

will be priced out in detail as for heating, and the rate of pay and consequently the charge for fitters' time is the same.

Hot Air.—Here again the work is mostly done to estimate, sometimes to the specification of a consulting engineer, and other times to a temperature clause and number of air changes required per hour, and in the case of a new building a set of plans is usually provided for the setting out of the scheme, that of the underground ducts being shown in detail, so that the builder can either do the necessary excavating for, or make provision for, piers or other means of support for the ducts, and in some cases builds the ducts to the engineer's drawings and instructions. The estimator has first to obtain the cubical contents of the rooms to be warmed, the number of air changes required ; often he has to settle this himself and takes as his guide the CO_2 ratio given in Chapter XI, keeping, as far as the limits of the estimate allow him, the lowest ratio possible.

Having ascertained the amount in cubic feet of the air required, allowing for all air changes per hour, he is now in a position to estimate the amount of heating surface required in the battery, and the size of the boilers which provides the heat, and next the size of the main duct or ducts, and length of same, position of branches, size of these, for delivering the warmed air into the building. The size and position of the ducts and branches will enable him to ascertain the frictional resistance he has to overcome, from which he calculates the size and horse-power of the fan. But he has also to bear in mind, when dealing with the fan capacity, the resistance of the filters, which in some types is considerable. He may further have to add for air conditioning, he will also have to allow for making large-size detail plans for boiler-house, heating battery, filtering plant, and main ducts for the builder's guidance.

Except that the items are much larger, the estimate is made out on the same lines as hot-water heating. The ventilating ducts take the place of the steam tubes. When estimating for the fan, provision must be made for the electric energy required, the cost of this being more or less according to the distance from the supply company's terminals. In day work the ducts are charged at per foot run, battery at per foot of heating surface, and gratings, fittings, etc., at per each, boiler and filters, screens, etc., being fully described and charged at per each, men's time being similar to hot-water or steam fitters'.

VENTILATION

Where this is obtained by hot air or the " Plenum " system, the foregoing description will apply, but for extract ventilation some additional data are necessary. The ducts in this case will probably be in the roof; the size will be according to the cubical contents and the number of air changes, and to the extract branches the estimator must allow for " trumpet " mouths, circular for preference, and grating to suit, which in ceilings are finished off with an ornamental moulding (formed by the builder). These, however, and the tubing are often exposed in a factory, on account of the cost of ceilings, etc. The fan for this class of ventilation is usually of the propeller type, and the estimator has to allow for its housing, unless it is included in the builder's work, and here the cost of laying on the electric energy is an item, for the fan is a considerable distance from the point of entry of the supply company's terminals. In factory work the fixing and supplying of suitable holdfasts also make an item which needs careful watching. Again, in old buildings the item of cutting away and making good, there being no builder on the job, is a considerable item, and being out of the ordinary rut, as it were, also needs close attention, for the writer has known occasions when this item alone has cost quite half the total estimate. It is not the cutting away that causes the trouble, but the making good, which is often made to mean matching existing colours, whitening the whole of the ceiling, etc. ; and very great and careful study is required here or a loss is bound to follow, in fact it is often a question as to whether it is wise to give an estimate or not, unless a properly drawn-up specification is provided for the engineer to work on.

GAS FITTING

This is either as per estimate or day work and material. If an estimate, it is either for a lump-sum price, inclusive of all fittings, or a price per point, and fittings extra to selection. In giving an estimate at per point, it must be made perfectly clear as to whether this price includes fixing the fittings selected, otherwise it is sure to be a bone of contention. Nowadays mostly iron piping is used for gasfitters' work ; composition, or " compo " pipe, as it is usually called, though being easier to run, does not make a reliable job, as it is liable to perforation by nails being driven into it, and its liability to sag, which allows the condensation to collect and makes the supply intermittent, so it is not advisable to use it, wherever it is possible to use the iron piping. The inlet of the gas meter is usually connected up by the Gas Company, but not always ; for instance, not by the London Gas Light and Coke Co., and this is taken as a separate item to the price per point, which in new buildings is termed " carcassing," and the pipes are often laid months before any connection to a gas meter is made, and then not always by the same contractor. The fittings are priced out per each in day work, and the gas barrel according to the different sizes at per foot run, while the gas burners and globes are priced at per each, also brackets and blocks and plugged points, clips and screws in a separate item. Day time for gas fitter and assistant or mate is at per hour, the same price as hot-water fitter and mate's.

Bell Hanging.—The old-fashioned bronze swing bells with pendulums mounted on " bell boards " are rarely met with now, having been super-seded by the electric bell. These are usually quoted for at per push, which includes indicator, battery power, wires and tube complete, and in the case of long runs " relays " as well. In day work all the various items are charged separately at per each, except the wire and tubing, the former in coils and the latter at per foot run. Day time as previous trades.

RENDERING ACCOUNTS

We now come to the most important part of the business, for it is on the prompt rendering of accounts principally that a business is made or marred. It is rarely possible to render a day-work account directly the work is finished, owing to the time sheets usually coming in weekly ; but so soon as all details are to hand, the account should be rendered at once, for a client may be solvent during and for some little time after the work is done, and then be made bankrupt. This is not so improbable as it might appear, for it has actually happened. Again, a client often gets suspicious when kept waiting for an account, and is far more inclined to query it, and there is no excuse for delay in payment when an account is promptly rendered. Accounts should not be too wordy, just sufficient description to give a clear idea of the item charged. No hard-and-fast rule can be given for pricing day-work accounts, and for small jobs it is wiser to simply describe the work done and price it as a lump sum, because when the material and time are separated, exception is often taken to the " men's time." One is told, " Your man was only here a few minutes, though two hours are charged," the client nearly always forgetting that the " man " has got to get to the job and back again, and all this time you have had to pay for, and naturally expect and have to insist on getting it back. Another objection is the " mate " : " What does he do ? wasn't wanted at all " ; though woe-betide the employer who sends out a plumber or fitter unattended, should an accident happen, for then he is not complying with the Statute, and if insured, would forfeit his rights. Where the person pricing the account has no knowledge of the work done, he should have a description from the foreman, or whoever supervised the work, so that he knows exactly how to apportion the time spent ; for instance, the measurement of piping on two jobs may be the same, but the amount of time spent on fixing may vary considerably owing to sets and fire bends and other labour, and of this the measurement gives no idea whatever. Most firms use a rough time book, in which each day's time is entered for each job, and a corresponding rough material book, into which all the material taken to the particular job is entered. Then when the job is finished, the totals are added together, and entered with the full description of the job in the " day book," the cost being in one column and the selling price in another, and a copy of this entry filled in with the selling prices on an account form is sent to the client. The totals from day book are entered into the ledger, from which the monthly " statement of account " is abstracted.

CHAPTER XVIII

LAWS AND BY-LAWS

PUBLIC HEALTH ACT, 1875 : Powers of Private Owners as to Public Sewers—Compulsory Powers of Sanitary Authority—Powers as to New Buildings—Notice to Remedy Defects—Factories and Workshops—Nuisances—Definition of Nuisance—Notices as to Nuisances—Power to Enact By-laws—Contracts by Urban Authorities. AMENDING ACTS : Restriction as to Matter Drained into Sewers—Cost of Connections to Sewers—Factories and Workshops. PLANS AND NOTICES TO BE DEPOSITED. WATER AUTHORITIES' REGULATIONS. LONDON COUNTY COUNCIL BY-LAWS, 1930.

PUBLIC HEALTH ACT, 1875

THE main law on which all subsequent Acts depend, and from which the Model By-laws were drafted as sent out by the Local Government Board (now the Ministry of Public Health), is the Public Health Act, 1875 (38 and 39 Vict., c. 55). As this Act contains 11 parts with in all 343 sections and 5 schedules, it forms a very bulky volume in itself, yet for all this there is very little in it which has no interest for the sanitary engineer, and any of the annotated editions are well worth study for their general information as well as for the various laws which must be observed.

The following are the chief items which most intimately concern the plumber and sanitary engineer :

Powers of Private Owners as to Public Sewers.—Section 21.—The owner or occupier of any premises within the district of a local authority shall be entitled to cause his drains to empty into the sewers of that authority on condition of his giving such notice as may be required by that authority of his intention so to do and of complying with the regulations of that authority in respect of the mode in which the communications between such drains and sewers are to be made, and subject to the control of any person who may be appointed by that authority to superintend the making of such communications. Any person causing a drain to empty into a sewer of a local authority without complying with the provisions of this section shall be liable to a penalty not exceeding twenty pounds, and the local authority may close any communication between a drain and sewer made in contravention of this section, and may recover in a summary manner from the person so offending any expenses incurred by them under this section.

Section 22.—The owner or occupier of any premises without the district of a local authority may cause any sewer or drain from such premises to communicate with any sewer of the local authority on such terms and conditions as may be agreed on between such owner or occupier and such local authority, or as in case of dispute may be settled, at the option of the owner or occupier, by a court of summary jurisdiction or by arbitration in manner provided by this Act.

Compulsory Powers of Sanitary Authority.—*Section* 23.—Where any house within the district of a local authority is without a drain sufficient for effectual drainage, the local authority shall by written notice require the owner or occupier of such house, within a reasonable time therein specified, to make a covered drain or drains emptying into any sewer which the local authority are entitled to use, and which is not more than one hundred feet from the site of such house ; but if no such means of drainage are within that distance, then emptying into such covered cesspool or other place, not being under any house, as the local authority direct, and the local authority may require any such drain or drains to be of such materials and size, and to be laid at such level, and with such fall as on the report of their surveyor may appear to them to be necessary. If such notice is not complied with, the local authority may, after the expiration of the time specified in the notice, do the work required, and may recover in a summary manner the expenses incurred by them in so doing from the owner, or may by order declare the same to be private improvement expenses.

Provided that where, in the opinion of the local authority, greater expense would be incurred in causing the drains of two or more houses to empty into an existing sewer pursuant to this section, than in constructing a new sewer and causing such drain to empty therein, the local authority may construct such new sewer, and require the owners or occupiers of such houses to cause their drains to empty therein, and may apportion as they deem just, the expenses of the construction of such sewer among the owners of the several houses, and recover in a summary manner the sum apportioned from such owners, or may by order declare the same to be private improvement expenses.

Section 24.—Where any house within the district of a local authority has a drain communicating with any sewer, which drain, though sufficient for the effectual drainage of the house, is not adapted to the general sewerage of the district, or is, in the opinion of the local authority, otherwise objectionable, the local authority may, on condition of providing a drain or drains as effectual for the drainage of the house, and communicating with such other sewer as they think fit, close such firstmentioned drain, and may do any works necessary for that purpose, and the expenses of those works, and of the construction of any drain or drains provided by them under this section, shall be deemed to be expenses properly incurred by them in the execution of this Act.

Powers as to New Buildings.—*Section* 25.—It shall not be lawful in any urban district newly to erect any house or to rebuild any house which has been pulled down to or below the ground floor, or to occupy any house so newly erected or rebuilt, unless and until a covered drain or drains be constructed, of such size and material, and at such level, and with such fall as on the report of the surveyor may appear to the urban authority to be necessary for the effectual drainage of such house, and the drain or drains so to be constructed shall empty into any sewer which the urban authority are entitled to use, and which is within one hundred feet of some part of the site of the house to be built or rebuilt, but if no such means of drainage are within that distance, then shall empty into such covered cesspool or other place, not being under any house, as the urban authority direct.

Any person who causes any house to be erected or rebuilt or any drain to be constructed in contravention of this section shall be liable to a penalty nor exceeding fifty pounds.

Section 26.—Any person who in any urban district, without the written consent of the urban authority, (1) Causes any building to be newly erected over any sewer of the urban authority, or (2) causes any vault, arch, or cellar to be newly built or constructed under the carriageway of any street, shall forfeit to the urban authority the sum of five pounds, and a further sum of forty shillings for every day during which the offence is continued after written notice in this behalf from the urban authority, and the urban authority may cause any building, vault, or cellar erected or constructed in contravention of this section to be altered, pulled down, or otherwise dealt with as they may think fit, and may recover in a summary manner any expenses incurred by them in so doing, from the offender.

Section 35.—It shall not be lawful newly to erect any house, or to rebuild any house pulled down to or below the ground floor, without a sufficient water-closet, earth-closet, or privy and an ashpit furnished with proper doors and coverings.

Any person who causes any house to be erected or rebuilt in contravention of this enactment shall be liable to a penalty not exceeding twenty pounds.

Notice to Remedy Defects.—*Section* 36.—If a house within the district of a local authority appears to such authority by the report of their surveyor or inspector of nuisances to be without a sufficient water-closet, earth-closet, or privy and an ashpit furnished with proper doors and coverings, the local authority shall, by written notice, require the owner or occupier of the house, within a reasonable time therein specified, to provide a sufficient water-closet, earth-closet, or privy and an ashpit furnished as aforesaid, or either of them, as the case may require. If such notice is not complied with, the local authority may, at the expiration of the time specified in the notice, do the work thereby required to be done, and may recover in a summary manner from the owner the expenses incurred by them in so doing, or may by order declare the same to be private improvement expenses. Provided that where a water-closet, earth-closet, or privy has been, and is used in common by the inmates of two or more houses, or if, in the opinion of the local authority, a water-closet, earth-closet, or privy may be so used, they need not require the same to be provided for each house.

Section 37.—Any enactment in force within the district of any local authority requiring the construction of a water-closet shall be deemed to be satisfied by the construction, with the approval of the local authority, of an earth-closet.

Any local authority may, as respects any house in which any earth-closet is in use with their approval, dispense with the supply of water required by any contract or enactment to be furnished to any water-closet in such house, on such terms as may be agreed on between such authority and the person providing or required to provide such supply of water. Any local authority may themselves undertake or contract with any person to undertake a supply of dry earth or other deodorising substance to any house within their district for the purpose of any earth-closet.

In this Act the term " earth-closet " includes any place for the reception and deodorisation of fœcal matter constructed to the satisfaction of the local authority.

Factories and Workshops.—*Section* 38.—Where it appears to any local authority by the report of their surveyor that any house is used, or intended to be used, as a factory or building in which persons of both sexes are employed or intended to be employed at one time in any manufacture, trade, or business, the local authority may if they think fit, by written notice require the owner or occupier of such house, within the time therein specified, to construct a sufficient number of water-closets, earth-closets, or privies and ashpits for the separate use of each sex. Any person who neglects or refuses to comply with any such notice shall be liable for each default to a penalty not exceeding twenty pounds, and to a further penalty not exceeding forty shillings for every day during which the default is continued.

Nuisances.—*Section* 40.—Every local authority shall provide that all drains, water-closets, earth-closets, privies, ashpits, and cesspools within their district be constructed and kept so as not to be a nuisance or injurious to health.

Section 41.—On the written application of any person to a local authority, stating that any drain, water-closet, earth-closet, privy, ashpit, or cesspool on or belonging to any premises within their district is a nuisance or injurious to health (but not otherwise), the local authority may, by writing, empower their surveyor or inspector of nuisances, after twenty-four hours' written notice to the occupier of such premises, or in case of emergency without notice, to enter such premises with or without assistants, and cause the ground to be opened, and examine such drain, water-closet, earth-closet, privy, ashpit, or cesspool. If the drain, water-closet, earth-closet, privy, ashpit, or cesspool on examination is found to be in proper condition, he shall cause the ground to be closed, and any damage done to be made good as soon as can be, and the expenses of the works shall be defrayed by the local authority. If the drain, water-closet, earth-closet, privy, ashpit, or cesspool on examination appear to be in bad condition, or to require alteration or amendment, the local authority shall forthwith cause notice in writing to be given to the owner or occupier of the premises requiring him forthwith or within a reasonable time therein specified to do the necessary works ; and if such notice is not complied with, the person to whom it is given shall be liable to a penalty not exceeding ten shillings for every day during which he continues to make default, and the local authority may, if they think fit, execute such works, and may recover in a summary manner from the owner the expenses incurred by them in so doing, or may by order declare the same to be private improvement expenses.

Definition of a Nuisance.—*Section* 91 (part only).—Nuisances, Definition of, for the purposes of this Act.

(1) Any premises in such a state as to be a nuisance or injurious to health.

(2) Any pool, ditch, gutter, watercourse, privy, urinal, cesspool, drain, or ashpit so foul or in such a state as to be a nuisance or injurious to health.

(3) Any animal so kept as to be a nuisance or injurious to health.

(4) Any accumulation or deposit which is a nuisance or injurious to health.

(5) Any house or part of a house so overcrowded as to be dangerous or injurious to the health of the inmates, whether or not members of the same family.

(6) Any factory, workshop, or workplace (not already under the operation of any general Act for the regulation of factories or bakehouses) not kept in a cleanly state, or not ventilated in such a manner as to render harmless as far as practicable any gases, vapours, dust, or other impurities generated in the course of the work carried on therein that are a nuisance or injurious to health, or so overcrowded while work is carried on as to be dangerous or injurious to the health of those employed therein.

(7) Any fireplace or furnace which does not as far as practicable consume the smoke arising from the combustible used therein, and which is used for working engines by steam, or in any mill, factory, dyehouse, brewery, bakehouse, or gaswork or in any manufacturing or trade process whatsoever ; and any chimney (not being the chimney of a private dwelling-house) sending forth black smoke in such quantity as to be a nuisance —shall be deemed to be nuisances liable to be dealt with summarily in manner provided by this Act.

Notices as to Nuisances.—*Section* 94.—On the receipt of any information respecting the existence of a nuisance, the local authority shall, if satisfied of the existence of a nuisance, serve a notice on the person by whose act, default, or sufferance the nuisance arises or continues, or, if such a person cannot be found, on the owner or occupier of the premises on which the nuisance arises, requiring time to abate the same within a time to be specified in the notice, and to execute such works and do such things as may be necessary for that purpose. Provided : First, that where the nuisance arises from the want or defective construction of any structural convenience, or where there is no occupier of the premises, notice under this section shall be served on the owner ; secondly, that where the person causing the nuisance cannot be found and it is clear that the nuisance does not arise or continue by the act, default, or sufferance of the owner or occupier of the premises, the local authority may themselves abate the same without further order.

Section 95.—If the person on whom a notice to abate a nuisance has been served makes default in complying with any of the requisitions thereof within the time specified, or if the nuisance, although abated since the service of the notice, is, in the opinion of the local authority, likely to recur on the same premises, the local authority shall cause a complaint relating to such nuisance to be made before a justice, and such justice shall thereupon issue a summons requiring the person on whom the notice was served to appear before a court of summary jurisdiction.

Power to Enact By-laws.—*Section* 157.—Every urban authority may make by-laws with respect to the following matters (that is to say) :

(1) With respect to the level, width, and construction of new streets, and the provisions for the sewerage thereof.

(2) With respect to the structure of walls, foundations, roofs, and chimneys of new buildings for securing stability and the prevention of fires and for purposes of health.

(3) With respect to the sufficiency of the space about buildings to secure a free circulation of air, and with respect to the ventilation of buildings.

(4) With respect to the drainage of buildings, to water-closets, earth-closets, privies, ashpits, and cesspools in connection with buildings, and to the closing of buildings as parts of buildings unfit for human habitation, and to prohibition of their use for such habitation. And they may further provide for the observance of such by-laws by enacting therein such provisions as they think necessary as to the giving of notices, as to the deposit of plans and sections by persons intending to lay out streets or to construct buildings, as to inspection by the urban authority, and as to the power of such authority (subject to the provisions of this Act) to remove, alter, or pull down any work begun or done in contravention of such by-laws. Provided that no by-law made under this section shall affect any building erected in any place (which at the time of passing of this Act is included in an urban sanitary district) before the Local Government Acts came into force in such place, or any building erected in any place (which at the time of the passing of this Act is not included in an urban sanitary district) before such place becomes constituted or included in an urban district, or by virtue of an order of the Local Government Board subject to this enactment. The provisions of this section and of the two last preceding sections shall not apply to buildings belonging to any railway company and used for the purposes of such railway under any Act of Parliament.

Section 173.—Any local authority may enter into any contracts necessary for carrying this Act into execution.

Contracts by Urban Authorities.—Section 174.—With respect to contracts made by an urban authority under this Act, the following regulations shall be observed (namely) :

(1) Every contract made by an urban authority whereof the value or amount exceeds fifty pounds shall be in writing and sealed with the common seal of the authority.

(2) Every such contract shall specify the work, materials, matters, or things to be furnished, had, or done, the price to be paid, and the time or times within which the contract is to be performed, and shall specify some pecuniary penalty to be paid in case the terms of the contract are not duly performed.

(3) Before contracting for the execution of any works under the provisions of this Act, an urban authority shall obtain from their surveyor an estimate in writing, as well as of the probable expense of executing the work in a substantial manner as of the annual expense of repairing the same, also a report as to the most advantageous mode of contracting, that is to say, whether by contracting only for the execution of the work, or for executing and also maintaining the same in repair during a term of years or otherwise.

(4) Before any contract of the value or amount of one hundred pounds or upwards is entered into by an urban authority, ten days' public notice at the least shall be given, expressing the nature and purpose thereof, and inviting tenders for the execution of the same, and such authority shall require and take sufficient security for the due performance of the same.

(5) Every contract entered into by an urban authority in conformity with the provisions of this section, and duly executed by the other parties thereto, shall be binding on the authority by whom the same is executed and their successors and on all other parties thereto, and their executors, administrators, successors, or assigns to all intents and purposes. Provided that an urban authority may compound with any contractor or other person in respect of any penalty incurred by reason of the non-performance of any contract entered into as aforesaid, whether such penalty is mentioned in any such contract, or in any bond or otherwise, for such sums of money or other recompense as to such authority may seem proper.

Section 293.—The Local Government Board may from time to time cause to be made such inquiries as are directed by this Act, and such inquiries as they see fit in relation to any matters concerning the public health in any place, or any matters with respect to which their sanction, approval, or consent is required by this Act.

Section 315.—Any by-law made by any sanitary authority under the Sanitary Acts which is inconsistent with any of the provisions of this Act shall so far as it is inconsistent therewith be deemed to be repeated.

Amending Acts

An amendment to this Act was passed in 1878, in so far as the supply of water by rural sanitary authorities is concerned, called the Public Health (Water) Act, 1878. Another amended Act, called the Public Health (Interments) Act, was passed in 1879, and again another in 1883 called the Public Health Act, 1875 (Support of Sewers) Amendment Act. In 1884 we get the Public Health (Confirmation of By-laws) Act and the Public Health (Officers) Act. In 1885 the Public Health and Local Government Conferences Act, the Public Health (Ships, etc.) Acts, the Public Health (Members and Officers) Act, and the Housing of the Working Classes Act.

In 1890 another Public Health Acts Amendment Act was passed, divided into 5 parts, part 3 dealing with sanitary and other provisions, and five sections of this Act are of interest to the plumber and sanitary engineer.

Restriction as to Matter Drained into Sewers.—*Section* 16.—(1) It shall not be lawful for any person to throw, or suffer to be thrown, or to pass into any sewer of a local authority or any drain communicating therewith, any matter or substance by which the free flow of the sewage, or surface or storm water may be interfered with, or by which any such sewer or drain may be injured.

(2) Every person offending against this enactment shall be liable to a penalty not exceeding ten pounds, and to a daily penalty not exceeding twenty shillings.

Section 17.—(1) Every person who turns or permits to enter into any sewer of a local authority or any drain communicating therewith— (*a*) any chemical refuse, or (*b*) any waste steam, condensing water, heated water, or other liquid (such water or other liquid being of a higher temperature than one hundred and ten degrees Fahrenheit) which, either alone or in combination with the sewage, causes a nuisance or is dangerous or injurious to health, shall be liable to a penalty not exceeding ten pounds and to a daily penalty not exceeding five pounds.

(2) The local authority, by any of their officers either generally or specially authorised in that behalf in writing, may enter any premises for the purpose of examining whether the provisions of this section are being contravened, and if such entry be refused, any justice, on complaint on oath by such officer made after reasonable notice in writing of such intended complaint has been given to the person having custody of the premises, may by order under his hand require such person to admit the officer into the premises, and if it be found that any offence under this section has been or is being committed in respect of the premises, the order shall continue in force until the offence shall have ceased or the work necessary to prevent the recurrence thereof shall have been executed.

(3) A person shall not be liable to a penalty for an offence against this section until the local authority have given him notice of the provisions

of this section, nor for an offence committed before the expiration of seven days from the service of such notice, provided that the local authority shall not be required to give the same person notice more than once.

Cost of Connections to Sewers.—Section 18.—(1) Where the owner or occupier of any premises is entitled to cause any sewer or drain from those premises to communicate with any sewer of the local authority, the local authority shall, if requested to do so by such owner or occupier, and upon the cost thereof being paid in advance to the local authority, themselves make the communication and execute all works necessary for that purpose.

(2) The cost of making such communication (including all costs incidental thereto) shall be estimated by the surveyor of the local authority, but in case the owner or occupier of the premises, as the case may be, is dissatisfied with such estimate, he may, if the estimate is under fifty pounds, apply to a court of summary jurisdiction to fix the amount to be paid for such cost, and if the estimate is over fifty pounds have the same determined by arbitration in manner provided by the Public Health Acts.

(3) A local authority may agree with the owner of any premises that any sewer or drain which such owner is required, or desires, to make, alter, or enlarge or any part of such sewer or drain, shall be made, altered, or enlarged by the local authority.

Section 19.—(1) Where two or more houses belonging to different owners are connected with a public sewer by a single private drain, an application may be made under section 41 of the Public Health Act, 1875 (relating to complaints as to nuisances from drains), and the local authority may recover any expenses incurred by them in executing any works, under the powers conferred on them by that section, from the owners of the houses in such shares and proportions as shall be settled by their surveyor or (in case of dispute) by a court of summary jurisdiction.

(2) Such expenses may be recovered summarily or may be declared by the urban authority to be private improvement expenses under the Public Health Acts, and may be recovered accordingly.

(3) For the purposes of this section the expression " drain " includes a drain used for the drainage of more than one building.

Factories and Workshops.—Section 22.—(1) Every building used as a workshop or manufactory, or where persons are employed or intended to be employed in any trade or business, whether erected before or after the adoption of this part of the Act in any district, shall be provided with sufficient and suitable accommodation in the way of sanitary conveniences, having regard to the number of persons employed in or in attendance at such building, and also where persons of both sexes are employed, or intended to be employed, or in attendance, with proper separate accommodation for persons of each sex.

(2) Where it appears to an urban authority on the report of their

surveyor that the provisions of this section are not complied with in the case of any building, the urban authority may, if they think fit, by written notice, require the owner or occupier of any such building to make such alterations and additions therein as may be required to give such sufficient, suitable, and proper accommodation as aforesaid.

(3) Any person who neglects or refuses to comply with any such notice shall be liable for each default to a penalty not exceeding twenty pounds, and to a daily penalty not exceeding forty shillings.

(4) Where this section is in force, section 38 of the Public Health Act, 1875, shall be repealed.

The above sections are those from which the by-laws are framed by the various Public Health Departments of our towns and boroughs, and the Urban and District Sanitary Authorities, which though they may differ in their wording in the various districts, are essentially the same as regards the facts, and those of the Corporation of the City of London are given here as a type of the requirements of the whole, and in these will also be found the Notices which it is always incumbent to give before commencing and finishing sanitary work in any new or old building.

PLANS AND NOTICES TO BE DEPOSITED

(1) All persons proposing to construct houses, drains, and w.c.s, or being " ordered " to reconstruct any existing w.c. or drain, or connect or disconnect any w.c., shall at least seven days before the work is to be commenced make application at the office of the Public Health Department of the Corporation at the Guildhall, on a form to be obtained there, and shall deposit a plan of the premises to be drained, drawn to a scale of 8 feet to an inch, with the lines of the proposed drains, their branches and inlets, shown thereon in red, together with their sizes and the depth of the lower floor of the premises below the footway kerb fronting the same. All existing drains to be shown by blue lines on the plan.

(2) Each house to have a separate and independent connection with the public sewer where practicable, and where impracticable a twin drain or some other method approved by the Public Health Department must be adopted.

(3) No work is to be commenced inside the premises until the connection from the sewer to the front of the building has been completed, excepting in cases of emergency, such as flood, etc.

(4) All work beneath the public way will be done by the contractor to the Corporation, and the applicant, before the works are commenced, shall pay the cost of such drain and any other works incidental thereto as estimated by the Engineer to the Corporation.

(5) All drains where practicable shall be laid in straight lines and outside the premises.

(6) All drains are to be formed of socketed, impermeable, glazed stoneware pipes, free from defects, and of a smooth surface inside, each

pipe to be in section a true circle and perfectly straight. All pipes of 6 inches diameter and under are to be at least ⅝ inch thick, and all over 6 inches are to have a thickness of at least one-twelfth of their internal diameter. If iron pipes are used, they must be at least ⅜ inch thick, and be coated internally with Dr. Angus Smith's, or other approved composition.

(7) The pipes are to be carefully put together, the butt end of one pipe being forced into the socket end of the next pipe as closely as will permit, and the space between them filled in with Portland cement of good quality, mixed with a little clean, sharp sand, the cement to be thoroughly worked in so as to fill the whole space and to cover the joint externally. The inside of each pipe to be carefully wiped out, so as to remove any cement that may have worked in through the joint. The joints of all iron pipes are to be run with lead and properly caulked.

(8) All drains where practicable shall be laid at least 12 inches below the floor level, measuring to the tops of the pipes ; and the ground shall be carefully excavated to true hanging lines and so made up that the pipes shall have a firm bearing throughout their entire length.

(9) All junctions shall be curved and made at the sides of the pipes and join the pipes in the direction of the flow. No T or right-angled junctions will be allowed.

(10) Taper pipes are to be used where the size of the drain is reduced, and inspection chambers with half-channel pipes and airtight covers as well as access pipes are to be provided if so directed at each change in the direction of the main drain.

(11) Where practicable, all 6-inch drains shall be laid to a fall of not less than 2 inches in 10 feet, and 4-inch drains not less than 3 inches in 10 feet.

(12) Where the drains are laid under any part of a building, they shall be laid on and surrounded with 6 inches of good Portland cement concrete, mixed in the proportion of six parts of fine clean ballast to one of cement.

(13) In laying the pipes, spaces are to be hollowed out of the concrete to receive the collars, so that the body of the pipes may rest on the concrete and have a firm bearing.

(14) No drain shall be deemed to have been laid to the satisfaction of the Public Health Department until it has been properly tested by the Sanitary Inspector in the case of old buildings, or the Inspector of Pavements in the case of new buildings, or other officers appointed to do such work, and each drain shall be tested with water once after the pipes have been laid and jointed, and if necessary, before and after the ground has been filled in. Where there are several inspection chambers in the building the drains can, if so desired, be tested in sections.

(15) All rainwater pipes shall discharge over or into trapped gullies fitted with movable iron gratings and fixed where practicable in the open air. All outlets or waste pipes from sinks, baths, and lavatories to be trapped and discharge into trapped stoneware gullies, fitted with movable

iron gratings, and fixed in the open areas. So many of the rain and waste waterpipes as is practicable shall be collected into one gully or trap, as near as may be to the head of the drain, the said gully being covered in at the floor level, if inside a building, with a movable airtight cover.

(16) No bell, whistle, tip, " D " or other non-self-cleansing trap will be allowed.

(17) No rainwater pipe shall be used as a ventilating pipe, excepting under special circumstances, as approved by the Public Health Department.

(18) All water-closets shall have external light and ventilation, and have at least one side next an external wall, overlooking a street or open space. In new buildings or buildings reconstructed from the first-floor level upwards, every water-closet shall be lighted naturally, and be provided with adequate means of constant ventilation, and shall be so constructed that at least one of its sides shall be an external wall abutting upon a street or open space. When constructed in or abutting on any room used for occupation or used as a factory or workshop, the water-closet must be enclosed by a brick wall at least $4\frac{1}{2}$ inches thick, extending the entire height from floor to ceiling, covered with an impervious material on one side, and be provided with proper door and fastenings. No water-closet shall open directly into any room where persons are engaged, but shall be approached by a lobby ventilated to the external air. In existing buildings all water-closets shall have direct communication with the external air, and where constructed in or abutting on a room used as a factory or workshop, or where any person is engaged, the water-closet must be enclosed by an impervious wall or partition extending the entire height from floor to ceiling.

(19) The water supply shall be separate and independent from the drinking supply.

(20) Each water-closet is to be fitted with a good apparatus of the wash-down or short hopper-class, and with improved waste-preventing cisterns, giving at least a two-gallon flush at each discharge, the connection between the cistern and the water-closet being made by a pipe at least $1\frac{1}{4}$ inches internal diameter.

(21) All water-closets in the lower floors of premises and all surface drains, sinks, gullies, rain-water pipes, and other inlets (excepting vertical soil pipes) shall be efficiently trapped by siphon or other improved traps, before being connected with the drains. All water-closets on the upper floors shall be trapped before being connected with vertical soil pipes. No " D " traps or containers will on any account be allowed.

(22) Where there is more than one water-closet connected with one vertical soil pipe, anti-siphonage pipes must be used if so directed.

(23) No waste-water pipes in the upper floors are to be connected with the soil pipes or traps to water-closets, and if connected with rain-water pipes, then only with such pipes as are outside the buildings, and are to be first trapped.

(24) All soil pipes shall be not less than 3½ inches internal diameter, formed of lead or iron, with all joints gastight and carried up without diminution of their area, with as few bends as possible, to above the highest part of the roof, and be fitted with a wire top or cage, and are not to be fixed near chimney-stacks, windows, dormers, or other openings. Where practicable, they shall be placed outside buildings, and when inside shall be of lead, weighing not less than 8 lb. to the foot superficial, with wiped joints, and fixed in grooves or chases so that they may be readily accessible.

(25) In connecting lead soil pipes to iron pipes, a brass thimble-piece is to be passed over the end of the soil pipe and then wiped on it. Some tarred yarn is then to be inserted in the space between the thimble and the iron socket, and the joint run with blue lead, and properly caulked.

(26) In connecting the lead soil pipes to stoneware drains, the thimble-piece must be wiped on to the soil pipe as before and the joint to the stoneware pipe filled in with cement. This method is also to be adopted when connections are made between the earthenware traps of water-closets and lead soil pipes.

(27) Every urinal and the floor and screens surrounding it is to be constructed of impervious material, and is to be furnished with an automatic flushing cistern or such other appliance for properly flushing same, as may be approved by the Corporation. The water supply is to be separate from the drinking supply, and the outlet is to be properly trapped and connected with an independent down pipe or drain properly ventilated.

(28) Before being connected with the public sewer the main drain must be trapped by means of a sewer intercepting trap, or siphon, fitted with a cleansing arm provided with an airtight stopper, such trap to be fixed between the sewer and an inspection chamber, formed of brickwork, built and rendered in cement. This chamber is to be provided with an airtight iron cover and ventilated by a pipe at least 3½ inches diameter carried from the top of the chamber as a fresh-air inlet, and terminating with a box fitted with mica valves.

(29) At least two untrapped openings shall be provided to the drains, one opening being at or near the surface of the ground to communicate with the drains by means of a suitable pipe which shall be taken into the inspection chamber as previously described, such opening in any case to be on the house side of the intercepting trap, the second opening to be made by carrying up from the drain, as far as may be practicable, from the first opening a ventilating pipe at least 3½ inches diameter to above the highest part of the roof and away from all window openings, dormers, chimney-stacks, etc. Zinc pipes will not be allowed.

(30) All inspection chambers, where practicable, to be constructed in the yards or areas of the premises to be drained.

(31) The overflow or warning pipes from cisterns shall, where practic-

able, discharge into the open air, and shall not in any case have any direct communication with a soil pipe or drain.

(32) All old brick or other disused drains and cesspools, etc., shall be broken up and destroyed, and the materials forming them and all foul earth and other substances shall be carefully removed, and, if necessary, dry earth or brick rubbish shall be brought in to fill up.

(33) The whole of the work shall be executed with the best materials of their several kinds, and the drains laid in accordance with the sections furnished by the Engineer to the Corporation, and all work to be done to the satisfaction of the Engineer, or other officer deputed by him to supervise that work.

(34) No drain shall be covered in until it has been seen and approved by such officer, and at least twenty-four hours' notice shall be given by the applicant to the Public Health Department of the Corporation at the Guildhall, when the drains are ready for inspection, and if any drain be covered in without such notice, the Corporation shall be empowered to uncover the work and recover the expenses of so doing from the person so offending.

WATER AUTHORITIES' REGULATIONS

We now follow with the regulations or by-laws of the Water Companies, taking the Metropolitan Water Act as a model, which is at present enforced by the Metropolitan Water Board.

(1) No "communication pipe" for the conveyance of water from the waterworks of the Company into any premises shall hereafter be laid until after the point or place at which such communication pipe is proposed to be brought into such premises shall have had the approval of the Company.

(2) No lead pipe shall hereafter be laid or fixed in or about any premises for the conveyance of or in connection with the water supplied by the Company (except when and as otherwise authorised by these Regulations, or by the Company), unless the same shall be of equal thickness throughout, and of at least the weight following, that is to say :

TABLE XCIX

Internal Diameter of Pipe in Inches.	Weight of Pipe in lb. per Lineal Yard.
$\frac{3}{8}$ inch	5 lb.
$\frac{1}{2}$,,	6 lb.
$\frac{5}{8}$,,	7$\frac{1}{2}$ lb.
$\frac{3}{4}$,,	9 lb.
1 ,,	12 lb.
1$\frac{1}{4}$,,	16 lb.

(3) Every pipe hereafter laid or fixed in the interior of any dwelling-house for the conveyance of, or in connection with, the water of the Company, must, unless with the consent of the Company, if in contact

with the ground, be of lead, but may otherwise be of lead, copper, or wrought-iron, at the option of the consumer.

(4) No house shall, unless with the permission of the Company in writing, be hereafter fitted with more than one communication-pipe.

(5) Every house supplied with water by the Company (except in cases of stand-pipes) shall have its own separate communication pipe. Provided that, as far as is consistent with the special Acts of the Company, in the case of a group or block of houses, the water-rates of which are paid by the one owner, the said owner may, at his option, have one sufficient communication pipe for such group or block.

(6) No house supplied with water by the Company shall have any connection with the pipes or other fittings of any other premises, except in the case of groups or blocks of houses, referred to in the preceding Regulation.

(7) The connection of every communication pipe with any pipe of the company shall hereafter be made by means of a sound and suitable brass screwed ferrule or stop-cock with union, and such ferrule or stop-cock shall be so made as to have a clear area of waterway equal to that of a half-inch pipe. The connection of every communication pipe with the pipes of the Company shall be made by the Company's workmen, and the Company shall be paid in advance the reasonable costs and charges of and incident to the making of such connection.

(8) Every communication pipe and every pipe external to the ouse and through the external walls thereof, hereafter respectively laid or fixed, in connection with the water of the Company, shall be of lead, and every joint thereof shall be of a kind called a " plumbing " or " wiped " joint.

(9) No pipe shall be used for the conveyance of, or in connection with, water supplied by the Company, which is laid or fixed through, in, or into any drain, ashpit, sink, or manure hole, or through, in, or into any place where the water conveyed through such pipe may be liable to become fouled, except where such drain, ashpit, sink, or manure-hole, or such other place, shall be in the unavoidable course of such pipe, and then in every such case such pipe shall be passed through an exterior cast-iron pipe or jacket of sufficient length and strength and of such construction as to afford due protection to the water pipe.

(10) Every pipe hereafter laid for the convenience of, or in connection with, water supplied by the Company, shall, when laid in open ground, be laid at least 2 feet 6 inches below the surface, and shall, in every exposed situation, be properly protected against the effects of frost.

(11) No pipe for the conveyance of, or in connection with, water supplied by the Company, shall communicate with any cistern, but, or any other receptacle used or intended to be used for rain water.

(12) Every communication pipe for the conveyance of water to be supplied by the Company into any premises shall have at or near its joint of entrance into such premises, and if desired by the consumer within

such premises, a sound and suitable stop-valve of the screw-down kind, with an area of waterway, not less than that of a ½-inch pipe and not greater than that of the communication pipe, the size of the valve within these limits being at the option of the consumer. If placed in the ground, such " stop-valve " shall be protected by a proper cover and " guard-box."

(13) Every cistern used in connection with the water supplied by the Company shall be made and at all times maintained watertight, and be properly covered and placed in such a position that it may be inspected and cleaned. Every such existing cistern, if not already provided with an efficient ball-tap, and every such future cistern shall be provided with a sound and suitable ball-tap of the valve kind for the inlet of the water.

(14) No overflow or waste pipe other than a " warning pipe " shall be attached to any cistern supplied with water by the Company, and every such overflow or waste pipe existing at the time when these Regulations come into operation shall be removed, or at the option of the consumer shall be converted into an efficient " warning pipe," within two calendar months next after the Company shall have given to the occupier of, or left at the premises in which such cistern is situate, a notice in writing requiring such alteration to be made.

(15) Every " warning pipe " shall be placed in such a situation as will admit of the discharge of the water from such " warning pipe " being readily ascertained by the officers of the Company. And the position of such " warning pipe " shall not be changed without previous notice to and approval by the Company.

(16) No cistern buried or excavated in the ground shall be used for the storage or reception of water supplied by the Company, unless the use of such cistern shall be allowed in writing by the Company.

(17) No wooden receptacle without a proper metallic lining shall be hereafter brought into use for the storage of any water supplied by the Company.

(18) No draw-traps shall in future be fixed unless the same shall be sound and suitable and of the screw-down kind.

(19) Every draw-tap in connection with any " stand-pipe " or other apparatus outside any dwelling-house in a court or other public place, to supply any group or number of such dwelling-houses, shall be sound and suitable, and of the " waste-preventer " kind and be protected as far as possible from injury by frost, theft, or mischief.

(20) Every boiler, urinal, and water-closet in which water supplied by the Company is used (other than water-closet in which hand-flushing is employed), shall, within three months after these Regulations come into operation, be served only through a cistern or service box and without a stool-cock, and there shall be no direct communication from the pipes of the Company to any boiler, urinal, or water-closet.

(21) Every water-closet cistern or water-closet service-box, hereafter

fitted or fixed, in which water supplied by the Company is to be used, shall have an efficient waste-preventing apparatus, so constructed as not to be capable of discharging more than two gallons of water at each flush.

(22) Every urinal cistern in which water supplied by the Company is used other than public urinal cisterns or cisterns having attached to them a self-closing apparatus, shall have an efficient waste-preventing apparatus, so constructed as not to be capable of discharging more than one gallon of water at each flush.

(23) Every down-pipe hereafter fixed for the discharge of water into the pan or basin of any water-closet shall have an internal diameter of not less than 1¼ inch, and if of lead shall weigh not less than 9 lb. to every lineal yard.

(24) No pipe by which water is supplied by the Company to any water-closet shall communicate with any part of such water-closet, or with any apparatus connected herewith, except the cistern service thereof.

(25) No bath supplied with water by the Company shall have any over-flow waste pipe, except it be so arranged as to act as a " warning-pipe."

(26) In every bath hereafter fitted or fixed, the outlet shall be distinct from, and unconnected with, the inlet or inlets, and the inlet or inlets ·must be placed so that the orifice shall be above the highest water-level of the bath. The outlet of every such bath shall be provided with a perfectly watertight plug, valve, or cock.

(27) No alterations shall be made in any fittings in connection with the supply of water by the Company without two days' previous notice in writing to the Company.

(28) Except with the written consent of the consumer, no cock, ferrule, joint, union, or other fitting, in the course of any communication pipe, shall have a waterway of less area than that of the communication pipe, so that the waterway from the water in the district pipe or other supply pipe of the Company up to and through the stop-valve prescribed by Regulation No. 12 shall not in any part be of less area than that of the communication pipe itself, which pipe shall not be less than a ½-inch bore in all its course.

(29) All lead " warning pipes " and other lead pipes of which the ends are open, so that such pipes cannot remain charged with water, may be of the following minimum weights, that is to say :

TABLE C

½ inch (internal diameter)	.	.	.	.	.	3 lb. per yard
¾ ,,	,,	,,	.	.	.	.	5 ,,	,,
1 ,,	,,	,,	.	.	.	.	7 ,,	,,

(30) In these regulations the term " Communication pipe " shall mean the pipe which extends from the district pipe or other supply pipe of the Company up to the stop-valve prescribed in the Regulation No. 12.

(31) Every person who shall wilfully violate, refuse, or neglect to

comply with, or shall wilfully do or cause to be done any act, matter, or thing in contravention of these Regulations or any part thereof, shall for every such offence be liable to a penalty in a sum not exceeding £5.

(32) Where under the foregoing Regulations any act is required or authorised to be done by the Company, the same may be done on behalf of the Company by an authorised officer or servant of the Company, and where under such Regulations any notice is required to be given by the Company, the same shall be sufficiently authenticated if it be signed by an authorised officer or servant of the Company.

(33) All existing fittings, which shall be sound and efficient and are not required to be removed or altered under these Regulations, shall be deemed to be prescribed fittings under the Metropolis Water Act, 1871.

LONDON COUNTY COUNCIL BY-LAWS, 1930

Deposit of Plans.—The deposit of properly drawn plans and sections is as set out elsewhere. Section 4 gives the following *exemption.* " Nothing in this by-law shall require the deposit of any plan or section in the case of any repair which does not involve the alteration or the entire reconstruction of any drainage work. Seven days' notice is required where alterations or reconstruction is to be undertaken."

There is a penalty of £2 for infringement and twenty shillings for each day after receiving notice of infringement. A period of grace is specified for Section 12. The by-laws do not apply to the area known as the City of London, this, of course, being a relatively small area.

Material of Waste Pipes.—The following abstract of the amended L.C.C. By-laws is accompanied by comments on the relative sections.

" A waste pipe for any fitment, such as any bath, lavatory basin, bidet or sink (not being a slop sink) and a waste ventilating pipe, shall be constructed of drawn-lead pipe, copper, cast iron, glazed stoneware or other equally suitable material."

There is an element of danger in the last phrase in that it is difficult to say what is an equally suitable material and what is not. It, however, admits of progress where any really suitable material is placed on the market. The new lead alloy, known as Ternary Lead Alloy would be suitable, but it is harder to say whether some of the new cement pipes could be considered equally so.[1] The inclusion of copper is new. The approval for glazed stoneware is a doubtful procedure for ordinary sinks as it is very easily damaged. Cases occur in cheap villa property where the end projecting through the wall has been knocked off in every case, leaving it so that the wall below the end and above the gully is saturated

[1] The Standing Committee on Water Regulations, having considered the question of these alloys passed the following resolution :

Resolved that those water authorities who are prepared to allow the use of ternary lead alloy pipe in the place of ordinary lead alloy pipe be advised that they may safely pass ternary lead alloy pipe of weight 30 per cent. less than ordinary lead permitted in their respective areas, but that this permission should, for the time being, be restricted to use above ground and within the building.

with wet and soapy compounds of filth. For chemical sinks, however, glazed stoneware is suitable in that the acids do not attack it. They should be encased so that they are not subject to mechanical damage from misusage or otherwise. Iron or stoneware wastes must not be less than $1\frac{1}{2}$ inches diameter.

Traps.—" All ablution fittings must be trapped with an approved form of trap having a water seal maintained at not less than $1\frac{1}{2}$ inches. The trap should be fixed immediately under the fitting and provided with means of inspection and clearing.

Exception.—" For sinks situated in outhouses, and where the waste pipe is not more than 3 feet 6 inches long, the trap may be omitted.

" Where two or more baths or lavatory fittings are fixed in a range the waste pipe may discharge below into a semi-circular open glazed channel, and without a trap on each waste. The channel must discharge to a trap."

The above, in the writer's opinion, is a dubious arrangement, as where the channel is not cleaned daily by hand it gets in a very foul condition from the splashes of soapy compounds and dust. Cleaners, for instance, may be found brushing the floor dirt into the channel.

Ventilation of Waste Pipes.—" Where a waste pipe is connected to two or more fittings fixed on different floors it shall be continued upwards *without diminution* of its diameter to terminate at such a position as to prevent any nuisance, or injury or danger to health from escaping gases."

It can be taken that if there are windows on the elevation within, say, 10 to 15 feet measured on a horizontal line, it should discharge above the eaves, though there is no such definite statement in the by-law.

Trap Ventilation.—" In order to preserve the seal of a trap such trap shall be ventilated whenever necessary by a pipe carried to terminate in a position where it will not be a nuisance or dangerous to health."

This permits for a single fitment that is known as a puff pipe terminating on the face of the wall, providing it is well away from windows, etc. It will also permit traps of unsiphonable construction, providing they are sanitary in other respects. (See Vol. I for type indicated.) Where there are two or more fitments on different floors connected to the same waste pipe the trap ventilating pipes must be carried up to discharge it a safe point, or may be connected into the main ventilating pipe at a height above that of the topmost fitting on the stack.

" Every trap ventilating pipe shall be connected at a point not nearer than 3 inches and not more than 12 inches away from the crown of the trap."

See Fig. 576 for this definition. It should not be nearer than 3 inches on the score that solids in the water would be thrown into the end and stick there, ultimately to choke the pipe and render it useless. On the other hand, 12 inches away as a limit may make it difficult to adopt such a system of ventilation as is very popular in America, and known as loop venting, which is shown in the chapter dealing with the "One-pipe" System of Sanitation. The method most general here and considered in the above by-law, is termed "*Crown Venting*" in distinction from "*Loop Venting*."

Size of Ventilating Pipes.—"The branch vent pipes may have a diameter not less than two-thirds that of the waste pipe."

This usually means it can be one standard size less, but a 1½-inch waste can have a 1-inch *trap vent*. The minimum diameter of any such trap vent is 1 inch and there is no need under the by-law to exceed 2 inches diameter. That is to say, a 4-inch or 5-inch waste pipe need only have a 2-inch branch vent. This, however, may need some adjustment when dealing with very high buildings with numerous closely grouped fittings discharging into the same stack.

Every waste pipe from ablution fittings must discharge above the water

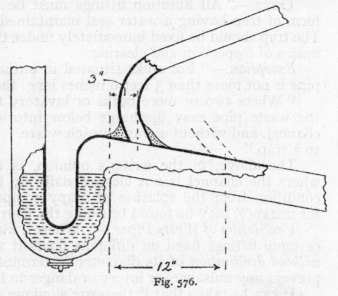

Fig. 576.

seal of a gully trap. It should terminate, however, below the grating to obtain the full flushing effect to the gully trap and to the drain ; also it avoids fouling the pavement from splashing.

Hopper Heads.—The Hopper head is not allowed, neither must waste matter discharge into any rainwater gutter.

The joints must be formed as previously described and light-gauge copper by means of compression joints or equally suitable manner.

Strength (or Weights) according to Position.—"Waste and waste ventilating pipes within a building, or outside when receiving the discharge from fittings fixed on two or more stories, then the weights and thicknesses shall be in accordance with the following table." (See next page.)

The inference is that waste pipes outside a building receiving discharge of fittings from one floor only can be of a lighter substance than given in table CI of minimum factors.

Joints, Waste Soil and Vent.—The joints *lead to stoneware ; lead to cast iron ; stoneware to lead*, etc., are as before and as illustrated and described in this work. For *light-gauge copper tubes to cast iron* the joint must be made by means of a thimble or flanged ferrule of copper, brass or other suitable alloy, connected to pipe or trap by means of a union nut or flange and to the iron by means of a gasket of yarn and metallic lead properly caulked or by means of flanges securely bolted.

Although the above is specified there should be no objection to a

TABLE CI

Diameter in inches.	Lead.	Copper.		Cast Iron.			
	Weight per yard in lbs.	Weight per yard.	Gauge.	Internal depth of socket in inches.	Caulking space in inches.	Thickness of metal in inches.	Weight per 6 ft. length, including sockets, etc., in lbs.
1	5	1·83	18	—	—	—	—
1¼	6·25	2·25	18	—	—	—	—
1½	7·5	2·7	18	2¼	¼	3/16	22
1¾	8·75	3·66	17	—	—	—	—
2	10	4·17	17	2½	¼	3/16	24
2½	12·5	5·19	17	2¾	¼	3/16	30
3	15	7·11	16	2¾	¼	3/16	35
3½	19·5	9·33	15	3	¼	3/16	41
4	22·5	11·85	14	3	¼	3/16	47
4½	29	13·29	14	3¼	5/16	3/16	54
5	35·5	14·76	14	3¼	5/16	3/16	59
6	50	17·64	14	3½	5/16	3/16	71

brass sleeve being welded or brazed on to the copper and then caulked into the iron socket. Cast-iron sockets should always be corrugated to form a key for the blue lead, whether it is copper to iron or iron to iron, as it is not an unusual thing to see the lead caulking wheedled out of the cavity by alternate expansion and contraction effects (see Fig. 577)

Fig. 577.—Inside of Socket showing Key for Lead Caulking.

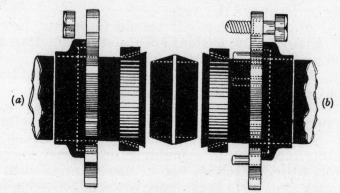

(a)   (b)

Fig. 578.—Compression Joint for large-diameter Waste Pipes and Soil Pipes in Copper.

(a) Flanged coupling before assembling.
(b) Showing inside sleeves, bolts and steady pins to ensure straight draw on copper pipe.

Fig. 578 shows a type of flange joint as obtainable for 2½-, 3-, 3½- and 4-inch copper pipe. Fig. 579 shows a Kontite form of fitting which is a particularly easily made joint and requires no tool to prepare, the end of the tube being simply pressed in and the fly nut tightened up. Fig. 580 shows a set of compression fittings for ranges of lavatories with light-gauge copper waste and ventilating pipes. This joint is also a favourite owing to the ease with which the joint, known as "The Instantor," is made. Fig. 578 is the "Securex," suitable for waste and soil pipe, etc., in copper in addition to suitability for water service. Joints lead to lead may be fused (lead-burnt) or wiped joints only.

Soil Pipes.—The materials are as for waste pipes, and a minimum diameter of 3 inches is now allowed as against $3\frac{1}{2}$ inches in the previous L.C.C. by-laws. There is a stipulation, however, that the outgo and trap from a w.c. connected to such a diameter has no part larger than 3 inches. The intention, no doubt, is to reduce risk of stoppage by large articles passing the trap and wedging in the pipe. This small diameter soil pipe is particularly suitable for the siphonic closet. There is a clause which can very well be reviewed stipulating that a soil pipe shall be situated outside the building wherever practicable. It may also be noted here that a 3-inch vent pipe to a drain is allowed, so that where

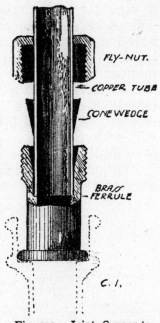

Fig. 579.—Joint, Copper to Cast-iron.

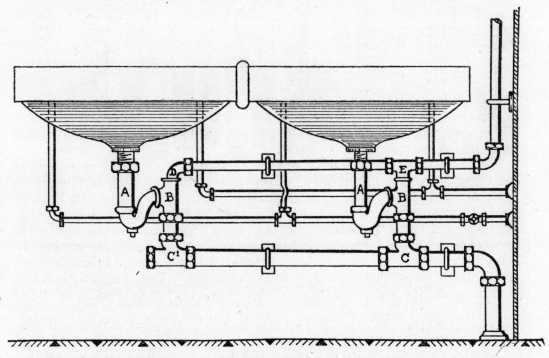

Fig. 580.—Waste Pipes Vent and Service in light-gauge Copper Tube and "Instantor" Compression Joints.

a w.c., etc., is situated near the head of a drain the soil with its vent will serve also the purpose of venting the drain. It should also be noted that small-diameter pipes give greater risk of siphonage than do large pipes, so that trap ventilation must be carried out in a thorough manner to avoid risk of the seals being broken. It has been stated by one authority that a 3-inch soil pipe is sufficient for one to three water-closets or slop-sinks. There has been a tendency in the past to over-size soil pipes and 6 inches diameter for w.c.'s only in a vertical stack will seldom be necessary in this country, while the height of buildings is so limited.

The minimum weights, etc., for soil pipes and soil ventilating pipes are as follows :

TABLE CII

L.C.C. SOIL AND SOIL VENTILATING PIPES

Internal Diameter in inches.	Lead.	Copper.		Cast Iron.			
	Weight per yard in lbs.	Weight per yard.	Gauge.	Internal depth of socket in inches.	Caulking space in inches.	Thickness of metal in inches.	Weight per 6 ft. length, including socket and ears, bead, etc. in lbs.
			S.W.				
1	5	1·83	18	—	—	—	—
$1\frac{1}{4}$	6·25	2·25	18		—	—	—
$1\frac{1}{2}$	7·5	2·7	18	$2\frac{1}{4}$	$\frac{1}{4}$	$\frac{3}{16}$	22
$1\frac{3}{4}$	8·75	3·66	17	—	—	—	—
2	10	4·17	17	$2\frac{1}{2}$	$\frac{1}{4}$	$\frac{3}{16}$	24
$2\frac{1}{2}$	12·5	5·19	17	$2\frac{3}{4}$	$\frac{1}{4}$	$\frac{3}{16}$	30
3	15	7·11	16	$2\frac{3}{4}$	$\frac{1}{4}$	$\frac{13}{64}$	40
$3\frac{1}{2}$	19·5	9·33	15	3	$\frac{1}{4}$	$\frac{13}{64}$	48
4	22·5	11·85	14	3	$\frac{1}{4}$	$\frac{13}{64}$	54
$4\frac{1}{2}$	32	13·29	14	$3\frac{1}{4}$	$\frac{5}{16}$	$\frac{1}{4}$	66
5	41	14·76	14	$3\frac{1}{4}$	$\frac{5}{16}$	$\frac{1}{4}$	78
6	57	17·64	14	$3\frac{1}{2}$	$\frac{5}{16}$	$\frac{1}{4}$	92

The materials of manufacture for waste pipes and vents from urinals and slop-sinks are as for soil pipes.

Sizes.—A urinal waste may not be less than $1\frac{1}{2}$ inches, or rather it may be as small as $1\frac{1}{2}$ inches (the previous minimum size having been 3 inches) for a single fitting, and not less than 2 inches in the case of urinals having not more than two basins, or two stalls not exceeding 4 feet 6 inches in total width. For more than two urinals the minimum diameter is 3 inches. Single basins must be trapped immediately below. Where two or more basins, or stalls, discharge into a glazed open channel, it is sufficient to provide one trap to the channel. The channel must not extend beyond the stalls. The minimum diameter for slop-sinks intended to receive the discharge of bedroom slops is 3 inches. The diameter for *branch* ventilating pipes is (*a*) 2 inches where connected with a soil pipe or a waste pipe 3 inches or more in internal diameter. (*b*) Two-thirds of the respective internal diameter of the branch and main waste pipes where the internal diameters of such pipes are less than three inches.

The points of connection and termination of ventilating pipes are as for soil ventilating pipes. It must be remembered that where a slop-sink has an ordinary sink attached with hot- and cold-water taps the waste pipe and the soil pipe if connected to such, should be of hard metal to better withstand the unequal strains of alternate expansion and contraction.

Drains.—The main features for drains are as previously mentioned, the main difference being that the wording of the by-law makes the fixing of an intercepting trap optional. The dwarf fresh-air inlet is not approved if situated near a building and where the intercepting trap is omitted only one vent pipe at the most distant point (as may be practicable) is required. Where the trap is fixed, two vent pipes are required, one at the head and the other as near to the trap as practicable and on the inlet side of the trap. The minimum diameter of these pipes is 3 inches as against $3\frac{1}{2}$ in the old regulations.

The stipulated minimum weights, etc., for drains are as follows :

TABLE CIII
L.C.C. 1930 CAST-IRON DRAIN PIPES

Diameter.	Internal depth of socket in inches.	Caulking space in inches.	Thickness of metal for pipes and fittings in inches.	Weight per 9 ft. length, including socket and beaded spigot or flanges, in lbs.
3	3	$\frac{7}{16}$	$\frac{5}{16}$	112
4	3	$\frac{5}{16}$	$\frac{3}{8}$	160
5	3	$\frac{3}{8}$	$\frac{3}{8}$	190
6	$3\frac{1}{2}$	$\frac{3}{8}$	$\frac{3}{8}$	230
7	4	$\frac{3}{8}$	$\frac{7}{16}$	350
8	4	$\frac{3}{8}$	$\frac{7}{16}$	400
9	4	$\frac{3}{8}$	$\frac{7}{16}$	450

The minimum diameter for a foul water drain is 4 inches.

Foundations.—The drain must be laid on concrete not less than 6 inches thick and projecting on each side of the drain 6 inches. The best way of laying the drains is to put 3 inches of concrete down and lay the drain on bricks behind each socket. This leaves plenty of room for making the joints. Three inches of fine concrete is then filled in and haunched up the sides of the drain.

The new widths of concrete are a little different to the old rule of width, which was equal to three diameters and works out as follows :

CONCRETE FOUNDATIONS FOR *CI* DRAINS

Diameter of drain in inches	3	4	5	6	7	8	9
Thickness of two pipe walls in inches	$\frac{5}{8}$	$\frac{3}{4}$	$\frac{3}{4}$	$\frac{3}{4}$	$\frac{7}{8}$	$\frac{7}{8}$	$\frac{7}{8}$
Add 12 inches for 2 projecting sides	12	12	12	12	12	12	12
Total width of concrete in inches	$15\frac{5}{8}$	$16\frac{3}{4}$	$17\frac{3}{4}$	$18\frac{3}{4}$	$19\frac{7}{8}$	$20\frac{7}{8}$	$21\frac{7}{8}$

The other general requirement for drains are as set out in these volumes and as set out in the older by-laws.   Greater latitude, however,

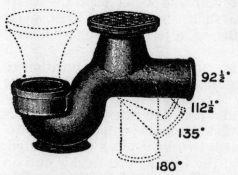

may be given to reduce the number of manholes, and in the case of terrace houses, for instance, to keep the drains at the back; the houses discharging into the one "*common drain*" with one intercepting trap on that drain before connecting to the sewer is a system to be encouraged against carrying a separate drain through each house.

92½°
112½°
135°
180°

Fig. 581.—Burns Bros. Access Gully Trap.

Again, for isolated gully traps it should be sufficient to provide a type of trap that has a rodding arm on the outgo with air-tight locking cover, and so save the cost of a manhole (see Fig. 581).

Another requirement, not included in the old set, is that a rodding arm or inspection eye is fixed at the base of vent pipes and soil pipes before entering the ground (see Fig. 582).

Testing.—Every drain shall be water- and gas-tight and proved so under a test with a 2-foot head of water."

As a drain is near this depth at the commencement and usually considerably deeper at the low end, the " mean head " would be more than 2 feet, so it should be sufficient to fill the drains with water up to ground level.   In the manholes a device similar to that shown in Fig. 488 can be used, but with an elbow at the base of the 1-inch pipe.

Traps.—" Water-closets, slop-sinks and urinals traps must be capable of retaining a water seal of 1¾-inch depth."

Other traps *on a drain* must be capable of retaining a seal of 2 inches depth.   If, or where, the regulations of a district permit the omission of an intercepting trap the open channel through a brick-built access

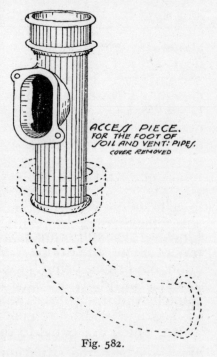

ACCESS PIECE.
FOR THE FOOT OF
SOIL AND VENT: PIPES.
COVER REMOVED

Fig. 582.

chamber is not permissible, as such chamber would be a large pocket for accumulations of sewer gas.   The access junctions must be fitted with water and air-tight plates, as indicated in Fig. 481.   If bolts and nuts are employed the latter at least should be of bronze to prevent them growing together with rust, in which case they would be practically immovable.

Water-closets.—Previously when the position of a w.c. was selected it was sufficient to show an adjacent open area containing 100 square feet; now such area must have a minimum width of 3 feet if open on one side (see Fig. 583). If entirely surrounded with walls the area must have a minimum width of 7 feet (see Fig. 584). If, however, more than one w.c. is required to abut on such an area, such area containing the 100 square feet should be sufficient as indicated in Fig. 585. The open area, so long as it is of a permanent character, can be 5 feet above the floor of a w.c. floor, but not more (see Figs. 586 and 587). For basement closets, i.e. closets with floor below 5 feet of adjoining open area, then the open area need only contain 40 square feet, but having a minimum width of 5 feet (see Fig. 588). If the open area, however, is constructed solely for lighting and ventilating a w.c. it is sufficient if the area contains 25 square feet (see Fig. 589). The floor of area must not be lower than 12 feet from adjoining open area.

Exception to External Wall.—Where the situation of a water-closet does not exceed 20 feet high, the water-closet may be so situated *as not to have an external wall*, if a street or

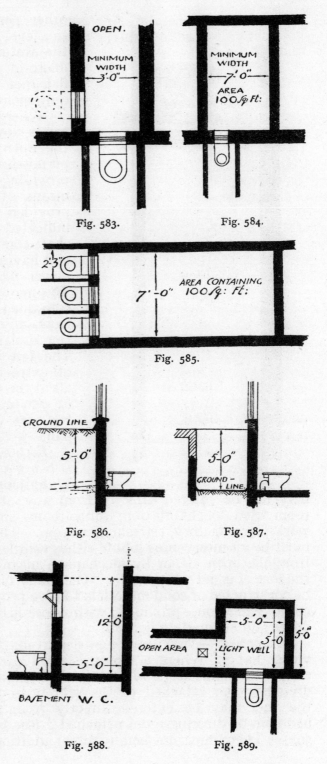

Fig. 583.   Fig. 584.

Fig. 585.

Fig. 586.   Fig. 587.

BASEMENT W. C.

Fig. 588.   Fig. 589.

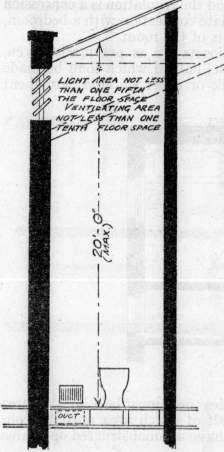

LIGHT AREA NOT LESS THAN ONE FIFTH THE FLOOR SPACE VENTILATING AREA NOT LESS THAN ONE TENTH FLOOR SPACE

20'-0" (MAX.)

DUCT

Fig. 590.—Open Area obtained above Roof.

other permanent open area exists at the level and abutting on the roof of the water-closet (see Fig. 590). The diagram shows a pitched roof, but a flat roof also naturally meets the requirement.

Where the proposed position of a water-closet cannot gain contact with the open air as indicated, then it is permissible to construct an apartment providing artificial and mechanical means of lighting and ventilation is provided (see Fig. 591). The means indicated entails an inlet and outlet shaft communicating with the open air and having a fan driven by mechanical power fixed in the extraction shaft. The motor and fan must be self-contained in duplicate, and separate from any other mechanical installation designed to ventilate the building. The fan and ducts must be capable of extracting air at the rate of 750 cubic feet per w.c. pan.

Entrance Lobby.—Water-closets may not be entered directly from any other room used for habitation, schoolroom, shop, work-place, factory, refreshment room. There must be an intervening lobby, either ventilated from the open air, or by mechanical means if the former is not practicable. The lobby must be constructed of solid materials to give proper aerial exclusion, provided with close-fitting doors and adequately lighted.

Exception.—An entirely new departure provides that: "Where a closet is used exclusively in connection with a bedroom or a dressing-room attached to the said bedroom, the w.c. may be entered directly from the bedroom or dressing-room attached" (see Fig. 592). There must not be any direct additional

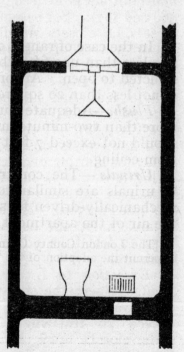

Fig. 591.—Internal w.c. with Mechanical Ventilation.

approach from a corridor or other place and the regulation is a concession to meet the need of a w.c. having immediate connection with a bedroom, such w.c. to be used only by the occupants of the room.

The general requirements for water-closets are as previously given, i.e. 2 square feet of glass exclusive of frame, half of which shall be made to open. There must also be an air brick or other suitable permanent opening.

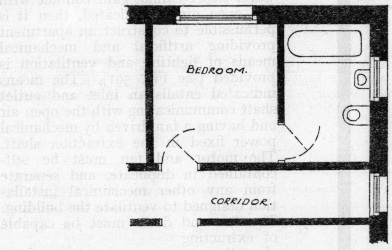

Fig. 592.

In the case of ranges of w.c.'s in cubicles there must be a lighting area not less than one-fifth the floor space, half of which area must be constructed to open. Air bricks, etc., must have an unobstructed open area of not less than 20 square inches per pan.

Flush.—Adequate flush provided to give succeeding flushes at not more than two-minute intervals. The height of screens between cubicles should not exceed 7 feet and give a clearance of 6 inches from floor and from ceiling.

Urinals.—The construction of the apartment and requirements as to urinals are similar to those required for w.c.'s in general. Where mechanically-driven fans are installed, they must be capable of changing the air of the apartment three times per hour.

[The London County Council have now in draft form amendments to the by-laws to permit the adoption of the "One-pipe" System.]

APPENDIXES

I. SERVICEABLE DATA

Roofing Data—Standard Sizes of Stoneware Pipes—Milled Lead—Expansion of Metal—Galvanised Corrugated Sheets—Sheet-Lead—Sheet-Zinc—Sheet-Copper—Specific Gravity, Specific Heat, Melting Point, and Breaking Strain of Metals—Weight in Pounds of Lead Pipes per Foot—Rainfall—Weight and Bulk of Water—Contents of Tanks—Hydraulic Memoranda—Service Pipes and Valves—Equivalents.

ROOFING DATA

Covering.	Inclination to Horizon.	Ratio of Rise to Span.	Weight of Roofing per Foot Square.
Tin	5° 43′	$\frac{1}{20}$	0·7 to 1·25 lb.
Lead	5° 43′	$\frac{1}{20}$	5·0 to 8·0 lb.
Zinc	5° 43′	$\frac{1}{20}$	1·0 to 2·0 lb.
Copper	7° 36′	$\frac{1}{15}$	0·8 to 1·25 lb.

STANDARD SIZES OF STONEWARE PIPES

	feet inches	feet inches	feet inches	feet inches	feet inches
Diameter	0 3	0 4	0 6	0 9	1 0
Thickness	0 $\frac{1}{2}$	0 $\frac{9}{16}$	0 $\frac{5}{8}$	0 $\frac{3}{4}$	0 1
Length	2 0	2 0	2 0	2 6	2 6
Depth of Socket . . .	0 2	0 2	0 $2\frac{1}{4}$	0 $2\frac{1}{2}$	0 $2\frac{3}{4}$

MILLED LEAD

In sheets 30 feet to 40 feet long, 7 feet, 7 feet 6 inches, and 8 feet wide.

Nearest Birmingham
Wire Gauge.

3 lb. per sq. foot =	in.	18
4 ,, ,, =	in.	16
5 ,, ,, =	in.	14
6 ,, ,, =	in.	12
7 ,, ,, =	in.	} 11
8 ,, ,, = $\frac{1}{8}$ in.	

EXPANSION OF METAL

Lead at between 32° to 212° F. will expand 1 part in 349
Copper   ,,   ,,   ,,   ,,   ,,   ,, 581
Zinc   ,,   ,,   ,,   ,,   ,,   ,, 340
Brass   ,,   ,,   ,,   ,,   ,,   ,, 532
Cast iron ,,   ,,   ,,   ,,   ,,   ,, 889

GALVANISED CORRUGATED SHEETS

Sheets 26 inches wide (with 8·3 inch corrugations), covering 24 inches when fixed, will weigh per sq. foot :

16	18	20	22	24	26	28	W.G.
40¼	39¾	31½	24½	20¼	15	13¾	oz.

SHEET LEAD

Weight in lb. per Foot Run.	Thickness.	Weight in lb. per Foot Run.	Thickness.	Weight in lb. per Foot Run.	Thickness.
1	·017	5	·085	9	·152
2	·034	6	·101	10	·169
3	·051	7	·118	11	·186
4	·068	8	·135	12	·203

SHEET ZINC

1 sq. foot of sheet zinc will weigh :

Gauge 4 approx. B.W.G. 34 .	. 4¾ oz.	Gauge 13 approx. B.W.G. 22 .	. 17 oz.
,, 5 ,, 31 .	. 5¾ ,,	,, 15 ,, 20 .	. 22 ,,
,, 8 ,, 28 .	. 9 ,,	,, 17 ,, 18 .	. 28 ,,
,, 10 ,, 25 .	. 11½ ,,	,, 20 ,, 16 .	. 29 ,,
,, 11 ,, 24 .	. 13 ,,		

SHEET COPPER

1 sq. foot of sheet copper will weigh :

1	5	10	16	20	22	24	26	28	B.W.G.
14·0	10·2	6·4	3·0	1·12	1·6	1·0	0·12	0·10	lb. and oz.

SPECIFIC GRAVITY, SPECIFIC HEAT, MELTING POINT, AND BREAKING STRAIN OF METALS

Metal.	Specific Gravity.	Specific Heat.	Melting Point in deg. F.	Average Breaking Strength per Sq. Inch.
Copper (cast)	8·6	—	—	19,000
,, (sheet)	8·79	·095	1,929	30,000
Lead (cast)	11·36	—	—	1,800
,, (sheet)	11·4	·031	618	3,300
Iron (cast)	7·3	·112	1,960	17,000
,, (wrought)	7·75	·113	2,912	50,000
Aluminium (cast)	2·58	—	1,157	17,000
,, (sheet)	2·68	·225	—	25,000
Tin (cast)	7·29	·052	446	4,500
Zinc	7·00	·093	779	7,400

WEIGHT IN POUNDS OF LEAD PIPES PER FOOT

Bore in Inches.	$\frac{1}{16}$	$\frac{1}{8}$	$\frac{3}{16}$	$\frac{1}{4}$	$\frac{5}{16}$	$\frac{3}{8}$
			Thickness in Fractions of an Inch.			
$\frac{1}{4}$	·303	·728	1·273	1·942	2·730	3·641
$\frac{3}{8}$	·425	·971	1·638	2·427	3·237	4·569
$\frac{1}{2}$	·546	1·214	2·013	2·913	3·944	5·097
$\frac{5}{8}$	·667	1·529	2·366	3·398	4·551	5·825
$\frac{3}{4}$	·789	1·699	2·731	3·873	5·157	6·552
1	1·032	2·184	3·457	4·851	6·371	8·009
$1\frac{1}{4}$	1·274	2·670	4·186	5·825	7·585	9·466
$1\frac{1}{2}$	1·517	3·155	4·915	6·796	8·796	10·923
2	2·001	4·127	6·372	8·734	11·223	13·883
$2\frac{1}{2}$	2·489	5·100	7·829	10·683	13·654	16·762
3	2·971	6·066	9·286	12·621	16·080	19·660
$3\frac{1}{2}$	3·456	7·033	10·731	14·55	18·491	22·553
4	3·941	8·003	12·186	16·49	20·916	25·463
$4\frac{1}{2}$	4·426	8·973	13·641	18·43	23·341	28·373
5	4·911	9·943	15·096	26·275	25·766	31·283
6	5·881	11·883	18·006	30·27	30·616	37·103

The lead pipes mostly used in plumbing are :

	$\frac{3}{8}$ inch	$\frac{1}{2}$ inch	$\frac{3}{4}$ inch	1 inch	$1\frac{1}{4}$ inch	$1\frac{1}{2}$ inch	2 inch
Bore							
Light	4 lb	5 lb.	8 lb.	11 lb.	14 lb.	18 lb.	24 lb.
Medium	5 ,,	7 ,,	12 ,,	16 ,,	21 ,,	27 ,,	33 ,,
Heavy	$5\frac{1}{2}$,,	9 ,,	14 ,,	21 ,,	28 ,,	36 ,,	48 ,,

RAINFALL

$\frac{1}{8}$ inch of rainfall equals ·585 gallons per sq. yard
$\frac{3}{16}$,, ,, ·885 ,, ,,
$\frac{1}{4}$,, ,, 1·171 ,, ,,
$\frac{5}{16}$,, ,, 1·463 ,, ,,
$\frac{3}{8}$,, ,, 1·756 ,, ,,
$\frac{7}{16}$,, ,, 2·049 ,, ,,
$\frac{1}{2}$,, ,, 2·343 ,, ,,
$\frac{9}{16}$,, ,, 2·635 ,, ,,
$\frac{5}{8}$,, ,, 2·928 ,, ,,
$\frac{11}{16}$,, ,, 3·220 ,, ,,
$\frac{3}{4}$,, ,, 3·514 ,, ,,
$\frac{13}{16}$,, ,, 3·806 ,, ,,
$\frac{7}{8}$,, ,, 4·099 ,, ,,
$\frac{15}{16}$,, ,, 4·395 ,, ,,
1 ,, ,, 4·687 ,, ,,

WEIGHT AND BULK OF WATER

1 cu. foot of water equals 6·25 gallons, 62·5 lb., or 1,000 oz.
1 gallon of water equals ·16 cu. foot, 276·48 cu. inches, 10 lb.

CONTENTS OF TANKS

To ascertain capacity of a square tank in gallons, multiply length by width and the product by the height in feet, and the result by 6¼.

To ascertain the capacity of a circular vessel take the radius (half the diameter) and multiply it by itself and the product by the standard figure 3·141, and the result by the depth.

HYDRAULIC MEMORANDA

1 cu. foot of water = 62·5 lb.
1 cu. foot of sea water = 64·11 lb. (approx.).
1 gallon of water = 10 lb., or ·16 cu. foot.
cu. feet × 6¼ = gallons
Gallons × ·16 = cu. feet.
A column of water 1 foot high and 1 inch square = ·434 lb.
A column of water 1 foot high and 1 inch in diameter = ·34 lb.
A column of water 1 foot high and 1 inch in diameter = ·034 gallons.
Head of water in feet × 62·25 = pressure in lb. per sq. foot of surface.
Head of water in feet × ·434 = pressure in lb. per sq. inch.
Head of water in feet ÷ 2·31 = pressure in lb. per sq. inch.

SERVICE PIPES AND VALVES

Height of Water in Cistern above Outlet.	Size of Pipes and Valves for Closets.	Size of Pipes for Sinks and Draw-offs.
4 feet and under 6 feet	1½ inch pipe ; 1½ inch valve	1 inch to ¾ inch
7 „ 12 „	1¼ „ 1½ „	¾ „ ½ „
13 „ 18 „	1 „ 1¼ „	½ „ ⅜ „
Above 18 feet	1 „ 1 „	½ „ ⅜ „

EQUIVALENTS

1 faggot of lead (London) = 2,184 lb.
1 seam of glass = 120 lb.
1 sq. foot of sheet lead ½ inch thick (7/0 Imp. wire gauge) = 29·59 lb.
1 sq. foot of sheet zinc ½ inch thick = 18·72 lb.
1 sq. foot of sheet copper ½ inch thick = 22·68 lb.

II. WORKSHOP RECIPES

Cements for Aquaria—Cement for Leaded Lights—Rust Cement—Cement for Glass to Metal
—Cement for Iron Pipe Joints—Resin Putty for Water Pipes—Cement for Wood to Iron or Stone
—Soft Solders—Hard Solders—Expanding Solder for Metal to Stone—Soldering and Brazing
Fluxes—Lacquering—To Clean Brass and Copper—Boiler and Piping Insulating Composition—
Watertight Putties.

CEMENTS FOR AQUARIA

(1) Powdered litharge . . . . 3 parts
  Fine white sand . . . . 3 ,,
  Plaster-of-Paris . . . . 3 ,,
  Powdered resin . . . . 1 part

Add sufficient boiled linseed oil to make a paste. Stand for 5 hours before
using, but it is useless after 15 hours.

(2) Common pitch . . . . 2 parts
  Gutta-percha . . . . . 1 part

Melt in an iron pot and pour out into cold water. Heat before using.

CEMENT FOR SLATE TANKS

Mix thoroughly equal parts of red and white lead with a little linseed oil. If
the tank is to contain soft water, paint over the cement with hot pitch.

CEMENT FOR LEADED LIGHTS

Mix equal parts of red and white lead with linseed oil into a stiff paste and paint
over the cement.

CEMENTS FOR GLASS TO METAL

(1) Resin . . . . . . 3 parts
  Caustic soda . . . . . 1 part
  Water . . . . . . 3 parts

Boil together until saponified; then mix with half its weight of plaster-of-Paris.
Use promptly.

(2) Copal varnish . . . . 15 parts
  Drying oil . . . . . 5 ,,
  Turpentine . . . . . 3 ,,
  Oil of turpentine . . . 2 ,,
  Liquid marine glue . . . 5 ,,

Dissolve in water bath and add 10 parts dry slaked lime.

Rust Cement

(1) Iron borings   .   .   .   .   200 parts
     Salammoniac in powder   .   .   2 ,,
     Flour of sulphur   .   .   .   1 part
          (Slow setting)

(2) Iron borings   .   .   .   .   80 parts
     Salammoniac in powder   .   .   1 part
     Flour of sulphur   .   .   .   2 parts
          (Quick setting)

Cement for Glass to Metal

Dissolve gelatine in water, add a small percentage of glycerine to render it slightly elastic, and a small quantity of bichromate of potash to make it insoluble.

Cement for Iron Pipe Joints

Iron filings   .   .   .   .   5 lb.
Powdered salammoniac   .   .   2 oz.

Mix with a little water.   Use at once and ram the cement tightly into the joints. If 1 oz. of sulphur is added setting is hastened, but the cement will not be so hard.

Resin Putty for Water Pipes

Resin .   .   .   .   10 parts
Cotton wool .   .   .   10 ,,
Calcined lime   .   .   .   10 ,,
Linseed oil varnish   .   .   3 ,,

Cements for Metal to Earthenware

(1) Milk .   .   .   .   .   1 pint
     Vinegar   .   .   .   .   1 ,,
     Sifted quicklime   (sufficient to form stiff paste)

Mix the milk and vinegar, remove the curd, and add sufficient quicklime to form a thick paste.

(2) Resin .   .   .   .   3 parts
     Caustic soda .   .   .   1 part
     Plaster-of-Paris   .   . $4\frac{1}{2}$ parts
     Water .   .   .   5 ,,

Make a soap by mixing the resin and soda in the water ; then add the plaster.

Cement for Wood to Iron or Stone

Dissolve cabinet-maker's glue to the consistency of liquid glue ; then add sufficient sifted ashes to attain the consistency of a thick varnish.   Apply warm, pressing the objects together.

SOFT SOLDERS

(1) Fine solder : Tin, 1½ parts ; lead, 1 part.
(2) Plumber's solder ; Tin, 1 part ; lead, 2 parts.

HARD SOLDERS

(1) Copper, 3 parts ; zinc, 1 part.
(2) Copper, 1 part ; zinc, 1 part.
(3) Copper, 4 parts ; zinc, 3 parts ; tin, 1 part.   (Given in order of hardness.)

EXPANDING SOLDER FOR METAL TO STONE

Lead . . . . 6 parts (by weight)
Bismuth . . . . . . 1 part
Antimony . . . . . . 9 parts

SOLDERING AND BRAZING FLUXES

For iron and steel : chloride of zinc or salammoniac.
Copper and brass : chloride of zinc, salammoniac, or resin.
New zinc : chloride of zinc.
Old zinc : hydrochloride acid.
Tin and pewter : resin or sweet oil.
  Equal parts of killed spirits, glycerine, and alcohol mixed makes a good soft soldering fluid.
  Borax is the best flux for soldering hard metals and alloys.
  All traces of hydrochloric acid must be wiped off after use.
  Acid should not be used in making jointings in electric conductors.

LACQUERING

For Copper : Shellac . . . 5 oz.
Sandarach . . . 5 „
Camphor . . . 4 „
Mastic . . . 3 „
Methylated spirits . 14 „

For Brass : Shellac . . . ½ lb.
Alcohol . . . 1 gal.

For Steel : (1) Buttonlac . . . ½ lb.
Resin . . . 1 oz.
Methylated spirits . 1 qrt.
Apply warm.

(2) Mastic . . . 8 oz.
Camphor . . . 4 „
Sandarach . . . 12 „
Gum alami . . . 4 „
Spirits of wine . 1 qrt.
Apply cold.

The lacquers may be tinted by the addition of a little red sanders or dragon's blood for red, annato for yellow, and a mixture of dragon's blood and annato for orange.

Articles may be either dipped or brushed over with a fluxing brush.

The metals must be thoroughly cleaned by washing with soap and water, drying, and then rubbing with methylated spirits.

If previously lacquered, remove the old by pickling in, or flooding with, the following liquid : sulphuric acid 10 parts, water 5 parts. Rinse well and wipe dry before applying the fresh lacquer.

To Clean Brass and Copper

Oxalic acid	1 oz.
Water	1 pint
Whiting . . (sufficient to form stiff paste)	

Dissolve the acid in water and apply to metal with a brush. Wash off ; rub on a little whiting and polish with flannel.

Boiler and Piping Insulating Composition

(1)		
Fireclay	1 gal.
Common clay . . .	1 ,,
Cow-dung	1 ,,
Fine ashes	1 peck
Tar	1 gill

Plasterer's hair, a small quantity. Mix all these ingredients with a little water, into a stiff mortar. Heat the boiler or pipe ; dab on the mixture in a thin coat with a brush, leaving it rough, and allow to dry. Then apply the mixture with a trowel, not more than $\frac{1}{2}$ inch, and allow to dry. Apply three or more coats if necessary. Should a smooth, polished finish be desired, add plaster-of-Paris to the mixture for the last coat.

(2)		
Ground limestone . .	10	parts
Ground coal dust . .	10	,,
Ground clay . . .	25	,,
Fine ashes from boiler flue .	30	,,
Water	60	,,
Sulphuric acid (50° Bé) . .	1	part
Cow's hair . . .	$1\frac{1}{2}$	,,

All proportions by weight ; apply as in first recipe.

Watertight Putties

One of the outstanding points demanded in connection with putties is that they should be absolutely watertight. In this respect the oil putties, consisting of oil varnish incorporated with minium, litharge, levigated chalk, etc., first come under consideration, by reason of their power of repelling, being therefore impervious to water. The hardening of these putties is ascribed to the formation of compounds between the metals and fatty acids in their components.

Resin putties are applied to the surface to be cemented either in a melted condition or as solutions, and are characterised by quick setting and impermeability as regards water. Their chief defect is a liability to crack, owing to the brittleness of the resin, but this may be combated by an admixture of oil putty or drying putty oil. Other putties esteemed for their resistance to liquids and chemical agents are those in which caoutchouc and gutta-percha form the main ingredients.

Linseed oil putty, prepared by boiling eight parts of linseed oil per half an hour with 12 parts of litharge, and incorporated by stirring with 88 parts of slaked lime, is very useful. The surface to be treated (crevices between stones, or flat roofs, or in closets, etc.) should be first coated with linseed oil varnish.

Resin putty, for wood that is exposed to wet, is made from 100 parts of shellac and 45 parts of strong spirits of wine.

For water pipes a very useful putty can be prepared from 10 parts of resin, 10 parts of cotton-wool, 10 parts of calcined lime, and 3 parts of linseed oil varnish.

The so-called "marine glue" meets with wide approval. It is prepared from 20 parts of asphaltum, 10 parts of rubber, 120 parts of petrol. It is applied hot and should be carefully melted by heating in a water-jacketed kettle. It is perfectly watertight and forms at the ordinary temperature very tough cement, suitable for metal, glass, wood, stone, etc.—THEODORE KOLLER.

TABLE CIV

MINISTRY OF HEALTH SPECIFICATION FOR LIGHT GAUGE COPPER PIPES (1924)

Internal diameter of tube in inches.	For pressures up to 50 lb. per sq. in.		Over 50 up to 125 lb.		Over 125 lb. up to 200 lb.	
	S. Gauge.	lb. per foot run.	S. Gauge.	lb. per foot run.	S. Gauge.	lb. per foot run.
¼	18	·17	17	·21	16	·24
⅜	18	·25	17	·29	16	·34
½	18	·32	17	·38	15	·50
⅝	18	·39	17	·46	14	·68
¾	18	·46	16	·63	14	·80
⅞	18	·54	16	·73	14	·92
I	17	·71	15	·93	13	1·21
1¼	17	·88	15	1·15	12	1·70
1½	17	1·05	15	1·37	12	2·02
1¾	16	1·40	15	1·59	12	2·33
2	16	1·60	15	1·80	12	2·65
2½	16	1·98	14	2·50	10	4·07
3	15	2·68	13	3·44	9	5·48
4	13	4·55	11	5·78	7	8·89

Lighter gauges may be adopted on approval of the Local Water Board, and providing suitable compression joints are used.

INDEX